Management and the Computer of the Future

Published jointly by

THE M.I.T. PRESS
Massachusetts Institute of Technology

and

JOHN WILEY & SONS, INC.
New York · London

1962

Martin Greenberger

EDITOR

Management and the Computer of the Future

*Royalties received from the sale of this book
are deposited in a fund established by the
School of Industrial Management at M.I.T.
The purpose of the fund is to advance education and research
in management applications of the computer
and of quantitative analysis.*

Preface

M.I.T. is now one hundred years old; the automatic digital
computer, more or less as we know it today, is not yet twenty.
It was born in 1944, and quickly learned to read, write, and remember, as well as to add, subtract, multiply, and divide. It was
indeed a precocious youngster, although it did make childish
mistakes.

In a brief span of years, the computer has grown remarkably
in every way except physical size. It has become faster, more
versatile, and more reliable; it has become a much better com-
municator with its external environment; it has developed a
memory of impressive speed and capacity; and it has become
articulate in many languages.

As the computer matured, we gradually delegated to it more
and more duties that we previously had discharged ourselves.
First we asked the computer to do only routine, repetitive calculation: to invert our matrices, solve our equations, and compile our lengthy numerical tables. Then we put it to work on
data processing and some other business chores: figuring our
payroll, writing our checks, and keeping our inventory and accounting records. Heartened by its dogged endurance, and in-

v

trigued by its ability to make choices by itself, we soon began to entrust it with certain responsibilities of a semisupervisory nature: the control of refinery operations, machine tooling, and other real-time processes. We also entrusted it with some military functions of awesome significance and proportions: information processing for continental air defense, surveillance of the seas, and anticipation of logistical requirements for massive troop movements.

It was not too long before we discovered that the computer was entirely capable of working with nonnumerical symbols and words as well as with numbers. Some of us felt a little uncomfortable about this at first, since we had become accustomed to thinking of the computer as a numerical specialist. But watching it differentiate complicated mathematical expressions, work out integration problems of freshman calculus, and even do some language translation, made us realize that we had underestimated its abilities.

As if to take heed of the adage about "all work and no play," during more frivolous moments we played games with the computer, such as checkers and chess. Some of this sport developed into serious interests. Playing with the computer provided us with *simulated* experience, which was obtained more quickly and less expensively than real experience. This led us to design business games and war games to help train our corporation executives and our military officers.

Gaming required that we simulate real systems, and therefore that we construct *models* which could be run on the computer. In some cases we found that we could make a model valid enough to increase our understanding of the system it represented. We also found that simulation on a computer could afford us a means for exploring properties of the model under laboratory-like conditions. If we had a reasonably accurate model of New York City traffic, for example, we could investigate the effect on it of alternate policies for controlling automobile and pedestrian flow, in order to see which policies resulted in lowest over-all waiting and congestion. The range of application of this simulation approach seemed to extend from the simplest inventory system to the most complex system of a national economy. We set out to see if we could develop the necessary models.

The more adventuresome among us entertained hopes of endowing the computer with problem-solving abilities of a relatively general nature. It was demonstrated that the computer could be taught to prove theorems of geometry and logic, read handwritten letters and other man-made patterns, solve puzzles, and even write sonatas. We came to refer to this activity as *artificial* intelligence, just to make sure that the line between the computer and us remained sharp and clear.

Now an artificially intelligent computer which can automatically control a live process at the same time that it simulates the process, appears, at least in the abstract, to offer very exciting possibilities for the future. While this computer is guiding the flow of traffic through New York City, it may also be evaluating potential improvements in policy which it has derived itself. A similar computer might be overseeing the operation of a factory, and still another computer might be routing warehouse shipments and ordering replenishments without assistance. Some people believe that one day the computer may "take over the business."

All in all, the computer has had a very rapid and extraordinary growth in the past two decades. This growth raises interesting and difficult questions for society, for government, for science, for education, and for management. The problems confronting the last group, in particular, prompted us to sponsor a series of eight lectures in the spring of 1961 to honor M.I.T. on the occasion of its one-hundredth birthday. This book is the product of that lecture series.

In planning the program of the series, it quickly became apparent that the topics of greatest importance to management in the long run were not directly in the management domain at present. It also was evident that the interests of society, government, science, and education could not altogether be neglected with clear conscience. These considerations strongly influenced the final selection of speakers and subjects.

The format of each lecture was the same. The speaker presented a main paper, after which each of two discussants delivered prepared remarks based on a prior reading of the paper. Then the speaker, who did not have the advantage of a prior reading of the discussants' remarks, was invited to reply. A general discussion followed, with members of the audience encouraged to air their own views or to ask questions of the panel. Audiences ranged in size from several hundred to almost two thousand, and represented a cross section of the university and industrial communities.

Tape recordings were made of all sessions. At the conclusion of the series the tapes were edited, in many cases substantially, and all contributors (speakers and discussants) were given an opportunity to review the edited version of the chapter to which they had contributed. The timetable for publication made it impossible to extend the same privilege to other participants in the general discussions, and, as editor, I take full responsibility for any distortions of meaning introduced as a result.

One of the most noteworthy aspects of the lecture series was the wide range of opinions evoked by the emphasis on the future. Spirited exchanges in the discussions were the rule rather than the exception. The "experts" contested points made by "amateurs," while the amateurs challenged the authority of the experts. One contributor referred to himself as "a little left of center" and characterized the complete spectrum in the following way: "On the far right were those who view computers as merely glorified slide rules useful only in carrying out computation, while at the far left were scientists who feel computers are already doing something pretty close to thinking." If the reader were to place the rest of the contributors in their places along this spectrum, he would find most of them falling between dead center and far left. This may be only the reflection of an unintentionally biased sample, or it may be a road sign to the future.

A selected bibliography at the end of the book is intended for the person who wishes to read further. The bibliography is based on the recommendations of the participants.

MARTIN GREENBERGER

Cambridge, Massachusetts
January 31, 1962

Acknowledgments

In working out the format and program of the lecture series, I benefited from the suggestions and ideas of many colleagues and friends. Sidney Alexander and Howard Johnson served with me on the program committee and took major roles in the planning. Also helpful during the early stages were Robert Fano, William Locke, Donald Marquis, Elting Morison, Philip Morse, Emanuel Piore, Claude Shannon, Herbert Simon, and Robert Solow. James Murphy of M.I.T.'s Kresge Auditorium and William Struble of the M.I.T. Public Relations Office assisted me greatly in making arrangements, as did my secretary Carmen Bach Ceder. A grant from the International Business Machines Corporation made the lecture series financially feasible.

In the preparation of this book, the very difficult and often dreary job of typing rough drafts from tape, and later drafts from my pencil-scratched revisions and re-revisions, was accomplished chiefly by Claire Curewitz. During the editing process, members of the M.I.T. Press, particularly Constance Boyd and Lynwood Bryant, provided me with much-needed aid. The contributors to the series were uniformly cooperative and understanding in meeting the many deadlines and accepting the many editorial modifications. My work has been made enjoyable by all of these people, and especially by my wife Ellen, who served as co-worker and colleague throughout.

M. G.

Biographical Notes

Included are thumbnail sketches of all contributors and session chairmen. Present positions are omitted, as a rule, since they appear elsewhere in the book. Following the sketches is a list of other identified participants in the general discussions, with titles and affiliations where obtainable.

Sidney S. Alexander was born in Forest City, Pennsylvania, in 1916. He received S.B., A.M., and Ph.D. degrees from Harvard, and served there as assistant professor of economics. He also studied at King's College, Cambridge University. Professor Alexander has been associated at different times with the Bureau of Economic Research, the Office of Strategic Services, the Treasury Department, the State Department, the RAND Corporation, and the International Monetary Fund. Before joining the M.I.T. faculty in 1956, he was economic adviser to the Columbia Broadcasting System.

Gene M. Amdahl was born in Flandreau, South Dakota, in 1922. He received a B.S. degree in engineering physics from South Dakota State College and M.S. and Ph.D. degrees from the University of Wisconsin. His doctoral thesis at Wisconsin contained the original design of the WISC computer. At IBM Dr. Amdahl has been project engineer for the design and development of the IBM 704 computer, as well as major systems designer for the IBM 709 and STRETCH computers.

George W. Brown was born in Boston, Massachusetts, in 1917. He received A.B. and A.M. degrees from Harvard and a Ph.D. degree from Princeton in mathematics. Professor Brown has been research statistician with R. H. Macy and Company, research associate at Princeton, research engineer with RCA's Princeton laboratories, professor of mathematical statistics at Iowa State College, mathematician with the RAND Corporation, and senior staff engineer at International Telemeter Corporation. He has been a vice president and director of General Analysis Corporation, and in addition to his post at UCLA is currently a director of CEIR, Inc.

Vannevar Bush was born in Everett, Massachusetts, in 1890. He received B.S. and M.S. degrees from Tufts College and an Sc.D. degree jointly from Harvard and M.I.T. Dr. Bush is best known for his pioneering work in computer technology and for his efforts in mobilizing science during World War II. He developed the Bush differential analyzer during the 1930's and was director of the Office of Scientific Research and Development during World War II. Dr. Bush is past president of the Carnegie Institution of Washington; he is one of the original founders of the Raytheon Manufacturing Company; and he is present chairman of the board of Merck & Company, Inc. Recipient of many awards, medals, and honorary degrees, Dr. Bush is coauthor of *Principles of Electrical Engineering* and author of *Operational Circuit Analysis, Endless Horizons,* and *Modern Arms and Free Men.*

Peter Elias was born in New Brunswick, New Jersey, in 1923. He received an S.B. degree from M.I.T. and A.M., M.Eng.Sci., and Ph.D. degrees from Harvard. At Harvard he was a Junior Fellow until he was appointed to the M.I.T. faculty in 1953. Professor Elias' major research interests include information theory and the analysis of pictures. He is coeditor of the journal, *Information and Control.*

Robert M. Fano was born in Turin, Italy, in 1917. After doing part of his undergraduate work at the School of Engineering of Turin, he received both S.B. and Sc.D. degrees in electrical engineering from M.I.T. He was formerly a group leader of Lincoln Laboratory, and during World War II a staff member of the Radiation Laboratory. In addition to his teaching at M.I.T., Professor Fano is a staff member of the M.I.T. Research Laboratory of Electronics. He has worked primarily in the fields of information theory, electromagnetic theory, and network theory, and has published a number of books in these fields, most recently, *Transmission of Information.*

Jay W. Forrester was born in Anselmo, Nebraska, in 1918. He took his B.S. in electrical engineering at the University of Nebraska, then came to M.I.T., where he worked on the staff of the Servo-mechanisms Laboratory and received an S.M. degree. Professor Forrester was responsible for construction of Whirlwind I, M.I.T.'s first high-speed digital computer. Later, as director of the Digital Computer division at the M.I.T. Lincoln Laboratory, he guided design of the SAGE System of continental air defense for the Air Force. Professor Forrester is author of the recent book, *Industrial Dynamics*.

Martin Greenberger was born in Elizabeth, New Jersey, in 1931. He received A.B., A.M., and Ph.D. degrees in applied mathematics from Harvard. Before joining the M.I.T. faculty in 1958, Professor Greenberger was manager of Applied Science Cambridge, the IBM group that cooperated with M.I.T. in the establishment and operation of the M.I.T. Computation Center. Professor Greenberger is coauthor of the recent book, *Microanalysis of Socioeconomic Systems—A Simulation Study*.

Charles C. Holt was born in Jennings, Louisiana, in 1921. He received S.B. and S.M. degrees from M.I.T., and M.A. and Ph.D. degrees from the University of Chicago. Before joining the faculty of the University of Wisconsin in 1961, Professor Holt was test engineer for the General Electric Company, staff engineer at M.I.T., and associate professor of economics at the Carnegie Institute of Technology. He is coauthor of the recent book, *Planning Production, Inventory, and Work Force*.

Grace M. Hopper was born in New York City, received an A.B. degree from Vassar College, and while teaching mathematics at Vassar, took her A.M. and Ph.D. degrees at Yale University. During World War II, Dr. Hopper served as mathematics officer with the Navy's Bureau of Ordnance in its computation project at Harvard. After the war, she joined the Eckert-Mauchly Computer Corporation as senior mathematician, played a leading role in the programming of the Binac and Univac computing systems, and later became director of automatic programming for the Remington Rand Division of Sperry Rand Corporation.

Ronald A. Howard was born in New York City in 1934. He received B.S. degrees in economics and electrical engineering, and

S.M., E.E., and Sc.D. degrees in electrical engineering, all from M.I.T. Professor Howard's interests are in operations research and systems engineering. In addition to his position at M.I.T., he serves as consultant to the Operations Research Group of Arthur D. Little, Inc. Professor Howard is author of the book, *Dynamic Programming and Markov Processes.*

Howard W. Johnson was born in Chicago, Illinois, in 1922. He received an A.B. degree from Central College and an A.M. degree in economics from the University of Chicago. He also did graduate work at the University of Glasgow, Scotland. He has been a member of the faculty of the University of Chicago, where he was director of management projects in the Industrial Relations Center. Dean Johnson came to the M.I.T. School of Industrial Management in 1955 as director of the Sloan Fellowship Program.

John G. Kemeny was born in Budapest, Hungary, in 1926. He served as assistant in the theoretical division of the Los Alamos Project at the end of World War II, then served as an assistant in teaching and research at Princeton University, where he received his A.B. and Ph.D. degrees. While at Princeton he was a research assistant to Albert Einstein in the Institute for Advanced Study. He went to Dartmouth as professor of mathematics in 1953. He is coauthor of *Introduction to Finite Mathematics, Finite Mathematical Structures,* and *Mathematical Models in the Social Sciences,* and is associate editor of the *Journal of Mathematical Analysis and Applications.*

Gilbert W. King was born in Long Eaton, Derbyshire, England, in 1914. He received S.B. and Ph.D. degrees in chemistry from M.I.T. He was a National Research Fellow at the California Institute of Technology, Harvard, and Princeton, and then served as an instructor at Yale and a research associate at M.I.T. During World War II, he was with the Office of Scientific Research and Development. His industrial associations have been with Arthur D. Little, Inc., International Telemeter Corporation, and IBM. At IBM he has directed programs in automatic language translation and information retrieval.

J. C. R. Licklider was born in St. Louis, Missouri, in 1915. He received B.A. and M.A. degrees at Washington University, St.

Louis, and a Ph.D. degree from the University of Rochester. He has been Research Associate and Fellow of the Psycho-Acoustic Laboratory at Harvard, and Associate Professor of the Psychology of Communications at M.I.T. Dr. Licklider was head of the Engineering Psychology Department and the Information Systems Research Department at Bolt Beranek and Newman before assuming his present position there.

William N. Locke was born in Watertown, Massachusetts, in 1909. He received an S.B. degree from Bowdoin College, attended the Middlebury College French Summer School, then studied in Paris at l'Ecole de Préparation des Professeurs de Français à l'Etranger and l'Institut de Phonétique. He received A.M. and Ph.D. degrees from Harvard. Professor Locke came to M.I.T. in 1945 as head of the Department of Modern Languages and in 1956 became Director of Libraries. He is coeditor of the book, *Machine Translation of Languages,* and of the journal, *Mechanical Translation.*

John McCarthy was born in Boston, Massachusetts, in 1927. He received a B.S. degree from the California Institute of Technology and a Ph.D. degree from Princeton. He was a member of the faculty at Princeton, Stanford, and Dartmouth before being appointed to the M.I.T. faculty in 1958. Professor McCarthy's principal interests include artificial intelligence, mathematical theory of computation, and computer systems design. He is coeditor of *Automata Studies.*

Donald G. Marquis was born in Two Harbors, Minnesota, in 1908. He received an A.B. degree from Stanford and a Ph.D. degree from Yale. He has been chairman of the departments of psychology at Yale and at the University of Michigan. During World War II, he was director of the Office of Psychological Personnel of the National Research Council, and he served in the Office of Scientific Research and Development. Professor Marquis is a past president of the American Psychological Association and was a member of the National Advisory Committee on Mental Health. He joined the M.I.T. faculty in 1959.

John W. Mauchly was born in Cincinnati, Ohio, in 1907. He received his doctorate in physics at Johns Hopkins University and served as head of the Physics Department at Ursinus College. Later, while on the staff of the Moore School of Electrical Engineering at the University of Pennsylvania, he and J. Presper Eckert invented and built ENIAC, the first electronic computer. Dr. Mauchly was president of the Eckert-Mauchly Computer Corporation from 1947 to 1950, when it was absorbed by Remington Rand. During this period he and Mr. Eckert designed and built UNIVAC, the first commercial electronic computer. Dr. Mauchly headed the UNIVAC applications research center until 1959, when he resigned to form his own firm.

George A. Miller was born in Charleston, West Virginia, in 1920. He received B.A. and M.A. degrees in speech from the University of Alabama, then came to Harvard for A.M. and Ph.D. degrees in psychology. Professor Miller taught at Harvard for four years. Later, while a member of the faculty at M.I.T., he worked on air defense problems as a group leader at Lincoln Laboratory. He rejoined the Harvard faculty in 1955. Professor Miller is now codirector of Harvard's Center for Cognitive Behavior. He is coauthor of *Plans and the Structure of Behavior* and author of *Language and Communication*.

Marvin L. Minsky was born in New York City in 1927. He received an A.B. degree from Harvard, and A.M. and Ph.D. degrees in mathematics from Princeton. Professor Minsky was a Junior Fellow at Harvard before going to the M.I.T. Lincoln Laboratory to work in artificial intelligence. He was appointed to the M.I.T. faculty in 1957, and is at present codirector of the M.I.T. Artificial Intelligence Group.

Elting E. Morison was born in Milwaukee, Wisconsin, in 1909, and received A.B. and A.M. degrees from Harvard University. Professor Morison has been a consultant to the Research and Development Board of the Department of Defense and a consultant to Houghton Mifflin Company. He also has been director of the Theodore Roosevelt Research Project. He is editor of *The Letters of Theodore Roosevelt* and *The American Style*, as well as author of *Admiral Sims and the Modern American Navy* and a biography of Henry L. Stimson, *Turmoil and Tradition*. Professor Morison joined the M.I.T. faculty in 1946.

Philip M. Morse was born in Shreveport, Louisiana, in 1903. He received an S.B. degree at Case Institute of Technology and M.A.

and Ph.D. degrees from Princeton. He also studied at the University of Munich and at Cambridge University before joining the M.I.T. faculty in 1931. During World War II, Professor Morse directed the Navy's Operations Evaluation Group. He also has served as scientific director of Associated Universities, Inc., and was the first director of the Atomic Energy Commission's Brookhaven National Laboratory. He is a trustee of the RAND Corporation. Professor Morse is coauthor of *Quantum Mechanics, Methods of Operations Research,* and *Methods of Theoretical Physics;* he is author of *Vibration and Sound, Queues, Inventories, and Maintenance,* and *Thermal Physics;* and he is editor of *Annals of Physics.*

Allen Newell was born in San Francisco, California, in 1927. He received a B.S. degree in physics from Stanford University and a Ph.D. degree in industrial administration from the Carnegie Institute of Technology. Before joining the faculty at Carnegie, Professor Newell was involved in large-scale organizational simulations at the RAND Corporation. He currently is working on the simulation of human thought processes and on the logical development of problem-solving programs.

Alan J. Perlis was born in Pittsburgh, Pennsylvania, in 1922. He received a B.S. degree from the Carnegie Institute of Technology and S.M. and Ph.D. degrees in mathematics from M.I.T. Before joining the faculty at Carnegie, Dr. Perlis was research mathematician with Project Whirlwind at M.I.T., mathematical advisor at the Multi-Machine Computing Laboratory, Aberdeen Proving Ground, Maryland, and assistant professor of mathematics at Purdue University. Professor Perlis is chairman of the American Committee on ALGOL and editor in chief of the *Communications of the Association for Computing Machinery.*

John R. Pierce was born in Des Moines, Iowa, in 1910. He received his B.S., M.S., and Ph.D. degrees from the California Institute of Technology, and has been with the Bell Telephone Laboratories, Inc., since 1936. Dr. Pierce served as director of electronics research at Bell before assuming his present position in 1955. He has written numerous popular science articles and short stories. Dr. Pierce is coauthor of *Man's World of Sound,* and he is author of *Electrons, Waves, and Messages* and *Symbols, Signals, and Noise.*

Emanuel R. Piore was born in Wilno, Russia, in 1908. He received B.A. and Ph.D. degrees from the University of Wisconsin, worked as research physicist with RCA, then went to CBS as engineer in charge of the television laboratory. During World War II, Dr. Piore served as senior physicist with the Navy's Bureau of Ships, later became head of the electronics branch of the Office of Naval Research, director of the ONR physical sciences division, and chief scientist of ONR. Before joining IBM, Dr. Piore was a director and vice president for research at Avco Corporation. He was appointed to the President's Science Advisory Committee in 1959.

Walter A. Rosenblith was born in Vienna, Austria, in 1913. He studied in Berlin, Lausanne, Paris, and Bordeaux. Before joining the M.I.T. faculty in 1951, he held teaching or research posts at the University of California at Los Angeles, the South Dakota School of Mines and Technology, and the Psycho-Acoustic Laboratory at Harvard. Professor Rosenblith is a research associate in otology at the Harvard Medical School and the Massachusetts Eye and Ear Infirmary. He is Acting Chairman of the Center for Communication Sciences at M.I.T.

David Sayre was born in New York City in 1924. He received an S.B. degree from Yale, then became a staff member of the M.I.T. Radiation Laboratory, where he was an editor of Volume 19 of the Radiation Laboratory Technical Series. Dr. Sayre received his doctoral degree from Oxford University, and was associated with the Johnson Foundation for Biophysics prior to joining IBM. His interests include automatic coding and artificial intelligence.

Claude E. Shannon was born in Gaylord, Michigan, in 1916. He received a B.S. degree in electrical engineering and mathematics from the University of Michigan and an S.M. degree in electrical engineering and a Ph.D. degree in mathematics from M.I.T. Professor Shannon attended the Institute for Advanced Study at Princeton and in 1941 joined the staff of the Bell Telephone Laboratories, Inc., where he remained until joining the M.I.T. faculty in 1957. Professor Shannon is coauthor of *The Mathematical Theory of Communication* and is coeditor of *Automata Studies*. He is best known for his pioneering work in information theory.

Herbert A. Simon was born in Milwaukee, Wisconsin, in 1916, and received A.B. and Ph.D. degrees from the University of Chicago. Before joining the faculty of Carnegie, he directed a program of administrative measurement studies in the Bureau of Public Administration of the University of California and was chairman of the Department of Political and Social Science at the Illinois Institute of Technology. Professor Simon is coauthor of *Planning Production, Inventory, and Work Force, Models of Man,* and *Organizations,* and is author of *Administrative Behavior* and *The New Science of Management Decision.*

Sir Charles Percy Snow was born in Leicester, England, in 1905. He received an M.S. degree in physics at Leicester University College, and a doctorate at Cambridge University, where he became a Fellow and later a tutor. During World War II, Sir Charles served as chief of scientific personnel for the British Ministry of Labor, and in 1945 was appointed Civil Service Commissioner. He also has served as physicist-director of the English Electric Company. Sir Charles is author of *The Two Cultures and the Scientific Revolution, Science and Government, The Search,* and a ten-novel sequence, *Strangers and Brothers.*

Robert C. Sprague was born in New York City in 1900. He is a graduate of the United States Naval Academy and received an S.M. degree from M.I.T. While assigned to the Office of Naval Construction at the Quincy Fore River shipyards, Mr. Sprague designed the landing gear of the nation's first aircraft carrier, the USS *Lexington.* He founded the Sprague Electric Company in 1926. Mr. Sprague has been president of the Electronic Industries Association and chairman of the Federal Reserve Bank of Boston. He also has been director of the Gaither Report Committee and consultant to the National Security Council.

Norbert Wiener was born in Columbia, Missouri, in 1894. He entered Tufts College at the age of 11 and received a B.A. degree in mathematics in 1909. After receiving an A.M. degree in 1912 and a Ph.D. degree in 1913 from Harvard, he was granted a traveling fellowship that enabled him to study with Bertrand Russell and G. H. Hardy. Professor Wiener's early teaching career included posts at Harvard and the University of Maine. He has been at M.I.T. since 1919. Professor Wiener is the author of *The Fourier Integral, Cybernetics, Extrapolation, Interpolation, and Smoothing of Stationary Time Series, The Human Use of Human Beings, Nonlinear Problems in Random Theory,* two autobiographies, and a novel.

Other participants in the general discussions included

PAUL W. ABRAHAMS, Research Assistant, M.I.T. Computation Center

DEAN N. ARDEN, Associate Professor of Electrical Engineering, M.I.T.

YEHOSHUA BAR-HILLEL, Professor of Logic and Philosophy of Science, Hebrew University, Jerusalem

DWIGHT M. B. BAUMANN, Assistant Professor of Mechanical Engineering, M.I.T.

PHILIP E. BEACH, JR., M.I.T. Fellow in Africa

NORMAN BEECHER, Project Manager, National Research Corporation

EDMUND C. BERKELEY, President, Berkeley Enterprises, Inc.

GORDON P. BRUNOW, Manager of Systems Services in Boston, Minneapolis-Honeywell Regulator Company

LAWRENCE F. BUCKLAND, Staff Engineer, Itek Laboratories

LEWIS C. CLAPP, Operations Research Group, Arthur D. Little, Inc.

HUBERT L. DREYFUS, Instructor in Humanities, M.I.T.

STUART E. DREYFUS, Assistant Professor of Industrial Management, M.I.T.

JAMES C. EMERY, Assistant Professor of Industrial Management, M.I.T.

EDWARD FREDKIN, President, Information International, Inc.

ROBERT P. FUTRELLE, Teaching Assistant in Physics, M.I.T.

CHARLES C. GARMAN, student, School of Industrial Management, M.I.T.

STEPHEN F. GRISOFF, student, Department of Mathematics, M.I.T.

ELIAS P. GYFTOPOULOS, Associate Professor of Nuclear Engineering, M.I.T.

STANLEY HERZOG, graduate student, Department of Chemical Engineering, M.I.T.

MILO P. HNILICKA, Assistant to Director of Research, National Research Corporation

JOHN H. HUGHES, Assistant Vice President, Systems and Programming, American Mutual Liability Insurance Company

THOMAS KAILATH, Instructor in Electrical Engineering, M.I.T.

MEYER M. KESSLER, Staff Member, M.I.T. Lincoln Laboratory

JACK LOWEN, Applied Physics Group, M.I.T. Lincoln Laboratory

EUGENE F. LUCAS, Systems Engineering and Management Operation, Sylvania Electric Products, Inc.

JAMES L. McKENNEY, Assistant Professor of Business Administration, Harvard University

JAMES CRAIG McLANAHAN, Manager, Terra Company, Baltimore, Maryland

FRANCO MODIGLIANI, Professor of Economics, Northwestern University

CALVIN N. MOOERS, Proprietor, Zator Company, Cambridge

ANTHONY G. OETTINGER, Associate Professor of Linguistics and Applied Mathematics, Harvard University

GUSTAVE J. RATH, Principal Scientist, Raytheon Company

JOHN C. REYNOLDS, Applied Mathematics Division, Argonne National Laboratory

EDMUND F. SHEDD, Data Systems Operations, Sylvania Electric Products, Inc.

JAMES R. SLAGLE, Staff Member, M.I.T. Lincoln Laboratory

HERBERT H. STEVENS, JR., Statistical Engineer, Texas Instruments, Inc.

PETER WEGNER, Research Associate, University of London

Contents

1 Scientists and Decision Making 2

C. P. Snow, *Speaker* 3
E. E. Morison, *Discussant* 13
N. Wiener, *Discussant* 21
H. W. Johnson, *Moderator*

2 Managerial Decision Making 36

J. W. Forrester, *Speaker* 37
C. C. Holt, *Discussant* 68
R. A. Howard, *Discussant* 74
R. C. Sprague, *Moderator*

3 Simulation of Human Thinking 94

H. A. Simon, *Speaker* 95
A. Newell, *Coauthor*
M. L. Minsky, *Discussant* 114
G. A. Miller, *Discussant* 118
S. S. Alexander, *Moderator*

4 A Library for 2000 A.D. 134

J. G. Kemeny, *Speaker* 135
R. M. Fano, *Discussant* 162
G. W. King, *Discussant* 166
W. N. Locke, *Moderator*

Contents

5 **The Computer in the University** 180

A. J. PERLIS, *Speaker* 181

P. ELIAS, *Discussant* 199

J. C. R. LICKLIDER, *Discussant* 203

D. G. MARQUIS, *Moderator*

6 **Time-Sharing Computer Systems** 220

J. McCARTHY, *Speaker* 221

J. W. MAUCHLY, *Discussant* 236

G. M. AMDAHL, *Discussant* 238

E. R. PIORE, *Moderator*

7 **A New Concept in Programming** 250

G. W. BROWN, *Speaker* 251

G. M. HOPPER, *Discussant* 271

D. SAYRE, *Discussant* 273

P. M. MORSE, *Moderator*

8 **What Computers Should Be Doing** 290

J. R. PIERCE, *Speaker* 291

C. E. SHANNON, *Discussant* 307

W. A. ROSENBLITH, *Discussant* 311

V. BUSH, *Moderator*

Selected Bibliography 327

Index 333

1

Scientists
and
Decision Making

1

Scientists
and
Decision Making

Speaker	**SIR CHARLES PERCY SNOW** Author London, England
Discussants	**ELTING E. MORISON** Professor of Industrial History Massachusetts Institute of Technology **NORBERT WIENER** Institute Professor, Emeritus Massachusetts Institute of Technology
Moderator	**HOWARD W. JOHNSON** Dean and Professor of Industrial Management Massachusetts Institute of Technology

SNOW. It is a great pleasure to be at M.I.T. tonight. Although you will not believe it, I am always saying kind things about M.I.T. behind its back. Indeed, I usually try to impress on my countrymen the absolute necessity of having an institution as reasonably nearly like it as we can manage. I have had so far absolutely no success in these efforts. But it is a real pleasure to be here. I love Cambridge. I love both parts of this great complex, and I owe very much to them.

It is also a special pleasure to be here with the discussants on the panel. From Professor Morison in his admirable book on Henry Stimson, I think I learned more about a certain kind of American politics than I have from any other single work. It is an enormous privilege and pleasure to be here with him.

As for Professor Wiener, he has been a great mythological

figure to me for nearly twenty-five years. It began because we happened to share a common friend, the great pure mathematician G. H. Hardy. Hardy used to tell me what a remarkable man Norbert Wiener was. It was very characteristic of Hardy that he should express it in the way I am about to describe. I think probably Professor Wiener will deny this story totally, but you must take it from me that it is true.

Hardy was a great mathematician. He was also extremely interested in the game of cricket, at which, in fact, he was quite a good performer. It was one of the inflictions on his foreign guests that they had to pay some attention to this peculiar pastime. Now cricket is a game roughly as complex as baseball, but complex in a rather different way. It has certain additional technical complexities because the ball is expected to hit the ground before it hits the bat, or at least that is the aim. The result is, as any of you who are familiar with baseball will at once perceive, that the ball can not only curve (what we call "move") in the air, it can also deviate off the ground; and most of the complexities of cricket in a technical sense derive from that simple fact.

Of all balls that a batsman or batter in cricket can receive, there are two which are very easy to play. One is the ball that does not hit the ground but just hits the bat directly; that is called the full toss. The other is the ball that hits the bat and the ground simultaneously, that is, pitches perhaps a foot in front of your left foot as you stand at the crease; that is called the half volley.

Hardy's story, which Professor Wiener is about to deny indignantly, is that Hardy took Professor Wiener to a cricket match and explained these technical aspects, to which Wiener with his astonishing insight said, "Yes, but between these two easy balls there must be one just a little bit in front of where the half volley was pitched and yet not quite so far on the bat as the full toss." Now, this is absolutely true. This happens to be a kind of ball called a Yorker. Why it is called a Yorker, no one knows. When a hard-bitten old professional once was asked, he said, "Well, I don't know what else you could call it."

Norbert Wiener, in his one and only acquaintance with cricket invented the theory of the Yorker. Hardy was fairly arrogant about mathematical accomplishment and would say, "Almost anyone of reasonable intelligence could do some sort of creative work in mathematics, but only a man of really distinguished intelligence, of something approaching genius, could have made this discovery about cricket at his first acquaintance with the subject."

The Luddites

I am standing before you tonight in a somewhat unusual position, or as I think it is now fashionable to call it, posture. In a little essay that I wrote, which I called "The Two Cultures and The Scientific Revolution," I had some harsh things to say about intellectual Luddites. I accused a lot of my literary intellectual friends of being, in effect, the intellectual Luddites of our day.

Ned Lud, just to remind you, was a poor unfortunate stocking weaver who lived during the early part of the nineteenth century in Nottingham in the Midlands of England, near where I was born. These stocking weavers did their work at home in their miserable cottages, which were mainly wattle and daub. These unfortunate people felt themselves menaced by the first mechanized looms. With surprising practicality, not usually possessed by intellectual Luddites, they went and destroyed the looms. That is what a Luddite was.

I have much more respect for the Luddites of that day than I have for the intellectual Luddites of our day, who simply deplore the introduction of the machine, while living off its profits; who regret the mechanical condition into which they were born, but take the fullest advantage of it. This attitude is not one which I can easily share, nor one for which I have much intellectual respect.

Nevertheless, tonight, for once in my life, I feel just a bit of an intellectual Luddite. For I am going to raise two questions of doubt as to the effect of the computer on decision making, particularly decision making in relation to scientific problems. I am not putting it more forcefully than this because I do not want you to think that I am fundamentally pessimistic on the topic. But I do feel obliged to raise two questions. There may be nothing in them, or they may be genuine warnings. Professor Wiener has forgotten more about computers than I ever knew, and he may easily be able to dispel some of these doubts or warnings.

Brownian Movement

I am going to begin quite a long way back. How are decisions made? This may sound like a trivial question, but it is the kind of question which society has never seriously examined. The concepts which people have of how decisions are made in our kind of society bear surprisingly little reference to the truth. You are the most legalistic people on earth by miles, and so you are always inventing legalistic diagrams of responsibility and are frightfully upset if they do not seem to correspond to reality. But usually they do not. We all know that even in nonsecret decisions there is a great deal of intimate closed politics, a subject to which I have given probably too much of my literary life. In your country, you elect a President; he initiates legislation (that is, he takes a decision as to which legislation to produce), and then the Congress takes the decision as to whether this legislation is to go into action.

In my country the procedure is more vague, but very similar: the country elects a Government and that Government collectively lays its decisions or its suggested decisions before the House of Commons. Those are the legalistic diagrams; and yet, in depth, I suspect that many of the most important decisions, although they may finish up with this format as a kind of rationalization after the event, do not take place in this way at all.

I believe that the healthiest decisions of society occur by

something much more like a Brownian movement. All kinds of people all over the place suddenly get smitten with the same sort of desire, with the same sort of interest, at the same time. This forms concentrations of pressure and of direction. These concentrations of pressure gradually filter their way through to the people whose nominal responsibility it is to put the legislation into a written form. I am pretty sure that this Brownian movement is probably the most important way in which the ordinary social imperatives of society get initiated.

Let me take two examples, one from my country, which has happened, and one from yours, which I think will happen. The one from my country which happened was the introduction of a National Health Service. All over England there had been people thinking, unconstrained by their party politics, that this was the kind of thing which our society must really set about, that health was too important a matter to be left entirely to the kind of money which you could reach for. This thinking was surprisingly general. One heard it on all hands. It was not a Labor matter, it was not a Conservative matter. It was weighted more on the Left than on the Right, but not very much more. Any government both could and would have had to find expression for this concentration of pressure. It was a perfect example, I think, of the way in which this anonymous Brownian movement finally found its way through into the written legalistic act.

As I go about the United States, I believe that a similar process is taking place here and now. I believe that all over this country there are people saying that although your college education is wonderful and can do everything which you ask it to do, your elementary and high-school education in certain respects leaves a great deal to be desired. I think that one feels and hears this kind of dissatisfaction everywhere one goes. I, myself, believe that the broad social generosity of your educational program is a fine thing. I believe that in strategy, in intention, your education is incomparably better than ours; but I have been in high schools where I felt it would be a good idea if the children sometimes were taught something. I am

7

just saying that as a friendly outsider who knows you pretty well, but I have heard it in much more virulent form from my American friends. Although the ramifications and the inter-connections of the federal system are the devil's own business to cut through, I am quite sure that within the not very distant future we shall see the widespread demand for a revised elementary and high-school curriculum enforced upon the people who in theory make the decisions.

Decisions in Secret by the Few

This Brownian movement is one of the ways in which any type of healthy society, not only a parliamentary democracy, makes some of its decisions. But the particular social situation in which we now find ourselves drives us into a very different kind of decision. We happen to be living at the time of a major scientific revolution, probably more important in its consequences than the first Industrial Revolution, a revolution which we shall see in full force in the very near future. We also have seen the two biggest political revolutions of all time and the two biggest wars of all time, and all this has happened within approximately forty years. This has meant a tempest of history which is not yet over and a rate of change which is going to accelerate more and more. We are not going to have a stable intellectual or social world within our lifetimes. That is the situation. As a result, many of the cardinal decisions of society are being taken in a way of which we are all aware, but which none of us like, a way which alters the entire structure of democracy and brings with it numerous consequences. This is what I was trying to say in the Godkin lectures in a neighboring institution.[1]

Unfortunately, partly through my own fault, the message that I was trying to convey got somewhat overshadowed by a personal anecdote.* I had to tell a personal anecdote because it demonstrated one of the essential features of this new type of secret decision which is taken by very few people — that

---

* The anecdote is the Tizard-Lindemann story recounted in Reference 1.

personalities matter very much more than they do in open, nonsecret politics. It is a curious irony, but I think there is no doubt of the fact. However, I showed poor literary tact in letting the personal story from which I was drawing examples obscure what I was trying to say. Now I can try to extract slightly more sharply the lesson I was wanting to be drawn. And this is that decisions which are going to affect a great deal of our lives, indeed whether we live at all, will have to be taken or actually are being taken by extremely small numbers of people, who are normally scientists. The execution of these decisions has to be entrusted to people who do not quite understand what the depth of the argument is. That is one of the consequences of the lapse or gulf in communication between scientists and nonscientists.

There it is. A handful of people, having no relation to the will of society, having no communication with the rest of society, will be taking decisions in secret which are going to affect our lives in the deepest sense.

I chose simply for convenience, because it was far enough in the past, two particular decisions in my own country. One was the matter of how we should defend ourselves before the Hitler War. The decision was taken to give highest priority to the radar chain. No more than fifty people, and at the point of action no more than five or six, were involved in that decision. My second example was the decision in 1942 to make strategic bombing, the bombing of the civilian population, a major part of the British war effort.

The second is a slightly different example from the first, because to some extent the decision to make bombing a major activity had some of the features of the Brownian movement which I described. That is, before the war and during its earliest years, a lot of English people felt with remarkable lack of strategic judgment that this was the one thing which we could do and ought to do. It was a great mistake, and it probably affected the judgment of those who finally had to take the decision. The final decision, of course, was taken again by very small numbers of persons, and you know the consequences.

9

We certainly disturbed the process of the war, and in my view, we certainly lengthened it.

These are characteristic decisions which in society now are being taken in secret by scientific persons and scientifically minded persons. As I look at it, it seems to me that there is very little to recommend this method. It may be partly inevitable, but some of it is not at all inevitable. The procedure would have nothing to recommend it were we not in the state of exaggerated world tension that we actually are. It has nothing to recommend it but speed.

As a general rule, very small groups of people are less wise than larger groups of people. Very occasionally, small groups can produce pieces of imagination and initiative which large ones would not. But, by and large, that is not true; by and large, maximum errors of judgment occur when concentrations of power result in decisions being taken by the smallest possible number of people. In fact, when I reflect on my experience as an observer of these things, the criticism I feel inclined to accept of my own attitude is that on the whole I accept closed and secret decisions too easily; that I have got used to them; that I know the way they work and in some ways find them even cozy; that I like them too much and do not realize how inhuman and contemptuous they tend to make the decision makers. I believe that is a criticism which I ought to take to heart.

A New Elite

Let us take this as the existing state of our world. And now, the computer comes on the scene. Previously, it seems to me, we have had two groups of persons in secret government: the circle of scientists who are knowledgeable about what is happening and which decisions must be made, and the larger circle of administrators and politicians to whom the scientists' findings have to be translated. My worry is that the introduction of the computer is going to lead to a smaller circle still. I am asking a question; I am not making a definite prediction. Instead of having the small group of scientists, knowledgeable enough to have something to add to the decisions, I am asking whether we are now running into a position where only those who are concerned with the computer, who are formulating its decision rules, are going to be knowledgeable about the decision. If so, instead of having a small circle of scientists and a large circle of administrators, we shall have a tiny circle of computer boys, a larger circle of scientists who are not familiar with the decision rules and are not versed in the new computer art, and then, again, the large circle of politicians and administrators.

It seems to me that it is going to require a tremendous effort to try to make all scientists in government literate in computers, and it is going to be quite impossible to make anyone else in government literate about computers at all. I know that you can do all kinds of things with these beasts. You can build in rules so that they defer to human judgment. Nevertheless, I suspect that the chap standing next to the machine, who really knows how it makes decisions, and who has the machine under his command, is going to be in an excessively influential position. If there is anything in this, we are running into an added danger.

What I would like to suggest is a piece of pure experimentation. The facts about the strategic-bombing controversies of 1942 happen to be exceptionally well documented. All the figures available in 1942 are there on the table. I should like to see two teams, one *pro* strategic bombing by inclination and one *anti* strategic bombing, both armed with their computer program or programs. It would be interesting then to see how the argument would have proceeded. Is this not a case where, with a little imagination, we could learn something from history?

Most decision making, of course, consists of finding arguments to justify what you know you are already going to do. I would guess that in these circumstances probably the *pro* strategic bombing characters would have come out with approximately the same answer that they did in 1942, and the *anti* strategic bombing experts would have come out with exactly the same answer as they did in 1942. But I believe it would be a valuable piece of research to try to see what difference, in reasonably accessible historical situations, the introduction of the computer really would make. It may make much more difference than I think.

The Gadget Charm

My second apprehensive question concerns an intellectual danger with great practical consequences. Cybernetics, as named by its founder, is a beautiful subject with great intellectual variety, depth, and complexity. I suspect, however, that the computer in certain hands could easily become a gadget. Gadgets are the greatest single source of misjudgment that I have ever seen, or that anyone has ever seen in scientific decisions in our time. People get fascinated by gadgets. They love them. They want everything to be explained in terms of their gadget. They think it is the answer to everything on heaven and earth. All the bad decisions I have seen have some element of gadgetry in them. And I suspect that computers in government are going to get into the hands of persons with mildly defective or canalized judgment and become gadgets. It will be astonishing if that does not happen.

Society Left Outside

Clearly we have not yet reached the stage of real danger. But dangers are usually much better met if you have anticipated them. Most things can be coped with if you recognize them in time. I think that with a certain amount of administrative and experimental skill we can reconstruct certain historical situations with the aid of a computer and see how the answers turn out. It will need some historical imagination, some scientific imagination, and especially some psychological imagination, but I am sure it is worth doing. Otherwise, the obvious and glaring danger is that the individual human judgment is going to take a part which will get smaller and smaller as the years go by. I am inclined to think that for a society which is really viable, and certainly for one which feels itself to be morally viable, there is no substitute for individual human judgment; and the wider it is spread, the healthier and more viable this society is likely to be.

It is not only that I am afraid of misjudgments by persons armed with computing instruments; it is also that I am afraid of the rest of society's contracting out, feeling that they have no part in what is of vital concern to them because it is happening altogether incomprehensibly and over their heads. I suspect that the feeling of being left out, being outside the decision-making party, as it were, is one of the causes of the malaise of our society. We must not let it go too far. I am not in the least pessimistic about our finding our way through these difficulties and dangers. I believe that the computer is a wonderful subject and a tool from which we can get great service. But if we let the individual human judgment go by default, if we give all the power of decision to more and more esoteric groups, then both the moral and intellectual life will wither and die.

Panel Discussion

MORISON. I shall make clear at the beginning two things that would, in any case, become obvious as I go along. First, I do not know very much about the subject of these talks, the computer. And second, I have spent my life in that culture which, as Sir Charles suggests, tends to produce nervous apprehension and depression of the spirit.

I do know that the computer in its present form is a relatively new machine; so I thought I might say a word or two as a historian on the way new machines and men have got on together in the past. I also know that the computer is a machine that will give answers to certain kinds of questions and supply solutions to certain kinds of problems. So I thought I might suggest what some men in my culture think they have found out about the perplexing dialogue between question and answer, problem and solution.

As for the first topic, no more than Sir Charles am I a Luddite. One of the things you can learn from history is that men have lived with machinery at least as well as, and probably a good deal better than, they have yet learned to live with one another. Whenever a new device has been put into society — the loom, the internal-combustion engine, the electric generator — there have been temporary dislocations, confusions, and injustices. But over time men have learned to create new arrangements to fit the new conditions. Anything that has the power to build also has, of course, the power to destroy, and this applies to machines in the hands of men. But, on the whole, and more often than not, men have always succeeded in organizing mechanical systems for constructive purposes and for the enlargement of human competence and opportunity. No one, I think, who compares the condition of life for the average person in the seventeenth century with the average condition of life today in our society can fail to reach this conclusion.

Partly for this reason, I am not as much of a Luddite as Sir Charles may be. Take his first apprehension — that the computer may measurably increase the tendency toward closed decisions in our society. Obviously, we shall have to think about this. Machines can, beyond doubt, alter some of our views of things — the multiengine plane, for instance, has changed somewhat our sense of time and space. But there is, as I understand it, nothing in the nature of the computer that will necessarily take us nearer to closed decisions — closed decisions such as those taken in the days of Wolsey or Richelieu or Caesar long before there were radar sets or computers. Both the machine and its programmers will have to work within a general scheme, a field of general decisions and determinations that can still, as Sir Charles says, be gathered out of the air if that is the way we want to do it. In determining the kind of life you want to have, the instrumentation is less influential than the nature of the culture you create to control what you want to use the instruments for.

For example, I do not believe that the rumble seat of automobiles increased the incidence, it merely changed the locus, of experiment in physical relations between boys and girls in the age of F. Scott Fitzgerald.

Then there is the apprehension about the computer as a fascinating gadget. It is obvious that there is always danger from the gadget-happy — whether the gadget is a machine, an idea, or a procedure. Amasa Stone, a very able man, killed a trainload of people because, against advice, he built a bridge at Ashtabula from a truss design for which he had an ancient attachment. I have no tonsils, nor have my brothers, nor have most of my generation, because an accomplished ear, eye, nose and throat man and his colleagues were all obsessed with the thought that the way to make a boy grow was to take out his tonsils.

In an age of new departures we have to live with all this, I suppose, but history suggests only for a limited period in each case. Over time the potentials of a new gadget are explored by trial and error until the real capacities are discovered and understood. Then, whatever it may be — Manichaean heresy, steam turbine, penicillin — it is fitted into a reasonable context.

I do not want to appear like a wise old head, made sager by my study of history than those like Sir Charles who have actually been there. Of course what he has said should cause any sensible man to think, and what I have said does not, I know, fully dispose of the complex problems he raises. Perhaps we can all talk about these things together afterwards. But now, I do not have much time, and I want to get on to a nervous apprehension of my own.

I think we may have more difficulty in exploring the full limits of the computer than we have had with earlier gadgets. I think there may be more danger in the period of trial and error than there has been with earlier devices. These earlier devices — looms, engines, generators — resisted at critical points human ignorance and stupidity. Overloaded, abused, they stopped work, stalled, broke down, blew up; and there was the end of it. Thus they set clear limits to man's ineptitudes. For the computer, I believe, the limits are not so obvious. Used in ignorance or stupidity, asked a foolish question, it does not

15

collapse, it goes on to answer a fool according to his folly. And the questioner, being a fool, will go on to act on the reply.

This at least is what my culture tells me often happens. Let me give you an example. In the play with which you are all familiar, Hamlet had a problem which he defined for himself as follows: What had happened to the late King of Denmark and what should he, Hamlet, do about it? Framing the question accurately — a good program — he took it to a ghost — the most sophisticated mechanism in the late sixteenth century for giving answers to hard questions. From the ghost he got back a very detailed reply, which included a recommendation for a specific course of action. Responding to these advices, Hamlet created a political, social, moral, and administrative mess that was simply hair-raising.

The trouble was that he had got the right answer — the answer he deserved — to a question that was totally wrong. He had asked about his father when he should have asked, as any psychologist will tell you, about himself and his relations with his mother.

My culture says, in other words, that it is much harder to ask the right question than it is to find the right answer to the wrong question.

Some of you, like some of my students, may say that Hamlet is only a play, so what does it prove? I therefore shall give you some further evidence about questions and answers taken from real history. We asked ourselves once, in the first days of the Republic, what a negro was really worth and came up in the Constitution with the answer that he was worth three-fifths of a white man. Somewhat later we asked ourselves how to increase the income of the average citizen and decided the answer was to coin silver at a rate of 16 to 1. And still later we asked how we could limit the arms race between Britain and us, and worked out the answer that for every British light cruiser we could have 1.4 American heavy cruisers. About the same time we asked ourselves how to make the nation "self-sustaining," and arrived at the answer of the Smoot-Hawley tariff which set an average ad valorem rate of 40.1 per cent for all schedules.

You will know, I am sure, that all of these answers caused us very real trouble of one kind or another. They did so because the questions they were designed to answer were framed in a wrong interpretation of events, a false conception of the actual problem. The answers supplied therefore gave the wrong solutions. They represented collectively what Ramsay MacDonald said of one of them: "an attempt to clothe unreality in the garb of mathematical reality."

The quotation from the Prime Minister suggests a further source of nervous apprehension — the tendency to simplify human situations and to do so, often enough, by reducing them to quantifiable elements. I have spoken of Hamlet so, by way of illustration, I will speak of him again. I remember two things my engineer-type students have said in explanation of his behavior. First, he had too much feedback in his circuits, and second, he was 16⅔ per cent efficient, because he had one person to kill and he killed six. This, purely incidentally, is about the thermal efficiency of the average internal-combustion engine.

What I want to suggest here is the persistent human temptation to make life more explicable by making it more calculable; to put experience into some logical scheme that, by its order and niceness, will make what happens seem more understandable, analysis more bearable, decision simpler. When you talk of 140 per cent of a cruiser, you can hope you have solved the underlying diplomatic issue you haven't dared to raise; when you pass a tariff with average rates of 40.1 per cent ad valorem to make a nation self-sustaining, you can assume that you do not have to look further for the causes of the worst depression in the nation's history — to which, incidentally, you have just contributed by passing the tariff. This is, I suppose, the way it does figure; and this seems to have been the human tendency from the time of Plato's quantification of the Guardian's role right on down.

I am not trying to suggest that the computer will soon bring us all under the cloak of the mathematical reality of its programs. But today the tendency to work with quantifiable elements and logical systems seems to me accelerating. There are more tests and measurements (the brain of a candidate for college works within a precisely graded scale from, presumably, 1 to 800), more rational systems like those of Keynes and Freud to assist us in ordering the economy and the personality, more mathematical models, and more efforts, as in this School of Industrial Management, to reduce administrative experience to quantifiable elements. This, in the name of clarification and the advancement of general understanding, is quite obviously all to the good. The aim of pure reason, which proceeds upon measurable quantities, is, presumably, to introduce increasing order and system into the randomness of life. But I have here the apprehension that as time goes by we may begin to lose somewhat our sense of the significance of the qualitative elements in a situation — such things as the loyalties, memories, affections, and feelings men bring to any situation, things which make situations more messy but, for men, more real. My apprehension is that the computer, which feeds on quantifiable data, may give too much aid and comfort to those who think you can learn all the important things in life by breaking experience down into its measurable parts.

I hope it is evident that I am for order and logic. But I do hope also that it remains clear that in all the really interesting questions and problems of life the measurable and the immeasurable are all mixed up. I think from time to time of the Pythagoreans, those men who came to believe that "all things are numbers" and who were supposed to have put to death a man who suggested the idea of the incommensurable. Even in an inventory program the risk one is willing to bear if he runs out of stock must be considered — and this risk is in part determined by the unknown size of the irritation of frustrated customers. Even in the strategic-bombing exercise suggested by Sir Charles, there is what might be called the Coventry factor to put in the program — the unrequited feelings of men and women who had been bombed with no redress.

Still, I am no Luddite. What I want to do, first, is to find out all there is to find out about the computer. And I must say this is hard enough. In my cursory researches I have been told a great many different things by people who have at least thought more about it than I: that it is and always will be simply an idiot doing what it is told to do; that it can now design fractional horsepower motors and electrical circuits; that it can already throw old data into new combinations — introduce intellectual surprise; that it may some day write a sonata; and that, if we can get enough vacuum tubes hooked up right (10^{10} is the figure), we cannot exclude the possibility that it may feel its own emotion and have a will of its own. The spread between assumed present capacity and the foreboded potential is, in other words, considerable.

In any case the computer is here, and no doubt it is going to develop. Everybody, or almost everybody, seems a little uneasy about this, and why not? This is man's first encounter outside himself with something that is exactly like some inside part of himself. It is not, as many other machines have been, like his arms or hands or legs in the work it does, it is like him. How much like him we do not yet know. But regardless of what happens in the future, we have already made a machine that simulates some part, a small part, of what we alone have been able to do in the past by thinking. Even this small advance begins to raise the large question we have succeeded so often in avoiding — as Hamlet did for instance. What is in fact our true image, what is our real likeness?

To assist us in examining this question, I propose, not that we bust up the machine, but rather that we explore it in a series of experiments suggested to me by Sir Charles's idea of replaying the bombing problem. I suggest a continuing experiment in which the machine would be asked to reconstrue a series of situations out of the past — situations taken from my own culture — in which men have acted most successfully on their own. One could begin with simple things — a successful plant relocation — and work up through, let us say, the Army and Navy decision on how to use the plane against the submarine, and then on to the most interesting situations — our method of limiting trusts and cartels as revealed in the Sherman Act and its subsequent modifying judicial interpretations, or the miracle of Queen Elizabeth I's foreign policy. I suggest for each situation a series of experimental programs — leaving some things out, adding some things, practicing ways to code things that seem uncodable, and so forth — to test various hypotheses and understandings by repeated trials against what may be called the real situation.

Some of the problems may be, at the moment, a bit far out, given the present state of the art. Also it is probable that the study of a particular past and nonrecurring situation would not produce the most desirable results. For instance, it has been suggested that a program designed from evidence taken from the record of six or eight different revolutions might well be useful in the attempt to discover how to control common elements — both the stabilizing and the disrupting — that operate in all revolutions, including the one we are in today. Or a program put to a computer on the problems of underdeveloped regions that are now developing under the energy of technology might well include data collected from the history of other regions that have passed through this stage of experience.

Whatever difficulties or defects there may be in these particular proposals, I am told a beginning of some sort could be made in the direction I suggest, and I hope it will be, for several reasons.

First, a good many people would have to learn some history — which is a good thing.

Second, it would be a way to capitalize on the ancient truth that fools persisting in their folly learn wisdom. We could acquire understanding of the uses of the machine without danger in a time of controlled trial and error.

Third, the machine would therefore become not so much a problem solver as a learning machine, which is today in fashion. Used as suggested, it would force us, again without danger, out from behind the silly or distracting questions we like to ask to the real questions we have to ask — and teach us to ask them more correctly. It would thus help us to sort out the things that can be thought from the things that can only be felt, and advance a little of our understanding of how much feeling goes into what we call thinking. Perhaps some of the things we now classify as feeling may turn out to be more identifiable and explicitly definable, as the work of Freud indeed suggests, than we think. But if not, if they cannot be programmed as they say, at least by this exercise we may well find out more about their meaning and influence. What I am suggesting here is, I trust, obvious: that we use the machine which simulates to explore fully what it is simulating — what image, what likeness.

For some, this assault by mechanism upon what e. e. cummings calls the single secret that is still man will be distasteful and to some appalling. It is not — at least not to me. Over on the other side good friends of mine are using accelerators to find out the secrets of other marvelous structures. The more they find, the more they seem to stand with respect, indeed with wonder, before their findings. If man working experimentally can learn more about himself from something he invented, can learn who he is, and who he is not, then he will have learned enough, I should think, to use himself as well as the machine that simulates more wisely and constructively.

And if in this process he finds, at length, the full answer to the single secret — well, that is what my crowd has been trying to do for twenty-five hundred years.

WIENER. I think we have been talking a good deal about computing machines on the basis of rather a shady account of what these machines are, and an even shadier account of what these machine are going to be.

I shall not confine my remarks to computing machines; I am going to talk about control apparatus in general. The difference between the two from our point of view is not very great. The computing machine is a general-purpose device that can be programmed to do very specific jobs, and it may be at the heart of the control apparatus for certain applications. But let us talk in general about control and communication machines, rather than specifically about computing machines.

As has been intimated by Professor Morison, we are starting to hear about a class of machines just coming into being — the learning machine. I want to say something more about the learning machine, because I think that both the greatest part of the difficulties which we have been discussing and the greatest part of the possibilities for relieving these difficulties lie in this machine.

Take the learning machine as it now exists. One form of it is a machine for playing checkers. Now, it is possible to play checkers with machines that are not learning machines. It is possible to write down at any stage of a game all the successive moves that are legally possible for the next stage; to rank them on a scale of values involving loss of pieces, mobility, control, and many other factors (I believe about fifteen factors have been considered in one game); and then to give these factors certain weightings, established at the beginning. This procedure leads to a machine that is a checker-playing machine to a limited extent, but not a learning machine. If you were to play against this machine, it would feel like a rigid personality. (By the way, if you play correspondence checkers or chess, whether with a machine or a person, you do acquire a feeling for the personality opposed to you.) When a rigid personality makes a blunder, it always repeats the same blunder in the same situation.

A machine with a less rigid personality can be achieved as follows. The machine plays as before, but now keeps a record of all plays made and all games played. At intervals it is run in a different way. Instead of evaluating moves in terms of a fixed scale of evaluation, it evaluates the scale of evaluation in terms of the games played. It determines which scale of evaluation would have led to wins more assuredly than any other. There are various tricks of accomplishing this which I need not describe here; they are not perfect, but they are valid. The machine, having determined which scale of evaluation would have been most conducive to winning, adopts it for further play. That is learning.

Such a machine, if you use it for playing checkers, as it has been used, would have a more flexible personality. The tricks that once worked against it might fail with its increasing experience and its re-evaluation of various considerations. Such a machine has been developed by Samuel of IBM.[2] At first the machine was able to defeat Samuel fairly consistently. Later on he learned a little more checkers and was able to defeat the machine more often. Nevertheless, the fact is that the machine can go beyond the person who programmed it. Even though Samuel caught up, there is always the possibility that the machine may catch up again later with more sophisticated programming.

The fact that a machine can defeat the man who programmed it means that having made such a machine does not give him completely effective control over it. If he had that, he would not let it beat him. Now, this is very important. Such a machine could be very useful in certain decision situations. It could be used to play games other than checkers: the business game, the war game, and the game of determining when to press the button for Armageddon — for the thermonuclear war.

How are you going to program such a machine? Well, you cannot program it based on prior thermonuclear wars. You would have to play the game according to a set of postulates which you constructed. You could make the machine learn to be more successful within the framework of these postulates. However, you receive no indication from this whether your postulates have the right values. Such a machine, in other words, can beg the question very badly and can be very dangerous.

What you have here is a situation not unlike that found in the folk tale, "The Monkey's Paw." "The Monkey's Paw" is a story told by W. W. Jacobs of England at the beginning of the century.[3] An old soldier returns from India to visit a friend. He has with him a talisman that he says has the ability to grant three wishes to each of three people. The first owner of the talisman had taken the first set of three wishes, two unknown to the soldier, but the third one for death. That is how the soldier became owner. The soldier took the second set of wishes for himself, but declines to talk about them. His experiences were too terrible. One set of wishes remains. With considerable reluctance the soldier yields to his friend's request for the talisman. The friend's first wish is for £200, and an official of the company where his son is employed comes in to tell him that his son has been crushed in the machinery. As a solatium, but without any admission of responsibility, the company has granted the father £200. The next wish is that the boy be back, and his mutilated ghost appears knocking at the door; the third wish is that the ghost go away.

The point is that magic is terribly literal-minded. It will give you what you ask for, not what you should have asked for, nor necessarily what you want. This will most certainly be true about learning machines. If you do not put into the programming the important restriction that you do not want £200 at the cost of having your son ground up in the machinery, you cannot expect the machine itself to think of this restriction.

"The Monkey's Paw" suggests a very real danger of the learning machine. The danger of these machines is greater than that of the simple computing machine, because you do not set down for it the tactics of the policy but only the strategy. You let the tactics work themselves out from the experience of the machine. The machine acquires a nature based on its experience.

So there are real dangers here. Is there any way of partially overcoming these dangers? The importance of learning machines is not how they act as pure machines, but how they interact with society. We thus are led to the concept of a system involving both human actions and machines. Is there any way in such a system to transfer values from the human being to the machine?

In a general, imperfect sense there is. Suppose you build a machine to translate a language. The value of the translation is a human value. The value depends upon whether people reading the translation will interpret it with the same meaning as the original. It is conceivable that you might attain a value system by having a complete logical code of translations, a superperfect grammar; but this would not be a really profitable way to proceed. Instead, you would have the machine do exercises, just as a human pupil does exercises. These exercises would be marked by a teacher who possesses human values. The machine would modify itself based on these marks, just as the checker-playing machine modifies itself based on its prior wins. It is at least theoretically possible to transfer values from the human being to the machine in such man-machine organizations. I think that the possibility of reproducing human values is of great importance, but in itself has dangers too.

The last thing I want to discuss is the temptation of gadgets. What are the tempting things about gadgets? What are the tempting things about machines? What are the tempting things about an organization with great compartmentation and high secrecy? These are the human questions that arise.

I am reminded here of the game of Russian roulette. At various times, in remote barracks and posts, officers have played this game of putting one bullet into their revolvers, spinning the chamber, and pulling the trigger, either at themselves or somebody else. This is obviously a means of expressing aggressive impulses either against oneself or against one's opponent. It is obviously a form of masochism or sadism. It is permissible, however, because one man has removed final responsibility for the act from himself, put it in the machine, and left it to chance. If he kills the other man, he has provided himself with a way (in his mind) of reducing his responsibility from what we ordinarily associate with murder to what we associate with manslaughter. He can blame chance.

This is very much like the game that is often played when a prisoner is taken before a firing squad. Each man in the firing squad has his rifle loaded with several blank cartridges and a single bullet. The result is that the men are more willing to fire because of the overwhelming likelihood that they will not kill the prisoner. This is a way of avoiding responsibility.

I am certain that a great deal of the use of gadgets for decisions, as it exists now and as it may exist even more in the future, is motivated by this desire to avoid direct responsibility. I am sure that a lot of the subdivision of effort in secret projects and highly compartmented projects has the same motive. The subordinate does not know enough about the project to feel responsibility, and the man in charge can place responsibility with the system. I believe that one of the greatest dangers at the present time has to do with the attempt to avoid responsibility in order to avoid the feeling of guilt.

SNOW. I find myself in very close sympathy with both discussants, which is a rather tedious position to be in. I share Professor Morison's passion for history in a very amateur sense, but in my view he, like all historians, slightly underestimates those few occasions in human affairs where there is a genuine discontinuity. I believe that the amount of energy we can now trigger is so grossly different from the amount of energy we could trigger in the very recent past, that a great many decisions take on a quite disproportionate significance. It is a significance which is unique in history. This discontinuity makes some of the language and attitudes of history, not exactly inappropriate, but often not entirely adequate.

I found Professor Wiener's remarks fascinating, but he provided more dangers than I ever could have imagined. Though intellectually stimulated, I do not feel really encouraged. My state of mild apprehension has not been dispelled.

MORISON. I do not in any way discount or deny that there is really an absolute change today to which certain of the precedents of the past do not apply. This is one of the things that worries me as much as anything we have discussed. There are many precedents which suggest that we can learn from our small-size errors, and historians tend to rely on these. It is the really large error that we do not know how to deal with very effectively, and I share Sir Charles's concern.

WIENER. There is a real possibility that changes in our environment have exceeded our capacity to adapt. The real dangers at the present time — the danger of thermonuclear war, the computing-machine sort of danger, the population-explosion danger, the danger of the improvement of medicine (to the extent that we shall very soon have to face not letting people live as part of the policy of letting them live) — all of these dangers make one wonder whether we have not changed the environment beyond our capacity to adjust to it, and whether we may not be biologically on the way out. We may not be, but this is not at all clear.

SNOW. What Professor Wiener has said is very real. Our tendency is to laugh it off, but it is not something that I would laugh off too easily.

WIENER. I think that the over-all danger from the total situation is much greater than the danger from any of its particular manifestations, such as the atomic bomb or the learning machine.

SNOW. I agree.

General Discussion

MINSKY. I should like to address a remark to Professor Morison, and I shall try to speak as an antihistorian. The experiment that you propose reminds me of the experiment that I feel historians have been avoiding very skillfully for many years; namely, to take a precise area of history about which not everything is generally known, but many facts can be found, and then have a group of professional historians study the facts and predict the outcome. It seems to me that members of your profession, and social "scientists" in general, have meticulously avoided any such experiments.

What brings this to mind is your sanguine attitude about

the way mankind will adjust to the computer — to this minor innovation or gadget. You look back at history as a professional historian and see a continual sequence of successful adjustments to dreadful or complicated gadgets. I, as an antihistorian, look back at history and see the most horrible sequence of disasters, with billions of people (or at least millions, before the population reached the precarious state at which it could be billions) being wiped out every few hundred years in virtually every culture. I do not get the impression of mankind's being capable of surviving even minor dislocations. It happens that a number of people seem to survive these disasters and start over, but I cannot see the flow of history as a neat adaptation to innovations.

MORISON.   I hope it was clear that in making my suggestion I was not above using the machine to improve the profession. I should agree with you that one of the things we as a profession have too much difficulty with is using the data in what you people would call a useful way, that is, to make generalizations and predictions. I think we have been timid in this respect. In fact, one of the reasons why I made the suggestion I did was to see what my historian friends would say. I thought it might force us all to think in new and different terms.

As for your second comment, I hope that I said (and I think I did) that we find it easier to live with machines than with each other. I think this is true. I think the disasters which you refer to were frequently not caused so much by machines directly as by our failure to accommodate to our fellow man.

WIENER.   There is one thing about the machine; the machine habit is like the liquor habit. If we drink enough of it, and we already have, it is an awfully hard thing to stop. We have made ourselves dependent upon the machine, on the car, for instance. We are suffering from the way the train is breaking down, and we cannot give up the airplane. We have made ourselves more vulnerable to machine failure than ever before. We cannot go back to the old agrarian civilization. The soil is not there. The habit of raising crops, the habit of living off your own patch of potatoes, are just not there anymore. In an emergency we should have a terrible time adjusting ourselves, if we ever could, to the way not only that our great-great-great-grandfathers lived, but even to the way that our grandfathers lived.

HNILICKA. One of the basic problems of history and of mankind is that all our thinking and philosophy are based on a static situation. We always assume that the way things are now in their static form is actually the right representation. Would the panel be so kind as to comment on whether the machine might help us interpret future stability, not from the static point of view, but from the dynamic point of view, so that we cannot just catch up but actually predict what is going to happen?

SNOW. This is an extremely interesting point. It is clearly true that societies like ours find it extraordinarily hard to understand change. The problem is very large, and I think that the machine might help us here.

WIENER. I should agree that the machine might help. It is true not only that the equilibrium of society must be dynamic, but that its possible breakdown must be dynamic, too. If we have a catastrophe, the final catastrophe, it probably will not be because our world has broken down statically, but because, as the engineers would put it, the transients have reached the explosive point. The idea of a dynamic equilibrium must be supplemented by the idea of a dynamic disequilibrium and a dynamic collapse. These also can be studied to some extent on the machine.

HERZOG. I am a little curious why Sir Charles is so worried about scientists' becoming an in-group in government. Certainly the militarists and the economists have been in-groups in government whom most of us could not understand. Does Sir Charles really think that scientists will do worse than politicians have done?

SNOW. I have been accused of some awful things in my time, but why in God's name do I get accused of this? Now, I have said very clearly that I should like to see many more scientists with direct responsibility in the affairs of government.

There are two things that frighten me: first, the assumption of power by very few people of any kind (scientists happen to be an exceptionally important group with extreme powers, and I would hate to see a solitary scientific overlord in any country); and second, the danger of even a relatively large group of scientists, with the actual legal decision-making power, communicating across a void. Both of these things I have said. But I have never said that I am especially frightened of scientists; this would be an absurd statement for me to make.

BEECHER. The training of a person in values takes anywhere from twenty-one to fifty years, depending on where the person is reared, before he is judged worthy to make a decision. Is there any reason to suppose that we could reduce the time with a learning machine? Also, how are we going to get the input? Are we going to send the learning machine to Sunday school, and then during the week teach it not to take what it learned too seriously, as we do with our children?

WIENER. With respect to breadth and depth of learning, man will be far superior to any machine that we are likely to see for a long, long time; very likely for all time. One of the advantages of the machine, however, is its ability to work faster and do many things in the same time that a man does relatively few. It is conceivable that over a limited scope the learning of the machine can proceed more rapidly than the learning of man. This will not be done without effort, but it is at least possible.

MORISON. I should like to ask Professor Wiener to go a little further and talk technically about how value can be programmed. How far have we gone on this?

WIENER. We have gone only a small distance, but the possibility is very clear. Consider a translating machine. You grade it on its translation and use this grade to modify the translating program, just as you use the past performance of a checker-playing machine to change the machine's playing of checkers — perhaps assigning 1 for winning and 0 for losing. In this way you teach the human values of what a good translation is to the machine.

You can transfer values from one machine to another in a similar way. This ability is really very important. It makes possible a self-reproducing machine that will make other machines in its own image. There is a definite mathematical theory supporting this possibility. We can use one machine to condition a second to have the same effect that the original does. And there are still other modes of interaction possible between machines. We can have criticism, and this criticism can be used to transfer values. This needs to be worked out in much greater detail, but it is the only promising way that I see for making a translating machine that will be any good.

MORISON. It would be fun to program the Book of Job on a machine that has made another machine in its own image and see how the relationship between God and man works out.

WIENER. In the machine that makes another machine in its own image you have the Book of Genesis, not the Book of Job. You have essentially the Book of Job in the checker-playing machine where a man plays a game with his own creation.

MORISON. I have lost on my own ground.

McCARTHY. I am wondering whether the speakers really take as gloomy a view of matters as they have indicated. In Professor Wiener's parable we have a magic paw that will grant wishes, and we supposedly have no idea just how it does this. But it seems to me that the computer engineer who designs a magic amulet probably does have some notion of how it is going to treat our particular wishes. If you want to insert some values, then you must convince the engineer.

WIENER. The point is that it is extremely difficult to insert the whole value system at the beginning. It generally will develop from continued interaction. You may ask, "Why can't we make the learning machine 'safe'?" The answer is that "safe" is a human value, and the machine cannot very easily state what safe is without reference to man. For example, if you have a machine for programming atomic war, there is no reason why the machine should care whether the human race is completely burnt up or not. "Safe" is a human idea. If you have not put this idea into the machine, it is unreasonable to expect it to get there by itself.

Another point is that since we do not have full control over the learning machine, as illustrated by the checker-playing machine's defeating the man who programmed it, the unsafe act may not show its danger until it is too late to do anything about it. It is possible to turn the machine off, but how are we to know when to turn it off? If there is any possibility of its going wrong, we should turn it off at the very start. Otherwise, by the time that anything becomes manifest about the danger, it may be too late to avoid the consequences that have come from the use of the machine up to that point. You cannot make a perfectly safe learning machine.

CLAPP. I should like to ask the panel a question. There is no doubt that the computer is here to stay. You may be correct in your gloom and your prognostications that we may all blow up because we have computers, but I wonder if there is not some middle ground?

WIENER. Obviously there is a middle ground. We have to make every effort to understand for ourselves what the dangers are, and this points up a fundamental thing about computers: They involve more thought and not less thought. They may save certain parts of our efforts, but they do not eliminate the need for intelligence.

SNOW. Even though we have expressed grave disquiet, not only about machines, but about the whole set of associated phenomena which are characteristic of our times, I do not think any of us feels that these problems are unsolvable. I do not think any of us wishes to give that idea. But it is going to take great intelligence, and in my view, great moral judgment.

GRISOFF. I wonder if the panel feels that man can ultimately build machines which will exhibit an intelligence basically different from human intelligence. I notice that there has been very little distinction made between machine intelligence and human intelligence, and I think that there might be a very basic difference here.

WIENER. As long as the machine has beat the man who programmed it in checkers, it will in some sense compete with human intelligence over a limited scope. My hunch is that for quick action over a limited scope, the machine can be made better than the man. For higher logical-type judgments, for vague ideas, and for a large class of other things, the machine is a long way from competing with the brain. I think that there will always be a shifting boundary between the two, but I don't dare to venture where it will lie.

LOWEN. Would it help us to remember the difference between intelligence and wisdom? The machine might help our intelligence, but as of now it has no bearing on our wisdom.

WIENER. This is connected with the question of logical type. Primitive statements — statements about one or two things — we shall call intelligence. Statements about statements will be more nearly wisdom. Statements about statements about statements will be even more nearly wisdom. I think the whole issue is closely connected with Russell's theory of types. The brain is at its best on relatively high types, and the machine is at its best on relatively low types.

GYFTOPOULOS. I should like to ask Sir Charles whether he feels that the big outer- and small inner-circle phenomenon in decision making is a sign of our times or whether it has always been in evidence historically. It seems to me that whenever I participate in a big group and a difficult question comes up, there is always a committee of two or three appointed to make the decisions.

SNOW. It is perfectly true that there have been times in the past when very little of what I described as Brownian movement was operating, and a whole set of decisions was taken by a very small oligarchy. The Council of Ten in Venice is one example. But I believe that from the time of the Industrial Revolution a very large number of important decisions typically have bubbled up out of society. It seems to me extremely important that this process should not be interrupted. One of my worries is that the current nature of world tension, the

33

nature of our particular problems, is throwing once again undue weight upon secret decisions by extremely small numbers of people.

MORISON. What troubles Sir Charles in this connection also troubles me. In this country, historically, Presidents and their cabinets have made decisions within a context of what they knew society would let them do. Examples are the prosecutions of trusts in the first ten years of this century, and the Monroe Doctrine. Society had enough general evidence available to gather out of the air, as Sir Charles said, an attitude within which the President had to operate. In the future, it may be increasingly difficult on certain kinds of very important questions to have that information available, so that in a sense men will be acting much more irresponsibly.

WIENER. There is something here that is analogous to a biological problem. A society in which those in control cannot act effectively is suffering from paralysis; a society in which those in control do not get sufficient feedback of the consequences of their actions is suffering from ataxia, which is just about as bad. If a man can move his muscles perfectly well, but cannot get any report from his sensory organs on what his muscles are doing, he is just about as badly off as if he were paralyzed.

REFERENCES

1. Snow, C. P., *Science and Government* (The 1960 Godkin Lectures of Harvard University), Harvard University Press, Cambridge, 1960.

2. Samuel, A. L., "Some Studies in Machine Learning, Using the Game of Checkers," *IBM Journal of Research and Development*, Vol. 3, 210–229 (July, 1959).

3. Jacobs, W. W., "The Monkey's Paw," in *The Lady of the Barge*, Dodd, Mead, and Company; also in *Modern Short Stories*, Ashmun, Margaret, Ed., The Macmillan Co., New York, 1915.

2

Managerial
Decision Making

2

Managerial Decision Making

Speaker	**Jay W. Forrester** Professor of Industrial Management Massachusetts Institute of Technology
Discussants	**Charles C. Holt** Professor of Economics University of Wisconsin **Ronald A. Howard** Assistant Professor of Electrical Engineering and Industrial Management Massachusetts Institute of Technology
Moderator	**Robert C. Sprague** Chairman of the Board and Treasurer Sprague Electric Company

36

FORRESTER. This series of lectures deals with information, information processing, and management. This evening I should like to concentrate on the relationship between information and managing. Management is the process of converting information into action. The conversion process we call decision making. Decision making is in turn controlled by various explicit and implicit policies of behavior. It is this area of decision making and the policies that control decisions which I want to discuss this evening.[1]

If management is the process of converting information into action, then it is clear that management success depends primarily on what information is chosen and how the conversion is executed. The difference between a good manager and a poor manager lies at this point. Every person has available a large number of information sources. But each of us selects and uses only a small fraction of the available information. Even then, we make only incomplete and erratic use of that information.

The manager sets the stage for his accomplishments by his choice of which information sources to take seriously and which to ignore. After choice has been made of certain classes of information and certain information sources to carry the highest priority, managerial success depends on what use is made of this information. How quickly or slowly is it converted to action? What is the relative weight given to different information sources in the light of the desired objectives? How are these desired objectives created from the information available?

This evening we shall look upon the manager as an information converter. He is a person to whom information flows and from whom come streams of decisions that control actions within the organization. There was a time when a person might have been properly viewed as a converter of information into physical action. The farmer or the craftsman used the available information to guide his day of physical labor. The manager, however, is not paid his premium salary in recognition of physical effort exerted. He is primarily an information converter at his own particular control point in the organization. He receives incoming information flows and combines these into streams of managerial instructions.

Viewing the manager in this way shows us immediately why we are interested in decision making and information flow. An industrial organization is a complex, interlocking network of information channels. These channels emerge at various points to control physical processes such as hiring employees, building factories, and producing goods. Every action point in the system is backed up by a local decision point whose information sources reach out into other parts of the organization and the surrounding environment. We shall concentrate here on the individual decision point with its information sources. We shall also need to be interested in the total structure whereby large numbers of these decision points are tied together into an operating organization, and how each draws on the available information to create the dynamic characteristics of the organization. The information sources used, the policies for converting information into action, and the way in which the various decision points are related to one another determine such important characteristics as corporate growth and stability of operations or, on the other hand, financial failure, extreme employment fluctuation, and a succession of short-term crises.

Information-Feedback Structure of the Managament Process

We have said that information is converted by the manager into instructions which lead to action. But, what effects do the resulting actions have on the succeeding information inputs to the next decisions? The manager uses information about conditions that he hopes to influence and control. He expects, therefore, that his immediate actions will have an effect upon the future values of the information which he will be using. This describes what is called an information-feedback system.

I should like to give an unusually broad definition of an information-feedback system:

An information-feedback system exists whenever the environment leads to a decision that results in action which affects the environment.

This is a definition that encompasses every conscious and subconscious decision made by people. It also includes those mechanical decisions made by devices called servomechanisms. Systems of information-feedback control are fundamental to all life and human endeavor, from the slow pace of biological evolution to the launching of the latest space satellite. Let me illustrate:

1. A thermostat receives temperature information, decides to start the furnace and changes the temperature.
2. A person senses that he may fall, corrects his balance, and thereby is able to stand erect.
3. In business, order and inventory levels lead to manufacturing decisions that fill orders and correct inventories.

39

4. A profitable industry attracts competitors until the profit margin is reduced to equilibrium with other economic forces.
5. The competitive need for a new product leads to research and development expenditures that produce technological change.

All of these are information-feedback control loops. The regenerative process is continuous, and new results lead to new decisions that keep the system in continuous motion. Such systems are not necessarily well behaved. In fact, a complex information-feedback system designed by happenstance or in accordance with what is "intuitively obvious" will usually be unstable or ineffective.

In an information-feedback system, it is always the presently available information about the past which is being used as a basis for deciding future action.

Everything we do as an individual, as an industry, or as a society is done in the context of an information-feedback system. The definition of such a system is so all-inclusive as to seem meaningless at first. Yet we are only now becoming sufficiently aware of the tremendous significance of information-feedback-system parameters in creating the behavior of these systems.

Information-feedback systems, whether they be mechanical, biological, or social, owe their behavior to three characteristics — structure, delays, and amplification. Structure, as it implies, tells how the parts are related to one another. Delays always exist in availability of information, in making decisions based on the information, and in taking action on the decisions. Amplification usually exists throughout such systems, especially in the decision policies of our industrial and social systems. Amplification is manifested by actions being more forceful than might at first seem to be implied by the information inputs to the governing decisions. We are only beginning to realize the way in which structure, time lags, and amplifications combine to determine behavior in our social systems.

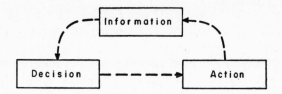

Figure 1   Decisions and Information Feedback

Figure 1 shows these relationships in simplest form. Information is the input to a decision-making point that controls actions that yield new information. The diagram shows the structural relationship. In each of these boxes are delays. Information about actions is not immediately available. The decisions do not respond instantaneously to available information. Time is required for executing the actions indicated by a decision stream. Likewise, each of the boxes contains amplification, which I use here in all of its positive and negative and nonlinear senses. In other words, the output of a box may be either greater or less than is seemingly indicated by the inputs. Likewise, the output may be noisy or distorted. The amplification, the attenuation, and the distortion at each point in the system can make the system more sensitive to certain kinds of disturbing influences than to others. It can make the system unstable, with tendencies toward internally generated fluctuations. We see this kind of instability in the boom and recession periods in our economic system. We see it in the way that automobile companies and household appliance manufacturers lay off hundreds or thousands of employees for two or three weeks while inventories are brought into line with current levels of business operation. We see it in the instability of copper prices and of most mineral and agricultural commodities.

The industrial system is, of course, not the simple, single information-feedback loop as shown in Figure 1. Instead, it is a very complex multiple-loop and interconnected system as implied by Figure 2. Decisions are made at multiple points throughout the system. Each resulting action generates information that may be used at several but not at all decision points.

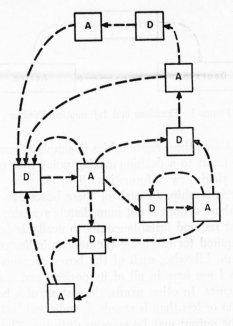

Figure 2 Multiloop Decision-Making System

This structure of cascaded and interconnected information-feedback loops, when taken together, describes the industrial system. Within a company, these decision points extend from the shipping room and the stock clerk to the board of directors. In our national economy, they extend from the aggregate decisions of consumers about the purchase of automobiles to the discount rate of the Federal Reserve Board.

Nature of the Decision Process

We should now examine in finer detail the decision process whereby information is converted to action. Figure 3 shows the system structure as it surrounds the decision point. A decision is based on the state of the system, which is here shown by the condition of various levels. Some levels describe the present instantaneous condition of the system, and others our

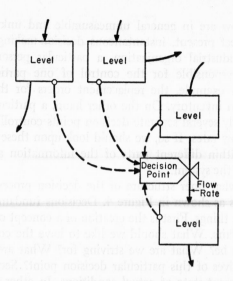

Figure 3   Decision Making in the System Structure

assumed knowledge about the system. A level may be an inventory, the number of employees, the average sales for last month, the accomplishment we believe has been made to date in a research project, the degree of optimism about the economic future, the size of bank balance, and so forth. These are the inputs to decisions. The output from a decision point controls the rate at which the system levels will change. I am using decision here in a very broad sense. This includes the filling of orders from an existing inventory, the placing of purchase orders for new replacement goods, the authorization of factory construction, the hiring of research scientists, and the authorization of advertising expenditures.

A very important part of the concept of this organizational structure is the directional relationship between the parts shown in Figure 3. The levels are the inputs to the flow of decisions. Decisions control flow rates between the levels. The flow rates between levels cause changes in the levels. But flow rates themselves are not inputs to the decisions. Instantaneous, present rates of flow are in general unmeasurable and unknown and cannot affect present, instantaneous decision-making.

In an industrial organization, a particular person may be primarily responsible for the control of one particular flow rate, as for example, the replacement orders for the mainte- nance of an inventory. On the other hand, a particular person may embody several separate decision points controlling several separate flow rates. If so, we should look upon these separately as lying within different parts of the information and action network of the system.

A somewhat finer structure of the decision process is of in- terest to us as shown in Figure 4. Decisions fundamentally in- volve three things. First is the creation of a concept of a *desired* state of affairs. What should we like to have the condition of the system be? What are we striving for? What are the goals and objectives of this particular decision point? Second, there is the *apparent* state of *actual* conditions. In other words, our available information leads us to certain observations that we believe represent the present state of the system. These ap- parent conditions may be either close or far removed from the actual present state, depending on the information flows that are being used and the amount of time lag and distortion in these information sources. The third part of the decision proc-

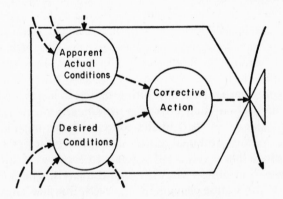

Figure 4   The Decision Process

ess is the generation of the kinds of *action* that will be taken in accordance with any discrepancy which can be detected between the apparent and desired conditions. In general, the greater the discrepancy between desired and actual conditions, the greater the resulting action. However, this entire process is highly nonlinear and noisy. Small discrepancies between apparent and desired conditions may seem of little consequence and create no action. A mounting discrepancy may lead to more and more decisive attempts to correct actual conditions toward desired conditions. However, as a maximum possible action rate is approached, further widening of the gap between desired and actual system states will no longer cause proportionate increases in action from decisions.

Decision making is being presented here as a continuous process. It is a conversion mechanism for changing continuously varying flows of information into control signals that determine rates of flow in the system. The decision point is continually yielding to the pressures of the environment. It is taking advantage of new developments as they occur. It is always adjusting to the state of affairs. It is treading a narrow path between too much action and too little. It is always attempting to adjust toward the desired goals. The amount of action is some function of the discrepancy between goals and observed system status.

One notes that we are viewing the decision process from a very particular distance. We are not close enough to be concerned with the mechanisms of human thought. We are not even close enough to see each separate decision as we ordinarily think of decisions. We may not be close enough to care whether one person or a group action creates the decisions. On the other hand, we are not so far away as to be unaware of the decision point and its place in the system. This proper distance and perspective are important to our purposes. We are not the psychologist delving into the nature and sources of personality and motivation, nor are we the biophysicist interested in the physical and logical structure of the brain. On the other hand, we are not the stockholder who is so far from the corporation as to be unaware of the internal structure, social pressures, and decision points.

Our viewpoint is more that of the managerial superior of a particular person who is charged with certain responsibilities. The superior is close enough to know how desired goals are established. He is in a position to observe and probably provide the information sources to be used by the subordinate to determine his concept of actual conditions. He knows in general the guiding policies and the manner in which the subordinate decision maker would respond to various kinds of circumstances.

Policy

We are now led to what I shall call policy. The word "policy" is here used as a broad term to describe how the decision process converts information into action. What actions will result from certain information inputs? What is the conversion relationship between information sources and the stream of resulting decisions?

We shall first define what is here meant by policy. We shall later turn our attention to whether or not such policy does exist and whether or not its form can be determined.

Policy is a formal statement giving the relationship between information sources and resulting decision flows. It is what has often been referred to in the literature as a decision rule. In physical systems, particularly in the field of servomechanisms, the corresponding term is "transfer function." The transfer function tells how the output of a particular box depends on the stream of inputs. The transfer function does not necessarily deal with the particular physical way whereby the conversion is accomplished. One is satisfied if the transfer function tells us adequately well, for a particular purpose, the present resulting action as a function of present and past inputs to the box.

Most of the literature of economics deals with what we are here calling policy. How will individuals and groups respond to various circumstances and pressures? If conditions change in a certain direction, what will be the direction of the response? In industrial organizations, some policy is very formal. It has been reduced to writing for the guidance of the decision makers in the system. Most of the guiding policy is informal but every bit as influential. It depends on habit, conformity, social pressures, ingrained concepts of goals, awareness of power centers within the organization, and personal interest.

We should here note that we have progressed through three different levels of decision-making abstraction. At the lowest level, we could imagine random unreasoned action, which does not depend on inputs and which has no basis. At the second level, we have unrationalized intuitive reactions, which in fact result from the available flows of information but where there is no comprehension by the actor concerning the structure and the basis of his actions. We can assume that this represents the thinking and the decisions of the lower animals. There is a basis and a reason for their decisions and actions, but they are totally unaware of such a basis and logical structure. At the third level of abstraction, there is an awareness of the formal reasons for decisions. Not only are decisions made, but we have self-awareness of why we make certain decisions, and we are aware and able to anticipate with some reliability the kinds of reactions that others will exhibit in response to changes in the state of their environment. The formal awareness for the basis of decisions, which I am here calling the guiding policy, certainly goes back as far as the written record of our civilization. Man is most conspicuously separated from the lower animals by this self-awareness of why he acts. In other words, much of history and literature devotes itself to the basis or policy that causes the human decision maker to react in a reasonable and expected way to his environment. When we say that there is a reasonable and expected reaction, we are in essence describing the policy whereby information will become a certain kind of action.

We should now consider whether or not we can detect the nature of the guiding policy with sufficient accuracy so that we can make use of it in better understanding the behavior of the industrial and social systems of which we are a part.

Clearly, people are of two minds on this question. Most of the literature on decision making implies great difficulty and subtlety in the subject. The social scientist makes very tentative simple experiments with groups of three or four people in an effort to determine how their decisions are reached in reacting to one another. When we raise the question of understanding the human decision-making process, the frequent answer from scientists is that not even a good beginning has yet been made. Yet the historian, the novelist, the manager, and every one of us in his everyday life has been much bolder. We all discuss why so-and-so acted in a particular way. In doing this we are discussing his guiding policy. We are discussing how he did respond or how he should have responded to information available to him.

The dichotomy in our thinking is illustrated by two recent encounters which I had with two different colleagues. One flatly stated that it was clearly impossible to introduce the actions of the Federal Reserve Board into a formal model of national economic behavior. The impossibility was argued on the basis that we do not know the process by which such decisions are reached. They are too subtle. They are subjective, intuitive decisions for which we do not know the guiding policy. The other incident took place in a doctoral oral examination. Another colleague, as a routine matter, casually asked the candidate to describe the factors that would lead the Federal Reserve System to make adjustments in various directions in its discount rate and open-market policies. In other words, the economics doctoral candidate was expected to know the essential nature of the policy that would guide the stream of Federal Reserve Board decisions. To be sure, there may be a high noise content that can cause timing variations and uncertainty in the extent of a response. However, the broad underlying outlines of guiding policy were expected to be within the understanding and comprehension of the student.

This contradiction in the opinions we hold about the process of decision making is very similar to what we observe in our thinking about the process of invention. There is great argument and little agreement in any discussion of how new ideas are generated and how invention and research results are achieved. Yet, we are almost in 100 per cent agreement in acknowledging that more intelligent and more experienced people, and greater research budget expenditure, and greater motivation, and greater need for the results will all enhance the probability of a successful outcome. This agreement on the nature of the conversion function that couples financial and manpower inputs to scientific output is the basis for Congressional action and military department appropriations in times of national emergency.

In short, our whole civilization is founded not only on the assumption that a basis exists for the guidance of human action but furthermore on the conviction that we know a great deal about the specific nature and extent of this guiding policy.

We find then that management decisions can be classified according to the form of the controlling policy, as in Figure 5. Here we see four regions, segregated in accordance with the extent to which the policies that guide decisions are known and agreed upon. In Group A are those decisions that are now made on a fully automatic basis by machines where the guid-

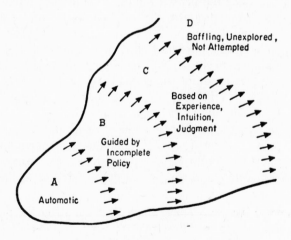

Figure 5   Scope of Management Decisions

ing policy is rigidly prescribed. For some time this region has included the rules for computing pay checks on the basis of wage rate and hours worked. In many organizations it includes a vast body of rules about the processing of accounting information and the flow and control of purchase orders, invoices, and shipping instructions. With the introduction of computing machines, this area is rapidly expanding to include the formal policies for production schedules and the management of inventory levels, with implications that carry over into production-rate and employment decisions. Group B represents those decisions which are not mechanized but which are made by a vast bureaucracy of middle management in our corporations according to well-understood guiding policy. This policy has not been reduced to explicit detailed operating rules, and yet it is clear enough that a supervisor generally knows what to expect from subordinate decision makers. Region C represents those decisions, usually nearer the top levels of the organization, where guiding policy does not appear in writing and where decisions are thought of as being based on experience, intuition, and judgment. Even here, however, there is a strong assumption about what constitutes proper action. In general, it is well known what the direction of effect of various changes in the system status will do to the resulting decisions. The current management press, such as *Business Week*, the *Wall Street Journal*, and *Forbes* magazine, is filled with the rationale for management decisions. Much of the printed material is devoted to a discussion of the pressures of the current state of affairs and the effects these will have on decision makers. Beyond Region C is one of great challenge but in which there is no basis for action in either experience or intuition. Into this unknown, beyond the frontier of traditional management actions, we reconnoiter on a random and haphazard basis to obtain information on which future intuitive judgment can be based.

The dividing lines between these regions are not sharp. The gradation from the automatic decision to the one that lacks even a basis in experience and intuition is one of continuous and gradual transition. The dividing zones between regions are moving upward and outward.

Many people seem to believe that there is a sharp break between Region A in Figure 5, where decisions are completely formal, and the other regions of management decisions. Such persons are unwilling to accept the possibility of even the existence of formal policies that could describe the major aspects of management in the other decision-making regions. I call your attention to an interesting contradiction in the attitude of many managers toward this matter of understanding the formal basis of the decision process. Any manager must of necessity admit the existence of the region of automatic decisions, since these are common practice. The majority of managers will argue that the region of the intuitive judgment decision is so subtle that no reasonable approximation can be made to it through formal decision rules. Yet, those same managers, when faced with a decision that they recognize as lying beyond the capabilities of their intuitive judgment, will once more fall back on formal decision-making procedures. I here refer to the whole field of sales and market and economic forecasting. Forecasting is essentially a decision-making process. It consists of taking past and presently available information and converting this into results that indicate a course of action. I am not a supporter of the wisdom and validity of the majority of this type of forecasting, but I simply point out the conflict in attitudes. There are those who relegate the simple decisions to automatic procedures. They rely, for lack of anything better, on certain formal statistical decision procedures with respect to some of the most subtle and difficult decisions. But they reserve the middle ground as a region for judgment which they assert is untouchable by formal decision rule.

It seems to me that there is now ample evidence to indicate that this middle region is not the obscure and subtle jungle that it has so often been pictured. Men are not good calculators of the dynamic behavior of complicated systems. The number of variables that they can in fact properly relate to one another is very limited. The intuitive judgment of even a skilled investigator is quite unreliable in anticipating the dynamic behavior of a simple information-feedback system of perhaps five or six variables. This is true even when the complete structure and all the parameters of the system are fully known to him. The verbal model and the mental model that we carry around with us to explain the dynamics of industrial and economic system behavior probably do not rank in effective dynamic complexity beyond a fourth- or fifth-order differential equation. We think that we give consideration to a much larger number of variables, but I doubt that these are properly related to one another in groups larger than five or six at a time. In short, I am saying that, in dealing with the dynamics of information-feedback systems, the human is not a subtle and powerful problem solver.

Furthermore, we have some massive examples of our ability to deduce these decision criteria and to go even so far as to automatize and mechanize them. Take, for example, the tactical decision making in the conduct of an air battle. In 1947, when I wrote a memorandum for the Navy on the use of electronic digital computers as automatic combat information centers, one could probably not have found five military officers who would have acknowledged the possibility of a machine's being able to analyze the available information sources, the proper assignment of weapons, the generation of command instructions, and the coordination of adjacent areas of military operation. Yet, in just ten years the situation was completely reversed. In 1947 no general-purpose electronic digital computer had yet operated. There was more justification then for the military officer than there is today for the manager to deny vehemently the possibility that there is a formal and orderly basis underlying the vast majority of management decisions. The military officer argued that the analysis of radar information, the determination of which data represented aircraft tracks and which were noise, the identification of friend or foe, the assessment of threat, the assignment of defensive weapons, and the generation of weapon-control orders necessarily required experience and judgment and a background of military training.

This of course overlooked the fact that the man at the decision-making point might be a second lieutenant who just two weeks before had been called up to military duty.

During the following decade the speed of military operations increased until it became clear that, regardless of the assumed advantages of human judgment decisions, the internal communication speed of the human organization simply was not able to cope with the pace of modern air warfare. This inability to act provided the incentive. The nature of the decision process was seriously studied. The policy that guided front-line military decision making was unraveled. In the early 1950's experimental demonstrations showed that enough of this decision making was understood so that machines could process raw data into final weapon-guidance instruction and achieve results superior to those then being accomplished by the manual systems. During the 1950's, thousands of man-years of effort went into a consideration of how military command decisions are made and how these can be reduced to an effective orderly system of decision-making rules. The military attitude was so completely reversed in a decade that we find in the proceedings of the Eastern Joint Computer Conference in December, 1958, an article by Colonel W. H. Tetley of the Air Defense System Integration Division out here at Hanscom Field in Bedford. The title of the paper was "The Role of Computers in Air Defense." Let me pick three separate quotations to give the general tone of that paper.

> In essence, this master air defense system is a giant servo-mechanism of really spectacular proportions. Although its reflex action is achieved by information feedback, it still suffers many vagaries of the simple feedback amplifier. Consider then, the weird prospect of a servomechanism, spread out over an area comparable to the whole North American continent, . . .
>
> . . . .
>
> In what follows, then, rather broad terms will portray what many in systems engineering believe lies ahead for the computer in air defense. . . .
>
> . . . .

First, there is the national level function which links together all regional computers and co-ordinates their actions by means of centralized control. This computer is able to exchange views with the Strategic Air Command operational computer and with that of the Office of Defense Mobilization, and thus co-ordinate air defense on the governmental level.

The only amazing thing about this paper is that it seemed to receive almost no notice from the audience. The reaction was, "So what?" The audience looked on it as a routine, ordinary paper presenting material that everyone already knew. Ten years earlier an Air Force colonel would have dared to give such a paper only at the risk of his military reputation.

You may say that the basis for conduct of an air battle is simpler than for the conduct of a business. It is. But, in the 1950's, on the basis of the knowledge then available, it was a great deal more complicated than will be the corresponding understanding of the practical aspects of management decision making in the decade of the 1960's.

The Management Laboratory

Now what is the practical significance of this discussion of managerial decision making in its framework of the information-feedback system? It means that if we can understand the mechanisms of a social system, we can construct effective and useful dynamic models of its operation.

These models open the way to what is essentially a management laboratory. The design of a corporation with its organizational structure and its managing policies can be brought to a level not unlike that of the design of an airplane with its wind tunnel and its aircraft models. It opens the way to what we might call "enterprise engineering" for the design of organizations to meet specific objectives and goals.

One might ask, is there any need to do this? Is there any room for improvement? New design methods are unimportant unless they lead to results that could not be achieved before. One can point to the present crises in Africa. Certainly we do not understand adequately the dynamics of growth of a new country with its complicated interactions between education, governmental structure, economics, technological change, monetary system, external investment, and the aspirations of its people. One can point to the large number of new industrial enterprises that are founded but to fail. On the other hand, there are those that begin and flourish with a growth rate of as high as 50 or 100 per cent per year. When the range in dynamic behavior is as great as this, there must indeed be some fundamental underlying reasons for success which can be better understood. We have the example of the electric generating industry. Electric demand is one of the most smoothly growing variables in our economic system. Yet the rate at which orders are placed for new turbines and electric generators fluctuates by as much as 10 to 1, with a periodicity of four, five, or six years. Actual production rate of this equipment fluctuates as much as 4 to 1, with the corresponding labor instability and individual and community hardship. Such behavior is a manifestation of the unstable interactions that can exist within an information-feedback system having certain managerial policies, certain time delays, and certain technological restraints. Changing any of these, and particularly the managerial policies over which one can exert control, will change the behavior of the system. There is every reason to believe that such undesirable system behavior characteristics can be greatly alleviated.

To begin to deal with the dynamic characteristics of social systems, we must be able to represent at least the central essential skeleton of the decision-making structure. To do this, we must be able to approximate the controlling policy at each significant decision point in the system. This understanding of policy can be accomplished if

1. We have the proper concept of what a decision is and of the significance of the policy that describes the decision process.
2. We have the proper structure relating system status to policy, to decisions, and to action.

3. We realize that the process is noisy and we shall not get and do not need high accuracy of decision-making representation.

4. We use to best advantage the extensive body of experience and descriptive information that probably contains 98 per cent of the essential information on decision making. The other 2 per cent will come from formal statistical and numerical data.

5. We realize that a formal, quantitative statement of policy carries with it no implications one way or the other regarding absolute accuracy. We can make a formal quantitative statement corresponding to any statement that can be made in descriptive English. Lack of descriptive accuracy does not prevent quantifying our ideas about decision policy. Assigning a number does not enhance the accuracy of the original statement. The common belief that we cannot quantify a decision rule because we do not know it with high accuracy is mixing two quite separate considerations. We can quantify regardless of accuracy. After that, we deal with the question of what is sufficient accuracy.

I feel it has been adequately demonstrated that these things can be done. We have the tremendous examples of corresponding accomplishments in the understanding of military control systems in the last decade. We have preliminary examples of the application of the same approaches to industrial systems. Let me touch quickly on an example.

Example

To give you an example of an application of the use of decision-making policy in the area of industrial operations, I shall mention some work that we have been doing with the cooperation of Mr. R. C. Sprague and with the financial support of the Sprague Electric Company.

There was a rather common but baffling industrial problem. In a particular product line there was substantial fluctuation of inventories and employment, and this fluctuation seemed much more extreme than could be explained by expected changes in the ultimate end demand for the product. The question arose: Could the fluctuating inventories and production rate come from interactions among the managerial policies in the complex information-feedback system comprising the company, its customers, and its employment and production policies?

Figure 6 shows a time history of how this system operates. The problems are clearly visible. We see that employment is fluctuating even more than the incoming-order rate. Furthermore, the excess employment is being created by the inventory fluctuation. This is very common in our mature industries. Unlike most electronic products, this particular product line is mature and well established and is showing little growth or decline from year to year. Note that inventory is rising rapidly at the time of the employment peaks, which occur only a little later than appear to be the high points in sales. Many people believe that inventories absorb fluctuations in demand and help stabilize production rate and employment. This is true of the very short run demand changes but is often quite the

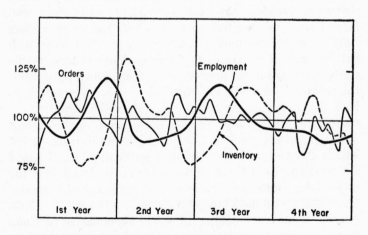

Figure 6   Behavior Shown by a Model of the System

reverse for longer-term fluctuations that create the major sales and employment problems.

Near the end of the first year and in the first half of the third year, employment is high. These employment peaks have been preceded by a period of above-average sales, but employment increased higher than did sales. The higher employment resulted from the attempt to recover the inventory depletion that occurred during the high sales period. The fact that inventory is rising during the sales peak and is falling during the sales valley causes employment to fluctuate more widely than sales.

Now as you look at this figure, you should know that it has been created entirely by a mathematical model that represents our estimate of the decision policies in the system and how these are related to one another. Furthermore, the model is completely closed except for an external demand that is absolutely constant and unvarying. In other words, here is a model that we believe represents point by point the decision functions of the system. Each of these decision functions, as we discussed earlier, recognizes the goals and objectives at the particular point, uses the information sources that predominantly influence that decision point, and generates the flow of decisions that we believe characterize each particular point in the system. Having done this, we find that the model has an interacting behavior within the multiple information-feedback loops such that it creates a pattern of the same qualitative nature as the real system, even in the presence of a constant final demand for the product. The model says that indeed it is quite possible to have widely fluctuating inventories and employment that far exceed any variation imposed upon the system from the outside.

We do not have time to dwell at length on this example, but let me give you an idea of what is involved. Figure 7 shows the most crucial of the decision points in the system and the major information-feedback loops that are involved. Actually, the mathematical model used for this system is a very nonlinear one of about 140 variables. Of these, about 30 are decision points represented by decision-making policy functions such as

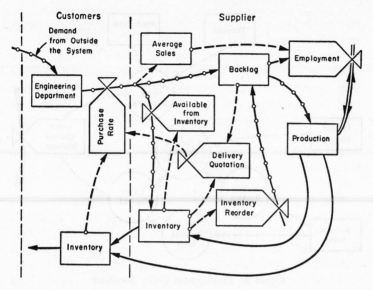

Figure 7   Major System Details

we have discussed. Of the 30, 5 can be singled out as especially important and these are shown in the figure. The 5 are the following:

1. The purchasing rate by the customers as it depends on design releases from their engineering departments, their inventory policies, and their response to changing delivery-delay quotations coming from the supplier.
2. The factors that determine the fraction of the incoming-order flow which the factory can fill from inventory.
3. The basis for quoting delivery delays from the supplier to the customer.
4. The basis for inventory reorder from the stock room to the production department.
5. The policies governing changes in employment and work week which control the production rate.

As an example of one of the decision-policy structures, we may examine that for the employment change rate in Figure 8.

59

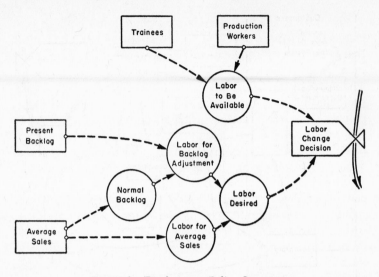

Figure 8   Employment Policy Structure

The rectangles represent the principal levels on which the decision depends. At the top the present production workers and the present people in training tell us the labor force that is to be available. This represents the present status of the system. At the lower left, average sales give a basis for determining what the normal backlog should be. This is a goal or desired condition as discussed earlier. This is compared with the actual present backlog representing present conditions, to determine the amount of labor desired for adjusting upward or downward the size of the unfilled-order backlog. Average sales also imply the amount of labor necessary for producing at the rate corresponding to average demand for the product. The labor for meeting average sales demand plus the labor increment for the adjustment of unfilled-order backlog combine to indicate the desired labor force. At the labor decision point there are then available the desired labor level and the actual labor level. The decision function then combines these, along with considerations of the rapidity with which changes can be made to yield a rate of employment change.

Turn now to Figure 9. Here are two time histories, both generated by dynamic models of the corporate system. It is clear that these differ in qualitative character. Conditions are much more stable in the lower time history than they are in the upper. The upper history is the one in the earlier figure and represents the behavior of the system model when it is set up with the policies that we believe have been governing the operations of this product line in the past. The lower history is the same model, in which some rather minor adjustments have been made in the sources of information used for certain decisions. The new system in the lower time history also specifies in several places longer averaging times and slower managerial responses to available information. In a number of respects there is very substantial improvement. Although inventories fluctuate through approximately the same amplitude as before, everything else is more stable. Employment fluctuations are about one-third as great. Although not on this simplified figure, the actual model results show that cash position is more stable,

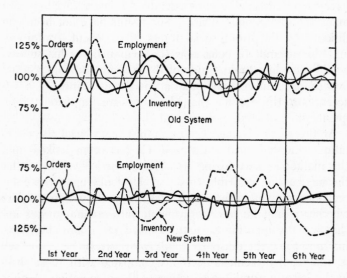

Figure 9   Comparison of Models of Old and New Policies

and unfilled-order backlog fluctuates less, as does delivery delay to the customer.

This illustrates what I believe to be a general characteristic of our industrial systems. They are so far from the best possible mode of operation that our first steps to improve them will often lead to improvement in nearly every variable of interest. One is not faced initially with the need to make a compromise wherein a heavy price must be paid in one factor to obtain improvement in another.

Decision Policy in the Corporation

It seems to me that management science has so far been very ineffective in dealing with this formulation and use of decision-making policy. I believe the past difficulties might be gathered into three categories.

First, there is the matter of perspective or viewing distance mentioned earlier. The social scientist has tended to look at the individual man, with emphasis on psychology and individual motivation. Many of the attempts at laboratory experiments have been with small groups assembled in an artificial environment for brief periods of time. The results have not been conditioned by the strong social forces of precedent, conformity, and the attempt to behave as the man believes his superior would want him to do. Study of the individual man, especially over short periods of time in an artificial environment, tends to accentuate the feeling that decisions are capricious, infrequent, disconnected, and isolated.

At the other extreme, the economist has viewed the corporation from too great a distance. He has often looked upon the market as maximizing its utility, whether or not it has the information available to do so. He looks upon the entrepreneur as a man who maximizes his profit without asking whether or not he has the available information sources and the mental computing capacity to find a maximum. This viewing from too great a distance tends to overstress the importance of the top-management decisions compared with those made in the lower and middle structure of the corporation. A directive from top management does not change the prejudices, habits, and self-interest objectives of the middle-level decision makers. For example, the public press has well documented the futility felt by the successive Secretaries of Defense who have tried their hands at changing the character, attitudes, and practices of our military department. It is a long, slow process. We tend to be misled by various "upheaval" incidents. A proxy fight followed by a complete change of top management and the firing of half of the middle-management structure will indeed change the attitudes and traditions of an organization. But this drastic surgery is not common.

For an understanding of the corporate information-feedback system it is very essential that we look neither at the individual person isolated from his environment, nor at the exterior of the system. It is at the intermediate viewpoint, from which we can know men and groups of men in their working environment, that we can capture the true character of the operation.

Second, I think that the understanding of decision making has been greatly handicapped by the assumption that it is a more subtle and more skilled process than it actually is. We have been too heavily influenced by the fact that the highest-speed computers cannot yet play chess as well as a person. This is not a typical example. The chess problem is essentially static. Full and exact information is available to the man. It is a problem of visualizing spatial relationships, which a man does quite well, and today's machines do poorly. There are other situations such as the time histories that I showed you earlier, where a computing machine can determine in five minutes what the consequences of a set of policies will be and where a group of men could argue inconclusively for a year about what follows from a given set of assumptions.

It is my feeling that in a dynamic information-feedback system the human decision maker is usually using a great deal less than the total amount of information available to him. Furthermore, the information available to him is a great deal less than that commonly assumed. In general, his actions with respect to any given decision stream will be almost entirely conditioned by less than ten information inputs. What he does with these few information sources is apt to be rather stereotyped. Some of them will be used to create a concept of desired objectives. Others will serve to form his impressions of the true state of affairs. From the difference will result reasonably straightforward and obvious actions. What seems obvious may not be best. Some of the biggest improvements that can be made in the dynamics of our industrial systems will come from following procedures that our traditions and our management folklore have led us to believe are precisely in the wrong direction. Our understanding of the dynamics of complicated information-feedback systems is so inadequate that our intuitive judgment can often not be trusted to tell us whether improvement or degradation will result from a given direction of policy change.

The third difficulty into which many seem to have fallen in attempting to understand decision-making policy has resulted from trying to skip one of the evolutionary steps in the hierarchy of decision-making abstraction mentioned earlier. You will recall that I suggested the lowest level of decision making would be that where actions were random and irrational. The second level would be one where actions are reasoned and rational but where there is no self-awareness of what the governing policies might be. Man was characterized as having, throughout recorded history, at least a verbal descriptive model of a rational policy that creates the stream of individual decisions. This is already a major fraction of the step toward the ability to formulate explicit quantitative policy governing decisions. The next level would be one in which the art and the intuitive judgment are applied to the development of a better understanding of policy.

Art, judgment, and intuition are at this new level no longer applied to the individual separate decisions but to the definition of a policy that governs the stream of individual decisions. This is the level of abstraction which is just emerging. This is the one wherein we can point to numerous successful examples but where there is not general agreement on method. At this level of abstraction, there is not a descriptive literature on what constitutes the practice of the art of detecting decision-making policy.

In spite of the gap in the art which exists at the policy-detection level, many economists have attempted to skip to the next level of the abstraction hierarchy. They have been attempting to develop statistical methods that can be applied as a routine matter to extract from quantitative data about a system the governing decision policies. This is still another level of abstraction in which intuitive art and judgment are applied to setting up rigid rules whereby the formal decision policies can be derived. I feel that we are not ready to attempt this last level of abstraction until we have achieved acknowledged success in applying art and judgment and intuition to the extraction of the decision policies themselves. After this process is well understood, it may then be possible to reduce this method of analysis of an organization to a rigid and orderly process. In general, the precedents seem to indicate that we must take these levels of abstraction one at a time. At each point in time, art and judgment are devoted to establishing the rules whereby the lower levels can be automatized.

An example has been the history of computing machine programming. Ten years ago one wrote the specific machine code for the solution of a particular problem. The next level of abstraction was to write a program of logical instructions to tell the machine how to create its own running program for a specific problem formulation. We now seem to be entering another hierarchy of abstraction in problem programming, in which the man develops concepts that allow the computer to formulate the specific statement of the problem which another computer program will, in turn, convert into machine language. This I feel is philosophically the equivalent of what I have been describing in the hierarchy of orderly rules related to decision making.

Future Implications

Let me close by commenting briefly on some of the implications that I see developing out of what we have discussed.

First, this does not imply automatic management. A better understanding of decision-making policy and its information-feedback context will not reduce the leadership demands on the executive. Quite the reverse. He will now have new methods to use and a new theoretical underlying structure to understand. The use of this new knowledge and these tools will not be automatic. The more skillfully these tools are selected and the more significant the goals, the more effective will be the application. New advances in physics have not led to automatic engineering. The skilled system engineer still produces the better chemical process plant or earth satellite. The great advances in physics have not yet led to automatic methods for selecting which principles should be applied or in what combinations.

We can, however, see that the emphasis in the corporation will change. Management education has concentrated on the making of individual decisions. The manager has been looked upon as a decision maker. On the other hand, the truly skillful managers have long recognized that their greatest contribution came through the establishment of a proper policy and framework for the guidance of the organization. This recognition of the importance of policy can be expected to spread very rapidly during the next two decades.

The manager who will be most in demand and who will command the highest salary will be the enterprise designer. He is the one who will be able to work with the way information sources and decision-making policy at each of the many points throughout the organization combine to create desirable results.

At the same time, there will be a thinning out of the present middle-management organization. It is in the middle-management levels that decisions are already highly routine and determined by formal policy and system structure and precedents.

Much of the middle-management structure is made up of frustrating and unrewarding tasks. The tasks are managerial in name only. They are actually steps in the information-processing production line. As these tasks are better understood, it will no longer be necessary to squander the talents of good men in these positions. The analogy to the physical-product production line is excellent. As the production process became routine, two things happened. Work on the production line became unrewarding. Also, once the tasks were fully understood, it became possible to design machines that would serve the function as well and would not suffer from boredom.

We spoke of hierarchies of abstraction with respect to our understanding of the decision-making process. I call your attention to a similar evolutionary hierarchy with respect to our industrial production processes. There was a time in an agrarian economy when man produced with his own labor to satisfy his immediate consumption needs. The next step was to specialize into a craft-trades economy, where judgment and intuition were acquired through apprenticeship to achieve greater manual skill and higher labor productivity. This evolved into the early industrial economy, where manual labor was subdivided and simplified so that people operated machines to produce goods for others. Skill and intuitive judgment were applied to the construction of machines that could produce what the craftsman had done before. At the next step, which we can call the advanced industrial economy, the creative level moved from machine construction to machine design. Then the concentration was on the principles and the art of machine design, with emphasis on kinematics, metallurgy, and thermodynamics. At the next stage, which we are now entering, the art of machine design is being formalized into logical rules. We can call this the automation economy. At this level, man designs methods and procedures that will permit machines to design machines that in turn will produce for human consumption. We have already taken a substantial step in this direction. Digital computers are today designed by digital computers. Computing machines design mechanical parts and lay out the piping and structure for chemical plants. The creative designer works with the formal concepts that govern how design should be done. At the next level, which we might call the "artificial-intelligence" level of economic development, machines will perhaps be instructed in how to develop the design concepts that machines can then follow to produce designs to produce equipment to produce goods for human consumption.

Each of these steps has led to a higher standard of living. Each hierarchy of abstraction is a multiplier that converts human effort into a higher standard of material welfare. Each step has created its social revolution as people find the old activities declining and new ones taking their place.

The manager, in rising to a new level of abstraction where he concerns himself with formal decision-making policy and with enterprise design, will be keeping pace with the evolution of our technological society.

Panel Discussion

HOLT. In discussing Professor Forrester's paper, I should like to give you my initial general reaction, which was enthusiastic, and then give you some second thoughts on a more detailed level.

At the risk of distorting Professor Forrester's intent, I should like to summarize very briefly the procedure that he proposes:

1. Make detailed studies of the decision making within a company (or other organization) and formulate a model of the *decision policy* for each important decision center.
2. Use an electronic computer to *simulate* the resulting model of the over-all decision system in order to determine its characteristics.
3. *Validate* the model by checking it against the actual performance of the organization.
4. Test proposed improvements in the system by performing *experiments* on the computer model.

5. *Introduce the improved policies* into the organization — and ultimately move toward *administration* of decision policies by the computer itself.

Let me indicate why I think this procedure is a most promising one to pursue. Detailed empirical studies of operating decision policies in the context of a complex decision system are all too rare. By such studies, we should learn a good deal about the way organizations actually behave, as contrasted to how they ought to behave. Although such studies obviously could have been carried out before electronic computers were available, it is important to recognize why they were not, at least not on the scale and with the rigor contemplated here. On one hand, the computer *forces* one to formulate an operationally complete system; and, on the other hand, the availability of the computer makes it possible, with a reasonable expenditure of resources, to find the implications of such studies instead of ending up with a huge and utterly indigestible case study.

Mathematical methods currently are limited, where general nonlinear equations are involved, to fairly small systems; so the emergence in recent years of electronic analog and digital computers capable of solving large-scale nonlinear equation systems constitutes a major breakthrough in the treatment of complex systems problems. Forrester's proposal to exploit this breakthrough in seeking solutions to problems arising in decision systems is thoroughly sound.

As any scientist knows, it usually is easy to formulate many hypotheses (or models) that are plausible. Consequently, there is a critical need for much careful testing in order to isolate the few hypotheses that yield empirically accurate predictions.

After the model has been validated and the researcher turns to proposing improvements in the system, he faces the fact that he too is the same kind of mortal as the businessman, in that he also is not a "good calculator of the dynamic behavior of complicated systems." Fortunately, computer simulation of models facilitates experimentation so that more or less random search guided by a few heuristics becomes feasible for the researcher in a way that was never possible for the business executive working with a live organization. Given the sad state of dynamic control in most business organizations, there is little doubt that recommendations can be made for changed policies that, if instituted, would yield substantial improvements in organization performances.

The potentiality of the computer to participate actively in the decision process "shoulder to shoulder" with men is still not generally appreciated. If anything, Professor Forrester has, under the pressure of time, understated his case.

Professor Forrester's approach certainly deserves to be exploited, and it can be counted on to yield substantial improvements. We all know that operations researchers working with much less powerful tools for dynamic analysis have found no great difficulty in achieving substantial improvements in present-day industrial practice. However, it needs to be emphasized that dynamic control problems are only *one* area of concern in the more comprehensive field of management science.

Perhaps it should be mentioned that other workers have used an approach that is somewhat similar to Forrester's: for example, Richard Cyert, Guy Orcutt, Alan Rowe, and Martin Shubik.

Now for my second thoughts on a miscellany of more detailed points. Forrester gives considerable stress to the definition: "An information-feedback system exists whenever the environment leads to a decision that results in action which affects the environment." He further states that "this definition . . . encompasses every conscious and subconscious decision made by people" and "everything we do as an individual, as an industry, or as a society is done in the context of an information-feedback system." I trust that what I am about to say will not be interpreted as meaning that I am against "feedback," but I think that I detect here a confusion between an intellectual model and the real world. Either an "information-feedback system" is defined so broadly that it applies to virtually all human phenomena, and hence cannot have much, if any, content as a statement about the real world; or it is not so universally applicable as is claimed. I should contend that the feedback model as expressed in Figure 1 is very useful for thinking about certain organizational phenomena, but we should guard against pretending that such models are true and exact statements about the real world. We should not confuse models that we use to think about the real world with the real world itself.

The notion of circular causality that is incorporated in Forrester's "information-feedback system" is an important analytical model which in any particular situation is capable of being either true or false. There is no denying that certain situations involve simultaneous determination (rather than uni-directional causality): for example, a manager with a budget constraint governing several different types of expenditure. It will not *always* be wise to limit ourselves to models based on circular causality in spite of the computational simplicity that may be obtainable by this approach. Forrester might argue that nothing can move faster than the speed of light, and hence, there can be no simultaneous relationships in a spatial system. To that argument, I can only answer that it rests on a hypothesis that is subject to empirical validation.

There is no question that the feedback concept supplies a useful perspective in examining a decision system. However, a somewhat finer distinction contributes to clarity. If we think of "feedback" as the decision response to the *state* of the system, then it is useful to introduce the additional concept of "feed forward" for decision responses to *anticipated future disturbances* on the subsystem being controlled by the decision maker. It is helpful in studying decision policies to be sensitive to the fact that a decision maker may be responsive to some off-beat and seemingly irrelevant information because it has some value, however indirect, in *forecasting* variables that *are* directly important.

I agree with Forrester that most psychologists and economists have been viewing the business firm from "distances" different from Forrester's, but I think it is only fair to say that most of them have been trying to answer questions different from the ones that he poses. Most psychologists and economists have not concerned themselves with solving the businessman's dynamic problems. Fortunately, many social scientists are now taking steps to remedy their sin of omission and increasingly are taking a serious interest in problems that arise in business organizations at all levels.

In trying to determine decision policies, there is an appealing directness in simply asking decision makers what they are doing. This is not an approach that has been overlooked by either psychologists or economists. It is well known that human beings are quite ready to supply rationales for their behaviors. It is also well known that when you ask a human subject to be his own social scientist and predict his own behavior the results usually do not stand up under critical empirical testing. In efforts to obtain reliable predictions, social scientists have been *forced* to use more subtle and devious methods than "interviewing the subject." There are very real dangers in being too simple-minded in our approach to this difficult research problem.

Although there is frequent mention in the paper of random noise in decision procedures, very little emphasis is given to the well-developed body of knowledge for treating such phenomena, namely statistics. This is quite surprising and suggests that the problem of validating the estimates of decision policies at the level of the decision center has not been adequately explored. It would take a wise man indeed to get 98 per cent of the information from a noisy, partly subconscious system and without benefit of statistics. As a scientist, I am unwilling to accept "agreement" on the determinants of invention as an adequate substitute for empirical tests.

I want it to be clear that I am not objecting to obtaining information in any way that we can, including interviews. But I would like to see some effort made to secure independent empirical tests of this information rather than simply assuming its accuracy. Statistical methods would be useful for such tests, and also might be useful for making estimates of the

72

decision policies themselves. To suggest that statistical methods are rigid and mechanical is, I think, to misinterpret the discipline.

When the simulated system has been assembled, there is a further nasty problem of validating the model to see whether its over-all interactions adequately mirror the organization that is being modeled. I am led to wonder about the adequacy of the test in the production and employment example that indicated that the model "generated patterns of the same qualitative nature as the real system." I urge that more emphasis be put on the validation of system models, even though I am aware of the morass of unsolved problems that are involved.

At the experimental stage when improved policies are being proposed and tested, Forrester refers to the wind-tunnel analogy. In that field there is a body of abstract theory that is of great help to the wind-tunnel experimenter. Similarly, we need theoretical insights that will help us to understand the organizational phenomena with which we are dealing. The fact that we can have a simulation model of the system for experimentation does not by any means make it an easy task to understand what is going on in the model. Thus the simulation model is not a panacea. There is still a great need for theoretical understanding of such complex systems.

The problem of implementing changes in organizations should be mentioned at least in passing, since operations research people often find that knowing what *ought* to be done is somewhat less than half the job. Often there is a great deal of work involved in bringing about changes in channels of communication and in decision policies. Indeed, a manager soon learns that the management role in a human organization involves a great deal more than just decision making.

In closing I should like to comment on the complementarity of alternative approaches to the problems that Professor Forrester considers. For example, a researcher might enter an organization and study not the prevailing decision policy but rather concentrate on the decision problem, i.e., the constraints and objectives that face the decision maker. Then by the use of mathematical decision theory and numerical methods, he could attempt to obtain *optimal* designs both of the organization and of the decision policies. This approach lends itself well to considering a few critical decisions while suppressing most of the detail in studying the rest of the organization. Such an approach, because of its narrow focus and great depth, has been found by me and others to offer considerable power and flexibility, but it also carries certain obvious dangers. Hopefully, such intensive normative studies might supply some of the theoretical insight whose need was mentioned before.

Since optimization problems involving complex dynamic systems are likely to prove difficult of solution, it is desirable for us to develop many alternative approaches. They will have a great deal to contribute to each other, and it is to be hoped that effective channels of communication can be established within and between research organizations in order to take full advantage of this interplay. The simulation approach presented by Professor Forrester has a very important contribution to make in this interplay, especially in the area of dynamic stability.

HOWARD. My first feeling on hearing Professor Forrester's comments was similar to the feeling I experienced upon graduation from the School of Engineering. With slide rule in hand I went forth to meet problems as Saint George went forth to meet the dragon, having full confidence that the engineer could do anything. All that was necessary was to grab the problem and wrestle with it. I am sadder and wiser now. Having wrestled with some problems, I no longer have as much confidence that our methods and approaches are omnipotent.

In discussing Professor Forrester's paper, I should like to treat and contrast two general approaches to the study of industrial and economic systems: industrial dynamics and operations research. Some of my colleagues in other fields seem to be confused about the relationship of Professor Forrester's industrial dynamics and the general field of operations research. Some individuals who are acquainted with Professor Forrester's work seem to believe that any approach to industrial problems that utilizes digital computers falls in the province of industrial dynamics. On the other hand, some operations research analysts, economists, and businessmen feel that industrial dynamics is not a discipline but rather a single isolated approach to industrial problems. Some researchers feel that industrial dynamics is the road to the future; others feel that it is a dead end. As usual, the truth probably lies somewhere between these views.

Industrial dynamics is a term coined by Professor Forrester to describe the method of studying industrial operations that he has developed. Professor Forrester has defined his approach as follows: "Industrial dynamics is an analysis of the interactions between the flows of information, money, orders, materials, capital equipment, and manpower in a company, an industry, or a national economy."[1] As the name implies, industrial dynamics is concerned with the time-varying or dynamic behavior of industrial organizations.

On the other hand, to define operations research is considerably more difficult because even the workers in the field cannot agree on a definition. However, for our purposes, the following definition will be useful. Operations research is a scientific method for studying men and machines performing repetitive operations. For convenience we shall refer to the people who make industrial dynamics studies as dynamicists and to those who make operations research investigations as analysts.

The question of the moment is: How is industrial dynamics related to operations research and what promise does each of these fields hold in the solution of management problems? To answer this question let us compare industrial dynamics and operations research with respect to their phenomena of study, their methodology, their research philosophy, and the state of the art in each field; finally, let us evaluate each approach and offer a few remarks about possible future courses of development.

Phenomena. Industrial dynamics is concerned primarily with industrial operational problems. Operations research is con-

75

cerned with the man-machine systems that are found in industry, government, and the military establishment. The dynamicist desires to study the highest-level problems of the enterprise: the basic forces controlling industrial growth and stability. On the other hand the analyst, up to the present time, has been content to concern himself primarily with lower-level decision problems: questions in the quantitative management of inventory, the establishment of effective marketing policies, and the improvement of distribution methods, for example.

Methodology. Computers are used extensively by both the dynamicist and the analyst. At the present time the most important models of the dynamicist are based upon a system of first-order difference equations that must be solved recursively. Because of the lofty aim of the dynamicist, only a digital computer has the computing and storage capacity necessary to provide the solution. As a result, the existence of large electronic computers is almost a prerequisite of industrial dynamics as we see it today.

On the other hand one can make a case for the point of view that computers are not necessary to the field of operations research in spite of their widespread use. The analyst attempts to build analytic mathematical models of the operations that he is studying, using such disciplines as mathematical programming, queuing theory, probability theory, and their equally imposing brethren. Although computers often have been necessary to obtain numerical results, there are many examples of studies in which significant contributions have been made without their assistance. Both the dynamicist and the analyst find useful the control theory of linear systems, although few of the systems that they encounter in practice are, in fact, linear. They also both use simulation, where computers are called upon to provide a working model of a complex enterprise.

Research Philosophy. The research philosophies of the dynamicist and analyst are markedly different. The general approach of the dynamicist is to describe a system by a large set of first-order difference equations. He is more likely to err on the side of too many variables rather than too few, because he has faith in the computational ability of his computer. The analyst, on the other hand, prefers to limit the number of variables as much as possible because he is looking for analytic rather than computational solutions. As a believer in Occam's Razor, the analyst will add variables only if they can be shown clearly to have an influence upon the total behavior of the system.

The goals of the two investigators differ in that the dynamicist's results are often descriptive rather than normative in nature. The dynamicist attempts to show how changes in time lags and amplifications throughout the system will produce qualitative differences in over-all system behavior. On the other hand the analyst's approach is normative. At his low level he attempts to find how decisions should be made in order to increase the effectiveness of the operation that he is studying. These differences in approach are responsible for much of the conceptual conflict that sometimes arises between the dynamicist and the analyst.

State of the Art. Much of the disparity in numbers between dynamicists and analysts at the present time can be explained by the fact that industrial dynamics is an area that has appeared only in the last few years. Although operations research is an infant science, it has been in existence about twenty years. Possibly as a result of its age, industrial dynamics has had little opportunity to provide convincing illustrations of successful applications. Operations research has a record of significant accomplishment, although there have been some unfortunate experiences.

Evaluation. Let us now attempt to evaluate the progress that has been made in each field. Industrial acceptance is probably not a good yardstick for evaluation. Although there are relatively few businessmen employing industrial dynamics, while many employ operations research, this fact could be explained by the relative ages of the two disciplines.

One basis for judgment might be the practical utility of

industrial dynamics models. Dynamicists claim that the behavior of an industrial dynamics model is usually quite similar to the behavior of the underlying phenomena. The question arises: Is mere similarity of behavior enough? Validation based on similarity alone is rarely convincing. Most observers agree that industrial dynamics will experience a significant increase in stature when its models have undergone irrefutable validation.

The main difficulty is, of course, that similarity can be misleading. In building industrial dynamics models, it may be fruitful to liken the industrial system to a complex fire-control system, but we must never forget in examining system responses that the measures of effectiveness for the two systems are quite different. For example, control engineers rightly maintain that oscillating systems are generally unsatisfactory. Suppose that we examined a company's past history and found a large oscillation over time in the amount of raw material purchased. Is this necessarily evidence of mismanagement on the part of the company or at least an indication that a better control system is necessary? Of course, that may be the case, but we cannot pass judgment until we examine the costs associated with this oscillation. Suppose we should find, for example, that the times at which raw-materials purchases were high were also the times at which raw-materials prices were low, and vice versa. Then we would praise rather than condemn management's control actions.

This example is rather extreme, but it does point out that the valuation of system responses is not a trivial problem. It is not sufficient to examine the behavior of industrial processes in the same offhand way that some people claim is appropriate for dealing with minimization of mean-squared error in physical systems. The result of fluctuations in each variable on the measures of effectiveness must be considered if the control system is to be satisfactory from an over-all point of view. It is the extremely perverse nature of business cost functions that makes perilous the naive extension of standard servomechanism theory to the theory of the firm.

A basic difficulty that dynamicists must face in building their models is that the rationality of decisions in the firm is often not determinable even if it exists. The input necessary for an adequate industrial dynamics model normally would require many man-years of work if the model were to be an accurate description of a firm's operations. Yet such careful study is necessary if the dynamicist is to make quantitative rather than qualitative statements about a firm's behavior. This is especially true if his efforts are to be compared with those of a rather unsophisticated observer of the firm's past history. For example, it does not require a digital computer to tell that if a company holds a major sale at a time when demand would be high in any event, then it is only going to increase the fluctuations in its sales pattern. The dynamicist should be judged not on his ability to make an absolute improvement in a firm's control but rather on his ability to improve the firm's operations beyond the improvement that could be achieved by having the operations subjected to the review of any careful observer.

On the other hand the analyst, in spite of his relatively mature field, still has a number of extremely difficult problems to solve. In many areas the relatively simple problems have long since disappeared. The analyst must look for second-order rather than first-order effects, and he finds that the tools to be employed must increase correspondingly in power. For example, the problem of controlling inventory is one of the most complex control problems found in any environment. The cost structure of the inventory system is complicated, the number of state variables necessary to describe the system is large, and there is a high degree of interaction between different parts of the system. Professional control engineers readily admit that the general inventory control problem is one of the most difficult control problems they have faced in any context, bar none. In the inventory control area it often happens that we can present the decision maker with the values of all variables on which a decision regarding inventory must be based and yet we cannot tell him how the decision should be made. Indeed, analytic solutions exist to relatively few problems in the area of inventory control.

Both the businessman and the dynamicist will be hampered in synthesizing new industrial control systems until the science of the analyst has been developed more thoroughly. The dynamicist may provide a real service to the analyst by pointing out the areas of an enterprise that most critically require study.

The Future. Scientists have gained an entrée into the world of the businessman through the field of operations research. The businessman has generally, but not always, found that the logical, methodical approach of science to his problems can increase his profits and his managerial control. Although the continued growth of the field of operations research seems assured, it is too early to tell whether industrial dynamics will be a sideline or mainstream of this growth. The main contribution of the dynamicists to date has been to attract attention to the higher-level decision problems of the enterprise. The importance of these problems assures that any approach which offers a deeper understanding of them will flourish. Only time will tell whether this will be operations research, industrial dynamics, or some new discipline of the future.

FORRESTER. I made no effort in what I said this evening to give a balanced picture. Had I tried to give a balanced picture, I should not have conveyed with enough clarity the points I was trying to make. The balance provided by the two discussants certainly is appropriate.

I should like to clarify my views on invention, which Holt used to argue for the necessity of statistical analysis. I said that there clearly was agreement on certain of the cause-and-effect relationships that control the process of invention, even if there was not agreement on how, in fact, it works. We agree that if we had more people, more budget, more research institutions, more quality in our people, by whatever standards we use, then the results would be better. Otherwise, we should not need M.I.T.; we should not have the large military research budget that we do; and one research man would contribute as much to technological advance as a multitude. This is what Holt does not believe without a statistical analysis.

HOLT. One word in rebuttal: Einstein.

FORRESTER. No, that is exactly what I mean. Einstein was not by himself. There was a vast structure of technology surrounding him, and this is exactly the point.

We do have a very large amount of knowledge and understanding for which there are no statistics in the formal sense. I did not say that one should not use statistics when one has them. I merely said that a very small percentage of our knowledge exists in this form. If we limit ourselves to information in statistical form, this does not give us enough to go on. My point was to call attention to the vast amount of information available in other forms.

General Discussion

LUCAS. Dr. Forrester, are you trying to develop a set of standard criteria that you could apply, not only to Mr. Sprague's industry, but to other industries as well?

FORRESTER. The answer to your question is, "No." There is no such thing as *the* model. There even is no such thing as a model that persists for as much as a week. You build a model to answer a question. You may build several models to answer several questions. In the airplane industry, you may build a wing-loading model to test with sandbags, a model to put in the wind tunnel, and probably many more. The issue of first importance is a hypothesis of what you think matters; then you develop a model to check the hypothesis. This is really an extension of what we necessarily do all the time in the management of an organization.

McLANAHAN. I am wondering if anything happens to your model as changes occur in the key personnel from whom you obtained your material, or in the way that they make decisions.

FORRESTER. Those of you who know a variety of business organizations well may characterize them as being different in various ways. There is the "successful" company; there is the "unsuccessful" one. One company has a high level of integrity, another has not. These are differences that do not come and go with the change of just a person or two. These characteristics are persistent. They partly determine how the people were selected in the first place. The kinds of people who are hired and the kinds who leave depend on the organization. Therefore, I should say that the types of things we are talking about are a great deal more stable than the coming and going of individual people.

SHEDD.   Dr. Forrester, I was wondering if you have been able to use the model of the Sprague operation to control employment in the company.

FORRESTER.   I cannot cite at this stage of the game documentary evidence of what has been achieved. Changes are still being made, and information flows are being set up. However, the situation is not so incomplete as perhaps has been implied. The procedures that we use are on a very sound basis in other professions. The pilot plant of a new chemical plant, for example, is essentially a hypothesis that a certain configuration will work. You build a model of it to see whether it will work, and if it does, you build the main plant along the same lines. This is an experimental procedure that is philosophically the same as ours. There is nothing new about the philosophy of the approach. The only thing new is the area to which it is being applied. The fact that it is a more nonlinear, less well-explored area makes it no more difficult as a next step than some of the earlier steps once seemed. Our knowledge goes up exponentially with time, and the next step always looks like a big one. I believe that we are ready to take this step in the next decade or two.

HOLT.   I should like to question Professor Forrester's going back and forth so facilely between a chemical pilot plant, a wind tunnel, and a simulation model for a computer. As we all know, one of the beauties of a computer is its flexibility. You can program on it practically any process involving information handling. Now, the wind tunnel and the pilot plant are governed by the same laws of nature that govern, respectively, the airplane and the full-scale pilot plant. We don't have to ask whether Mother Nature is really applying the same rules or physical laws to the model phenomena which she is to the full-scale phenomena. On the other hand, when we go into a business organization and observe its structure and come home and build a model with our bare hands, there is a very real question as to whether we have brought home the baby. I think the problem of validating the model here is extremely critical in the effective use of this sort of approach.

I should particularly like to emphasize at M.I.T. the difference between tests in the real world and tests on an abstract model because I think that engineering education often is deficient in drawing this kind of distinction clearly. Engineers are expert at using scientific theories in solving practical problems, but they learn relatively little about the scientific method that yields the theories. They are sensitive to the problems of finding workable approximations to theory when they want to bring it to bear on a problem, but they are not sensitive to the fact that the theory itself is at best an approximation to reality — a hypothetical model subject to empirical verification. In a well-developed field like electrical engineering, it may not be too serious to fail to draw a clear distinction between the relationships in the real world and the relationships incorporated in Maxwell's equations, a hypothetical model. However, in a field where our models are still shaky, it leads to no end of mischief to confuse models with reality.

ANONYMOUS. An earlier question was addressed to you [Forrester] about the effect of changes in management personnel. In answering, you referred to the relative stability of both successful and unsuccessful companies. If an unsuccessful company was wise enough to employ your approach, and arrived at what we hope is the right answer, then how does the company implement it in light of the stability of management's viewpoint?

FORRESTER. If it is a poor enough company and stable enough, it will not try the approach. It seems to me that one of the reasons for being poor is not so much an insistence on following traditional policies as it is a lack of understanding of what various alternative policies will do. It is the innovating companies, willing to experiment, who will be most interested in the approach.

ANONYMOUS. Do you [Forrester] expect that the actual results obtained by a company which has altered its procedures based on the theoretical results of a simulation will be comparable with the theoretical results?

FORRESTER. In general we are shooting for improvement so great that there would be no doubt about there having been an improvement. If you can cut down the employment fluctuation by a factor of 3 or 4, this will be fairly conspicuous. Of course, no one could prove that the improvement was attributable to the changes that had been made. But after the changes were tried successfully a few times, the evidence would be strong enough to be persuasive.

In terms of money, we are aiming at gains comparable with the present profit margin of the company. For example, in one company familiar to me, the officers began to wonder about some of the things that we have been discussing. In reviewing historical data, they found that in a particular year production had varied by 400 per cent from minimum to peak. During that same year retail sales fluctuated by only 30 per cent. Their estimate of the avoidable costs had they followed different policies — of the costs avoidable had they not stopped and started production lines, had they not transferred people, or laid them off and later rehired them, had they not had to let things obsolesce in the warehouse — their estimate of possible avoidable costs for the year was some $75,000,000. This was about the profit that they made that year.

HOWARD. Jay [Forrester], it has always seemed to me, primarily because industrial dynamics is such a young field, that it presents an insubstantial target at the present time. It does not appear possible to pin you down and make you validate your assertions. We are used to seeing in the sciences one curve labeled "predicted" and another labeled "observed."

These curves allow us to make evaluations such as "This is good" or "This is not so good." Is there any reason in principle, assuming that you have a good model of the decision-making process, why you cannot take actual sales, production, and inventory data, use your model to obtain "predicted" sales, production, and inventory figures for the corresponding period, and make a comparison?

FORRESTER. Yes, there is a reason why you cannot. These decisions are all noisy. Suppose you take two models, absolutely identical in structure and parameters, but both having noise components in their decision mechanisms. If you start these models from identical initial conditions and let them run, their behaviors will diverge so quickly that there is no way of predicting what will happen on a specific day. Yet the two models will exhibit similar qualitative performance characteristics. They will both be stable or unstable, for example. And should you change the design of one of these models in the presence of the same noise as before, it will be better or worse by virtue of the induced change in its qualitative characteristics.

Thus, one must predict, not the particular event, not the shape of the particular time history, but one must predict the change in the performance characteristics: profitability, employment stability, and characteristics such as these. The test you [Howard] suggest of comparing a particular time history with the output of a model is not a test that you can expect to use, although it is a test that many people have been attempting for many economic models. I think we can demonstrate that this test, in fact, cannot be met. And it is not necessary to meet it to have tremendously useful results.

HOWARD. But I think that you have to have some quantitative measure of how good your model is. It may be that you should make several replications and then apply a statistical analysis, as Holt suggested. In other words, how can we possibly criticize you when you say, "It has the same qualitative behavior"? We both look at the same simulated history, and I say it does not look at all like the real thing, and you say it does. You say that you cannot with your model duplicate the actual sales data because of the noise in the system. All you can do is get a signal that has the same characteristics as the actual data. I say that this statement has no content. What you might view as the same characteristics, I might not. How can we get a quantitative agreement on what constitutes the same characteristics?

FORRESTER. I think that this is a matter of judgment. The man who is operating the company has got to make a decision. He is doing it now. If you disagree with the decision, then your judgment about the issue is different from mine. And if it is your company, you had better use your judgment. If it is my company, I shall use mine.

This is really an academic point, though, because I have yet to see the difference arise with the working people, including managers and analysts. This is a very troublesome question in the abstract, and yet in the actual specific case it is not answered in the rigorous objective sense that you speak of; neither is it in any of our real-life activities. I think you are trying for something here that we do not have in other areas of human endeavor. We do not have it in medicine or law or engineering. You are trying for something here that is more nearly perfect, more objective than in fact we know how to do anywhere else. I do not disagree with the desirability of it. I say we do not have it, and we are not ready for it. Where we seem to have it in certain of the statistical model tests, I believe it is misleading and on an essentially unsound foundation.

HOLT. It is interesting to contrast Professor Forrester's willingness in model formulation to quantify such unstructured concepts as "integrity" with his unwillingness in model testing to accept quantitative tests of the models. Even where *quantitative* data are available for such variables as employment fluctuations both from the company and from the model, he accepts *qualitative* judgments on similarity as perfectly adequate.

ARDEN. In technical investigation a researcher often has more than one motive. He may desire to solve a particular problem, but he also may wish to find better methods for solving a class of problems. I wonder if Professor Forrester will comment on what insights he may have gained, not to solutions of particular problems, but to methods for solving these problems. I know, in one sense, that applying a computer to a problem is a method; but I am really looking for insights a little beyond that.

FORRESTER. The field that we are talking about occupies a position in the social sciences not unlike the position of engineering between the physical sciences and society. We do not teach at M.I.T. how to be an inspired designer; we do not arrange it so that everybody who graduates from here creates the best engineering system or the best communication system. What we do is to provide the student with some tools and approaches and attitudes that he can apply. The rest is up to him. Some people are just plain better at applying than others. This point relates to what I said a while ago. We are now at a stage where the procedures that you are asking for lie essentially in the art and judgment area.

What I am doing is retreating into the same refuge that the manager often does. We tell the manager that we are going to understand his decision policies and how he runs his business. And he says, "Oh no you aren't. It is art and judgment." You ask me how we determine the characteristics of these systems, and I tell you it is art and judgment. But this is really where engineering stands. This is where medicine stands. I can discuss with you what the art is; I can discuss the approaches with you; but I cannot give you an objective set of rules that anybody can go out and apply step by step to come up with the right answer. I cannot do it.

HOLT. It seems to me significant that Jay [Forrester] has selected medicine and engineering as his examples, not physics and chemistry.

FORRESTER. No, they are not pertinent.

HOLT. [To Forrester] The point is that at times you have been very critical of the strivings of management science toward a scientific body of knowledge. There is a real distinction between the kind of professional problem solving that we associate with engineering, where the object is to get the job done, and the kind we associate with fundamental scientific research, where the object is to obtain knowledge. It seems to me that you have directed yourself more toward the question of solving practical problems and less toward the question of obtaining knowledge.

If your aim is simply to improve an operation, how do you decide how complicated to make your model? In your example you had thirty decision centers of which five were important. Suppose that an operations researcher, after careful study, set up a mathematical model that incorporated the five important decision centers and was able to solve this model analytically. Would you still argue in this case that the industrial dynamics approach is superior to the operations research approach?

FORRESTER. Generally you find out which five are important only after you have considered all the ones that seem to be operating in the system. This information unfolds as you observe the process. It is not obvious in the first place.

HOLT. You do not think that it is possible to spot the five critical decision centers at the start?

FORRESTER. In retrospect, yes, for the example I cited, and perhaps for similar examples. But in general I should be willing to assert that it is not possible.

HOWARD. Professor Forrester's procedure reminds me of Galileo trying to discover the laws of falling bodies by throwing up feathers and pillows and everything else, and measuring each one individually, instead of sitting down and thinking, "Well, maybe if I use an inclined plane I can slow down this action, and if I standardize the shape of the body I can refine my analysis." I rebel at the shotgun approach. Whenever someone says, "This is a 400-variable analysis-of-variance problem, and this is a 225-variable linear programming problem," my first reaction is, "What's the matter, couldn't you understand the process?"

HOLT. If you have some good empirical tests, you can try the 5-variable model to see if it fits. If it does not, then you can try another model. There is a lot to be said for starting off with simplicity and adding complexity, instead of vice versa.

MODIGLIANI. I am still disturbed about this question of testing, because it seems impossible to pin you [Forrester] down to some definite position. As I understand what you say, the test of whether a model is reasonable is whether I think it is reasonable. I completely agree that you would not want to test the model in terms of its behaving in exactly the same way as the real system. I also agree with the idea of using certain qualitative features of the situation such as frequency, amplitude, and lag. But it seems to me essential that we do worry about finding some criteria for pinning ourselves down. Someday we want to have a common ground for agreeing that a model is or is not reasonable.

FORRESTER. Anything qualitative certainly has quantitative measures. What are the qualitative characteristics? Things like periods, intervals between peaks, phase relationships, turning points, and the relative succession of peaks. All of these qualitative characteristics most certainly have a quantitative basis. And these are the characteristics that we use in comparing two model runs, just as you might compare a model run with real life. You compare it on the basis of amplitudes and periods and the tendency for disturbances to die out or to be amplified.

But the distinction I was making is between the qualitative tests, which indeed have quantitative bases, and the test that a lot of people seem to expect: the test of whether a model can predict a specific future event. I assert that this is not a really significant and worthwhile test. Any economic model that I can conceive of at this stage will not predict whether in July 1965 we are going to be at the top or bottom of an economic cycle. This is what I mean by an inability to predict a specific event.

HOWARD. You say that we cannot predict a specific event primarily because of the noise that is introduced into the system at the various decision points. But isn't this noise known *a posteriori?* Don't we know what the actual outside variables were at the particular time?

FORRESTER. No, these are buried throughout all the decision points.

HOWARD. But you could design an experiment in which you took a detailed data account of all information flows within the company and set the parameters in your model according to the actual noise values observed in these flows. Then you could see if you were able to predict the over-all behavior of the company. This would be analogous to checking out a computer program containing random elements by fixing these random elements to deterministic values.

FORRESTER. Oh, I should not want to assert that your suggestion is impossible. But I think you are calling for a volume of information that we cannot expect to be available. For example, in one company's data we found periods when production exceeded sales, yet inventory was falling. This is impossible. But this is the kind of information that usually is available. I certainly cannot say that your suggestion is impossible, but it requires a job that is tremendously expensive and overwhelming in its implications; and I do not think that it will contribute anything that is essential.

HOLT. Our discussion tonight seems to have pointed up a clear difference in approach. Industrial dynamics seeks to develop models that can be used to generate, test, and sell improvements in decision policies; the models are good enough if management will accept them. Operations research and management science share these practical objectives (although the latter often takes a longer view in seeking practical payoffs), but in addition they aspire gradually to accumulate a body of *tested* knowledge. Hence, they are more willing than is Forrester to accept the discipline of the scientific method. They accept at least in principle the search for objective empirical tests of their models as an integral part of their research process.

To be sure, industrial dynamics as expounded tonight also seeks knowledge; but the *art* of improved practice comes first, the understanding and theory come later. This process will "work," of course, but there is a question of relative efficiency. In my view, if scientific research leads to reliable knowledge, improved practice will follow soon enough and progress will be faster than if we concentrate our energies on the short-term payoff. And there is a danger to a new and immature field in using as the final test "acceptability to the manager." If a recommended policy fails in practice, the manager loses his profit, but industrial dynamics loses reputation. The latter may be far more difficult to repair.

The reluctance of industrial dynamicists to face the validation problem is understandable enough; for we know very little about testing complex nonlinear hypotheses. However, this shortcoming in our methodological tool bag is not apt to be remedied by skirting the issues, and one might hope that industrial dynamicists could be influenced seriously to concern themselves with these problems.

But even if they do not, there are plenty of problems to go around. There is little to be gained by methodological bickering and criticism, since it is clearly understood that the two approaches are quite different and each has merit. Either way, we cannot fail to learn more than we now know.

REFERENCE

1. Forrester, J. W., *Industrial Dynamics*, The M.I.T. Press and John Wiley & Sons, Inc., New York, 1961. Portions of Professor Forrester's talk are based on material appearing in this book.

3

**Simulation
of
Human
Thinking**

3

Simulation
of
Human
Thinking

Speaker	**HERBERT A. SIMON** Professor of Administration and Associate Dean Graduate School of Industrial Administration Carnegie Institute of Technology
Coauthor	**ALLEN NEWELL** Institute Professor of Systems and Communications Sciences Carnegie Institute of Technology (Also Consultant, the RAND Corporation)
Discussants	**MARVIN L. MINSKY** Associate Professor of Mathematics Massachusetts Institute of Technology
	GEORGE A. MILLER Professor of Psychology Harvard University
Moderator	**SIDNEY S. ALEXANDER** Professor of Industrial Management Massachusetts Institute of Technology

Simon. The use of computers to simulate human thinking has a prehistory and a history, as well as a present and a future. During the prehistorical period, prior to World War II, there were no computers, in the modern sense, but there were a number of successful attempts to construct teleological mechanisms — analog devices that simulated one aspect or another of an organism's adaptive behavior in relation to its environment.[1]

History begins in earnest, however, with the rapid growth of servomechanism theory during World War II and with the appearance of the first stored-program digital computers, two of the three legs on which Professor Wiener's cybernetics stands. Grey Walter's "tortoises" and W. Ross Ashby's Homeostat represent important early progress, as does an analog simulation of a self-organizing network that Professor Minsky constructed in 1951.

Computer simulation had already begun to take definite form as a field of research by the time of the well-known session on learning machines at the 1955 Western Joint Computer Conference, a session in which Professor Miller also participated.[2] At that session, Clark and Farley of Lincoln Laboratories described a computer simulation of a self-organizing "nerve net" system; Selfridge and Dinneen, also of Lincoln Laboratories, described a pattern recognition program; and one of the authors, Newell of the RAND Corporation, outlined a program for a chess-playing machine.

One of the discussants at that session, Walter Pitts, observed that there were two main lines of attack represented: the first taking as its point of departure some features of the human nervous system and sensory apparatus, the second, the organization of symbolic processes to perform complex thinking tasks. As Mr. Pitts put it:[3]

> The speakers this morning are all imitators in the sense that the poet in Aristotle "imitates" life. But, whereas Messrs. Farley, Clark, Selfridge, and Dinneen are imitating the nervous system, Mr. Newell prefers to imitate the hierarchy of final causes traditionally called the mind. It will come to the same thing in the end, no doubt. . . .

Most workers in this field continue to believe that it will come to the same thing, but the end is not yet, and these two main strands of research are still clearly discernible in the work going on at the present time. Our remarks this evening will be concerned almost exclusively with the second, with the imitation of mind. This strand has already begun to make contact with important potential areas of application, business administration and teaching among them.[4] Our purpose tonight, however, is not to speculate about applications. We shall be speculative enough, we are sure, for your tastes; but we shall speculate about the form that fundamental theory in this field is taking, rather than about the implications of that fundamental theory for everyday affairs.

The Proof of Possibility

With this decade of history and several decades of prehistory behind us, it is no longer necessary to argue that computers can be used to simulate human thinking, or to explain in general terms how such simulation can be carried out. A dozen or more computer programs have been written and tested that perform some of the interesting symbol-manipulating, problem-solving tasks that humans can perform, and that do so in a manner which simulates, at least in some general respects, the way in which humans do these tasks. Computer programs now play chess and checkers, find proofs for theorems in geometry and logic, compose music, balance assembly lines, design electric motors and generators, memorize nonsense syllables, form concepts, and learn to read.[5]

With the proof of possibility accomplished, we can turn to more substantive questions. We can ask what we have learned about human thinking and problem solving through computer simulation: to what extent we now have theories for these phenomena, and what the content of these theories is. Since we want to talk about these substantive matters, we shall simply make the following assertions, which are validated by existing computer programs.

1. Computers are quite general symbol-manipulating devices that can be programmed to perform nonnumerical as well as numerical symbol manipulation.

2. Computer programs can be written that use nonnumerical symbol manipulating processes to perform tasks which, in humans, require thinking and learning.

3. These programs can be regarded as theories, in a completely literal sense, of the corresponding human processes. These theories are testable in a number of ways: among them, by comparing the symbolic behavior of a computer so programmed with the symbolic behavior of a human subject when both are performing the same problem-solving or thinking tasks.

The General Problem Solver

The theory we shall have most to say about is a computer program called the General Problem Solver. It is not "general" in the sense that it will solve, or even try to solve, all problems; it obviously won't. It is called "general" because it will accept as tasks all problems that can be put in a specified, but fairly general, form, and because the methods it employs make no

97

specific reference to the subject matter of the particular problem it is solving. The General Problem Solver is a system of methods — believed to be those commonly possessed by intelligent college students — that turn out to be helpful in many situations where a person confronts problems for which he does not possess special methods of attack.

Before general methods can be applied to any particular class of problems, of course, the problem solver must also learn, or be taught, the rules that apply to that particular problem domain. The General Problem Solver will not prove theorems unless instructed in the rules of proof in the particular branch of mathematics to which the theorems belong. Thus, in any particular problem domain, the resources available to the General Problem Solver include information about the task environment as well as its own repertory of methods.

Missionaries and Cannibals

Let us introduce the General Problem Solver (which we shall call GPS) by means of a simple example. Many of you are familiar with the puzzle of the missionaries and cannibals, and some of you saw a young lady solving the puzzle in a recent CBS television program celebrating M.I.T.'s centenary. There are three missionaries and three cannibals on the bank of a wide river, wanting to cross. There is a boat on the bank, which will hold no more than two persons, and all six members of the party know how to paddle it. The only real difficulty is that the cannibals are partial to a diet of missionaries. If, even for a moment, one or more missionaries are left alone with a larger number of cannibals, the missionaries will be eaten. The problem is to find a sequence of boat trips that will get the entire party safely across the river, without the loss of any missionaries.

Suppose, now, that we encountered this puzzle for the first time. We are endowed by nature and nurture with certain abilities that enable us to tackle the problem. We might or might not solve it, but we could at least *think* about it. In what would this thinking consist? In particular, how could we bring to bear our general problem-solving skills, which make no reference to missionaries and cannibals, on this particular situation?

Clearly, we have to form some kind of abstraction of the problem that will match the abstractness of our general methods: We have some people and a boat on *this* side of the river and we want them on *that* side of the river. Stated abstractly, we have a certain state of affairs, and we want a different state of affairs. Moreover, we can describe both states, and we can also describe what the differences are between them, between what we have and what we want.

In this case, the differences between the given and the desired are differences in physical location. Our men are on one side of the river; we want them on the other. But we have had vast experience with differences in location, and that experience (stored somehow in memory) tells us that boats are useful devices for reducing differences of location on water. So we begin to consider the possible sequences of boatloads that will get our party across the river without casualties.

It is clear from this formulation of the problem what part is played in its solution by our general problem-solving techniques and what part by our knowledge and experience of the particular problem domain in question. A general solution technique is to characterize the given and desired situations, to find the differences between them, and to search for means — implements or operators — that are relevant to removing differences of these kinds. Our knowledge of the task and our experience tell us what the given and desired situations are, and what kinds of operators may be relevant for getting from here to there.

Structure of GPS

We can now characterize the program of the General Problem Solver more formally.[6] The program deals with symbolic *objects* that describe or characterize situations: the given situation, the desired situation, various intermediate possible situations. The program also deals with symbols representing *differences* between pairs of objects, and with symbols representing *operators* that are capable of inducing changes in the objects to which they are applied. (Table 1, first column.)

Goal Types. The processes of GPS are organized around *goals* of three types:

1. *Transformation* goals, to transform object *a* into object *b*.
2. *Difference Reduction* goals, to eliminate or reduce difference *d* between objects *a* and *b*.
3. *Operator Application* goals, to apply operator *q* to object *a*.

TABLE 1

Comparison of Basic Categories in GPS,
Speech Learning, and Organismic Adaptation

GPS	Learning Speech	Adapting to Environment	
objects	perceptual symbols (audited phonemes)	AFFERENT	
differences	comparison between adult-child phoneme images		state language
relevant operators	changes in motor symbols (control of speech production)	EFFERENT	process language

Methods. With each type of goal in GPS there is associated one or more methods, or processes, that may contribute to the attainment of the goal. The principal methods in the present version of GPS are three in number, one for each type of goal:

1. Method for transformation goals, to transform *a* into *b*:
   (a) Notice a difference *d* between *a* and *b*.
   (b) Establish the goal of reducing *d* between *a* and *b*.
   (c) Try to attain this new goal.
   (d) If successful, find a new difference and repeat.

2. Method for difference reduction goals, to reduce *d* between *a* and *b*:

   (a) Recall an operator *q* that is relevant to differences of the type of *d*.

   (b) Establish the goal of applying *q* to *a*.

   (c) Try to attain this new goal.

   (d) If successful, return to the previous transform goal.

3. Method for operator application goals, to apply operator *q* to *a*:

   (a) Compare conditions for application of *q* with object *a*.

   (b) If these are not satisfied, establish and try to attain the goal of transforming *a* into an object that meets these conditions.

   (c) When the conditions are satisfied, apply *q* to *a*, and return to the previous difference reduction goal with the modified object *a'*.

This is a rather simplified description of what goes on in GPS, but it gives the broad outline of the program. GPS, to put it simply, is a program that reasons about ends and means. It is capable of defining ends, seeking means to attain them, and, in the process of so doing, defining new subsidiary ends, or subgoals, to the original end.

As a theory of human problem solving, GPS asserts that college students solve problems — at least problems of the sorts for which the program has been tested — by carrying out this kind of organized means-end analysis. It does not assert that the process is carried out consciously — it is easy to show that many steps in the problem-solving process do not reach conscious awareness. Nor does the theory assert that the process will appear particularly orderly to an observer who does not know the program detail or, for that matter, to the problem solver himself. It does assert that if we compare that part of the human subject's problem-solving behavior which we can observe — the steps he takes, his verbalizations — with the processes carried out by the computer, they will be substantially the same.

Abstracting and Planning Processes. Before we leave this description of GPS, we should like to mention one other kind of process that we are incorporating in the program, and that certainly must be included if we are to explain and predict the behavior of our subjects, particularly the brighter ones. We call these additional methods *abstracting* and *planning* processes. Briefly, abstracting consists in replacing the objects, the differences, and the operators, with new symbolic expressions that describe the situation in much more general terms, omitting the detail.[7] For example, we might ask GPS to prove a trigonometric identity:

$$\cos^2 x + \sin^2 x = \tan x \cot x$$

Here, GPS might take as *a* the expression "$\cos^2 x + \sin^2 x$" and as *b* the expression "$\tan x \cot x$." In using the planning method, these might be abstracted to *a′* "an expression containing cos and sin" and *b′* "an expression containing tan and cot," respectively. Then, the methods of GPS could be applied to transforming the abstracted given object *a′* into the abstracted desired object *b′*. If this goal were attained, the steps employed for this transformation would generally provide a *plan* for transforming the original, detailed given object *a* into the original desired object *b*. In the particular case illustrated, the plan might be something like: "First eliminate cos and sin from the expression, and then introduce tan and cot."

The Generality of Means-End Analysis

The processes incorporated in GPS have actually been observed in the behavior of our human subjects solving problems in the laboratory. By analyzing the tape-recorded protocols of their problem-solving efforts, we can identify the occurrences of the three goal types and the four methods. Moreover, the augmented GPS, containing the planning method, incorporates a substantially adequate set of processes to explain our subjects' behavior in some of these simple theorem-proving, puzzle-solving situations.[8] By the adequacy of GPS, we mean two things:

1. We do not find in the subjects' protocols evidences of processes quite different from those postulated in GPS. This may mean only that we don't know how to look for them.
2. But when we have compared the trace of the GPS computer (or hand simulations of the computer program) with the protocols of a subject solving the same problem, we have found that the two often follow the same path — noticing the same things about the problem expressions, establishing the same subgoals, applying the same operators, running down the same blind alleys — over periods of time ranging up to several minutes. That is to say, the processes in GPS are sufficient to produce a stream of behavior in a given problem situation quite similar to that produced by the human subject.

These kinds of tests, even if broadened, would still not say much about the generality of GPS as a theory of human thinking and problem solving. It might turn out that if we examined tasks quite different from those used in developing the program, and made the same careful records of subjects' protocols, we should find many new processes exhibited that are not contained in GPS. However, extensions of GPS in fair detail to problem domains that were not considered when the program was developed indicate that its processes are adequate at least to these other domains. For example, the problem of the missionaries and cannibals, which was first suggested as a possible task by Mr. Thomas Wolf of the Columbia Broadcasting System, has been solved by the current version of GPS, not without some reorganization of the program but without addition of new goal types or methods. Similarly, the applications to algebraic and trigonometric identities and to certain learning tasks appear to require no enlargement of the basic repertory of methods. Less detailed analysis of a variety of other tasks shows GPS to be adequate for these also.

Still, these additional tests do not carry GPS beyond a fairly limited range of formal problem-solving situations. It would be of considerable interest to explore, even qualitatively, the powers and limitations of GPS when it is confronted with a thinking or learning task of quite a different kind from any of these. We should like now to carry out a reconnaissance along these lines. First, we shall describe, on the basis of what is now known, the processes that humans use in a task that appears, superficially, to be quite different from problem solving. Then, we shall propose a framework which shows that these processes can be subsumed under those already incorporated in the General Problem Solver. The particular task we shall examine was chosen because quite a bit is known about it, and because it will allow us to call on our discussants for a maximum of assistance this evening.

The Acquisition of Speech

There are many human activities to which we should apply the term "thinking" but not the term "problem solving." There are also many activities we should usually call "learning" rather than "thinking." We should ordinarily call a child's acquisition of speech, "learning." We propose to consider the acquisition of speech as an example of human cognitive activity that is at something of an opposite pole from the rather highly verbalized, somewhat conscious, practiced problem solving of an intelligent and educated adult. We can then judge whether the processes at these two poles are quite different or basically the same.

Speech acquisition has been about as well studied as any non-laboratory complex human activity, and a review of the literature indicates that there is general consensus about the particular facts we shall use.[9] If we are wrong in that assumption or in our interpretations of the facts, Professor Miller is one of the best-equipped men in the country to put us straight.

Central Representations

We consider an infant who has already learned the names of a few objects, as evidenced by the fact that he can point to them or fetch them when they are named by an adult, but who has not yet pronounced their names. From his behavior, we can infer that when the child perceives the spoken word "ball," his perception has some kind of internal representation in the brain that permits it to be associated, through previous experience, with some internal representation of a visually perceived ball.

To *say* the word "ball," the child must, in addition, store some kind of program capable of energizing, through motor (efferent) channels, the muscles involved in speech production, in the production of the specific phonemes of that word. Let us call the "whatever-it-is" in the central nervous system that represents internally a perceived sensory stimulus an *afferent* or *perceptual symbol*. Let us call the "whatever-it-is" that represents the program for initiating the motor signals an *efferent* or *motor symbol*.

Learning to speak, in this formulation, means acquiring the motor symbols that correspond to perceptual (auditory) symbols of words already known, and associating the former with the latter. Now the difficulty is that there is no way in which the corresponding perceptual and motor symbols can "resemble" each other, can symbolize the appropriateness of their association by resemblance. The correspondence is purely arbitrary.[10] The infant is faced (if he only knew it!) with the immense inductive task of discovering which motor symbols will cause speech production that, when he hears it, will produce, in turn, an appropriate auditory symbol to be perceived and recognized. And the task appears at first blush to have little structure that would permit it to be approached with some less arduous technique than trial-and-error search.

There is ample evidence that much trial-and-error search is indeed required before the infant acquires the skill of speaking. The child imitates the adults around him, and he imitates himself (echoic speech). Gradually, over many months, he acquires the motor symbols that enable him to produce sounds which he hears as the expected auditory symbols. In the early stages, the child's acquisition of a speaking vocabulary appears to be paced by the task of developing the new motor symbols.

At later stages, he is able to produce a word relatively easily once he has learned to recognize the corresponding auditory symbol.

Factorization

A little reflection will persuade us that something more than trial and error is involved. If that were all, the three hundredth word would be no easier to pronounce than the first. The child learns to learn. In what does this consist?

Although the motor symbol cannot be compared with the perceptual symbol, the *correct* perceptual symbol for a word can be compared, through imitation, with the perceptual symbol produced by the attempt to pronounce the word. If these are different, modification of the motor symbol can be attempted until an auditory symbol resembling the correct one is perceived.

Thus far we have been assuming that the units in terms of which these transactions take place are words. But there is no reason for this assumption — the child might well attend to particular syllables, phonemes, or even components of phonemes. The auditory symbols for words can be compound symbols or *expressions*: strings of phonemes, each phoneme itself encoded in terms of its component frequencies and other characteristics. It is even more plausible to suppose that the motor symbols would be constructed from smaller units, for each word involves a temporal succession of syllables, each syllable a temporal succession of phonemes, and each phoneme a whole set of signals to the several muscles involved in that part of the speech act. Thus, one of the many components of the motor symbol for the spoken word "dog" might be the signal that pushes the tongue against the palate in the initial "d" phoneme of this one-syllable word.

The Learning Process

There is considerable evidence today that this picture of the processes of word recognition and word production is correct, at least in broad outline. Many of the components involved in both auditory and motor symbols have been tentatively identified, and there is good experimental evidence for some of them.[11] But what does the picture, if true, contribute to our understanding of the child's acquisition of speech?

It means that the inductive learning need not be blind inductive learning — attempting to associate by pure trial and error each of a large number of words with an appropriate motor symbol chosen from the myriad of producible sequences of speech sounds. On the contrary, to the extent that specific factors in the auditory symbol vary with specific factors in the motor symbol (e.g., as one of the formant frequencies in vowel sounds varies with the size of the resonating mouth cavity), the search for the correct symbol can be very much restricted. Components can be corrected on a one-at-a-time basis. For example, the child trying to pronounce "dog" can at one time attend to the correctness of the vowel, at another time to the correctness of the initial consonant, or even to the aspect of the initial consonant associated with tongue position.

Thus, the hypothesis of factorization is supported both by experimental evidence that it does take place, and by theoretical reasons why it "should" take place — why speech acquisition would be very much easier with it than without it. Trial-and-error acquisition of words without factorization would require a search, in each instance, for the correct motor symbol from among tens of thousands of possible symbols. Trial-and-error acquisition of phonemes would require a search from among only a few hundred phonemes (much fewer are actually used, of course, in any single dialect). Trial-and-error search among phomene *components* would be even more restricted; there are, for example, probably only a half dozen distinguishable tongue positions. Thus, by factorization of the total space of possibilities, a very limited trial-and-error search of the factors can be substituted for an immense search of the product space. Moreover, once the child has acquired motor symbols corresponding to the common phonemes, acquisition of new words (new combinations of these same phonemes) can be very rapid.

Summary: The Child's Acquisition of Speech

Let us now summarize our description, partly factual, partly hypothetical, of the speech acquisition process. The child acquires perceptual auditory symbols corresponding to words he has heard and has associated with visual symbols. He tries, on a trial-and-error basis, to produce words, hears his productions, and compares these auditory symbols with those already stored. When he detects differences, he varies the motor symbol to try to remove them. As he learns, he detects that changes in certain components of the motor symbols alter only certain components of the auditory symbols. Thus he is able to factor the correction process and thereby accelerate it greatly.

The Acquisition of Speech by GPS

Now it is very easy, with a few changes in vocabulary, to translate this whole descrpition back in terms of GPS. When the translation has been made, we shall see that the processes just described are the methods of GPS.

Let us, in this translation, call the auditory symbols *objects*. (Table 1, second column.) We assume that there exist central processes that modify motor symbols, that change one or more of their components. We shall call these processes *operators*. A change in a motor symbol will, in turn, change the auditory symbol that is perceived when that motor symbol produces a sound.

The child detects *differences* between the object he has produced (i.e., his perception of the sound) and the correct object (his perception of the sound when produced by adults). He applies operators to the motor symbol to modify the sounds he produces, hence the object perceived; and he compares the latter again with the correct object. This search process continues until he can reproduce the perceived object.

But this does not account for the factorization, which we have argued is so crucial to the efficiency of the learning process. How will GPS learn (1) which differences in objects are associated with which operators upon the motor symbols, and

(2) how to factor objects and operators? Although the answers to these questions are far from certain, a scheme we have proposed elsewhere would enable GPS to handle these tasks also.[12] We shall sketch it briefly:

1. Given a set of differences and a set of operators, GPS can, with modest amounts of trial and error, detect which operators are relevant to producing or eliminating which differences. To take a crude, but simple, example: It takes relatively little trial and error to discover what differences in the perceived sound are associated with changes in the rounding of the lips while producing a vowel. The factorization has already largely been carried out by nature, so to speak, because changes in only a few aspects of the motor signal will change only a few aspects of the perceptual symbol.

2. The GPS processes can themselves be employed to discover inductively a "good" factorization, a "good" set of differences. To do this, GPS must be supplied with some very general criteria as to what constitutes such a good set. The criteria would be of the following sorts:

   (a) Only one or a few operators should be relevant to each difference (so that, given a difference, an appropriate operator can be found without too much search).

   (b) Only one or a few differences should be associated with each operator (so that the sounds produced can be varied factor by factor).

and a few others of the same general kind.

With such a set of criteria provided, finding a good set of differences simply becomes another kind of problem to which GPS can apply its problem-solving methods. What are the objects, differences, and operators in terms of which this new kind of problem is formulated? To avoid unnecessary confusion, we shall capitalize the terms OBJECTS, DIFFERENCES, and

OPERATORS in speaking of the new problem context, in order to distinguish them from the objects (perceptual symbols), differences, and operators (changes in motor symbols) involved in the original task of acquiring speech.

The OBJECTS for the new problem-solving task are the *sets of differences* in the original task environment. The new DIFFERENCES designate to what extent particular sets of differences meet the *criteria* we have just listed. OPERATORS are processes for altering the set of differences under consideration by deleting differences from the set, adding differences, or generating new differences for possible inclusion. GPS then tests in what respects particular OBJECTS (sets of differences) are DIFFERENT from the desired OBJECT (as indicated by the criteria). It seeks to remove these DIFFERENCES (modify the set of differences) by applying OPERATORS (by adding, subtracting, or modifying differences).

Since this scheme has not been realized on a computer, we cannot tell how effective GPS would be in handling it. All we can say is that it is a problem whose solution can be attempted with the means at the disposal of GPS.

A due respect for parsimony would suggest, then, that instead of postulating quite different processes for the acquisition of such skills as speaking from those postulated for adult problem solving, we embrace tentatively the hypothesis that the processes are in fact the same, that the General Problem Solver provides a description of both processes. This hypothesis would provide a sharp focus for empirical research into the early speech behavior of the child.

The State-Process Dichotomy

Let us accept this hypothesis for the moment: that the same system of means-end processes is involved in learning speech and in problem solving. Can we explain why a system of means-end analysis should provide the basis for adaptive behavior in both classes of situations? We shall try to provide an explanation for the generality of means-end processes by showing how these arise quite naturally from the problem that any organism must solve if it is to use its motor and sensory apparatus effectively to survive.

Relation of Perceptual to Motor Symbols

The terms "perceptual" and "motor," or "afferent" and "efferent," reflect the dual relation that every adaptive organism has with its environment. It perceives aspects of the environment, and it acts upon the environment. It must be able, therefore, to transmit, store, and operate upon internal representations — perceptual symbols — that stand for its perceptions; and it must be able to transmit, store, and operate upon internal representations — efferent or motor symbols — that can serve as signals to its effectors. The organism survives by associating appropriate motor symbols with the perceptual symbols that stand for various classes of perceptions.[13]

In particular, the organism can perceive, at least grossly, its own behavior caused by its efferent signals. Hence, among the perceptual symbols that it can store are symbols that stand for the perception of corresponding motor signals. Languages are especially adapted to facilitate this correspondence. Language behavior, built from limited alphabets of unit behaviors, is highly stylized so that to each distinct language "act" will correspond an easily perceivable and distinguishable perceptual symbol.

Nevertheless, the relation of a particular language efferent, say, that which energizes the word "dog," to the corresponding perceptual symbol is arbitrary. There is no more resemblance between the auditory "dog" and the motor symbol which produces that word than between "dog" and "Hund." If it is to be learned, the correspondence must be learned as a pure fact. By building up a dictionary relating motor with perceptual symbols, including language-symbols, the organism gains the ability to produce the actions it "intends." In the last section we explored how this ability could develop in the case of speech.

The duality of our relation with the environment reveals itself in the vocabulary of natural languages, particularly in the distinction between nouns and adjectives, on the one hand, and verbs, on the other. We have *clean* clothes (a perceptual symbol) because they have been *washed* (a motor symbol). It is a fact stored in our "table of connections" that when we wash clothes they become clean. As we build up our vocabulary, however, we pass more readily from the one mode of discourse to the other. Thus, the clothes, in the last example, might also have been *cleaned*. As we learn what actions have what effects, changes in objects are named by the processes that produce them, and processes by the effects they create.

The Problem of Translation

It is precisely this duality of language or, more broadly, of the internal symbols employed in thought that makes behavior problematic. The world as it is and as it is desired is described in a *state language*, a language of perceptual symbols.[14] Possible actions are described in a *process language*, a language of motor symbols. (Table 1, third column.) The problem of adapting is the problem of finding the statement in the process language that corresponds to the difference between existing and desired states of affairs in the state language.[15]

But the problems that GPS was designed to handle can be viewed in exactly the same way. What is involved in discovering a proof for the Pythagorean theorem? The *theorem* is a symbolic object in the state language: "The square on the hypotenuse of a right triangle is equal to the sum of the squares on the sides." By comparing this theorem, so stated, with the axioms and previously proved theorems, we detect differences between them. A *proof* of the theorem is a symbolic object in the process language. This object, the justification that we generally write down alongside the successively modified axioms and theorems, describes the sequence of operations that eliminates the differences between axioms and desired theorem. Given a set of axioms, for every theorem defined in the state language, the theorem can be represented in the process language by the sequence of operations that constitutes its proof.

Thus mathematics, and problem solving generally, is an imitation of life. Problem-solving activity uses the very fundamental processes that all adaptive organisms must have if they are to coordinate successfully their perceptual and motor pictures of the world.[16] Ends-means relations, far from being highly special, are reflections of the basic state-process dichotomy, the dichotomy between perceiving and acting.

The Difficulty of the Environment

How hard a problem will be depends on the simplicity or complexity of the rules that define the correspondence between the two languages. An example of a relatively simple correspondence is the relation between the decimal and octal representations of integers. There is a simple and direct algorithm that solves all problems of the form: If *a* is the decimal representation of a number, what is its octal representation?

At the other extreme, the correspondence between the vocabularies may be purely conventional or arbitrary. Then rote learning is the only means for building up the translation dictionary, and if the correct translations must also be discovered, immense amounts of trial-and-error search may be required.

The aspects of the environment with which we, as organisms, deal effectively reach neither of these two extremes. The translation between the state language that describes our perceptions of the world and the process language that describes our actions on the world is reducible to no simple rule, but it is not, on the other hand, arbitrary. Most of our skill in dealing with the environment is embodied in elaborate *heuristics*, or rules of thumb, that allow us to factor, approximately, the complex perceived world into highly simple components and to find, approximately and reasonably reliably, the correspondences that allow us to act on that world predictably. This is the skill that the adult businessman uses when he makes a decision, the skill of the scientist in his laboratory, the skill of the subject in a problem-solving experiment, the skill of a child learning to speak.

What we have proposed this evening is that at the core of these heuristics (the portion that is not bound up in special skills) is the organized system of ends-means processes, of state-process translations, that the General Problem Solver describes. We have proposed that here, in Mr. Pitts's words, is a first approximation to "the hierarchy of final causes traditionally called the mind."

Panel Discussion

MINSKY. In discussing the differences that Pitts's quotation suggests, I shall group artificial intelligence and the simulation of human thought, and distinguish these research areas from work on initially less structured models: "self-organizing" models and "random neural net" models. The first two areas are very similar. The third area is very different in methods and goals. It has a physiological orientation and alleges to be based on an imitation of the brain. Incidentally, I have many reservations about accepting any theory that alleges to be an imitation of the brain, since almost nothing is known about how the brain forms a concept, recognizes a pattern, and so forth. I shall say more about this later.

In the case of people (myself included) who are working on artificial intelligence, we feel free to employ mechanisms that are not at all lifelike if they will help our programs solve difficult intellectual problems, such as the problem of the missionaries and cannibals. The trouble is that we really have not encountered very many such mechanisms. If we examine the machines that play chess, or prove theorems in geometry and the calculus, it is hard not to be reminded of the approach of the human game-playing machines. "If he goes there, I shall go there," and so on. It is not clear that anything new is being used.

In the case of Simon and other people working on the simulation of human thought processes, I really doubt that they could long resist the temptation to exploit some new, non-human technique that would make their machines significantly more intelligent. I believe that their interest in psychology might play second fiddle to any possibility of attaining more intelligent machines.

Efforts in artificial intelligence and efforts in simulating human thought will eventually diverge, particularly in specialized areas where computers most easily can be made to transcend human limitations. This is naturally already the case in numerical computation. There are also less-evident areas in which simulation of human methods would yield distinctly poorer performance than other kinds of heuristic programming, e.g., areas in which the inability of the human to retain and handle more than a few things at a time is a serious weakness. Professor Miller has written on this subject.

In any case we might suppose that the province of the psychologist will not remain limited to human problem solving after artificial intelligence has matured. Computers may become our intellectual successors; their training and management will not run smoothly. Future psychologists may envy the simple problems we faced when we had only to deal with human thought.

It is curious that with all the general interest and publicity in the field there are only a very few research groups directly concerned with artificial intelligence. In view of the obvious romance of the field, why is there so little activity?

For one thing, the technical problems are very difficult. Each major advance has involved two or three years of work, usually of several capable people. Ideas that are both new and good are hard to conceive, formulate, and realize in a performing program. GPS is a very good idea. The essentials of its description, when formulated several years ago, fit on a very few pages; its realization has occupied several man-years of irreplaceable talent. There also are many bad ideas around, equally concise, that have consumed even more time, but presumably of more easily replaceable talent.

It is very difficult to take apparently common-sense procedures, such as those described in Polya's books on practical heuristics in mathematical problem solving, and put them into machine-usable form. It requires people with first-class talent both to get the ideas and to formalize them in a satisfactory form. The rarity of this combination, plus the fact that such people find other things to do, accounts in part for the limited activity in the field.

Whenever there is an alternative to the prospect of hard work, people tend to turn toward it. It seems to me that interest is being attracted, or diverted, to the apparent alternative which goes under the name of "self-organizing" systems. A considerable number of people are studying large, more-or-less random network models to find learning or evolutionary capabilities. Some of these models supposedly are patterned along the lines of the nervous system; others are more deliberately designed to evolve adaptive learning. But since essentially nothing is really known about the physiology of how the nervous system learns and manipulates concepts, these efforts can be grouped together. People have obtained certain kinds of simple learning behavior from such networks. My impression, however, is that there is still no evidence that the kinds of models these people are considering today can solve even slightly difficult problems. Today's results in this area seem little better than those of a decade ago. Yet I have the impression that, for example, every aircraft company in the country is sponsoring such a project.

While the results of such work may prove interesting and useful, people should be aware that there is at present no promise that self-organizing models constitute a *direct* approach either to artificial intelligence or to simulation of human problem solving. Solving difficult problems takes a great deal of organization in cases where competely blind trial and error is out of the question; and this includes almost everything. Even GPS must be, or must become, considerably more complex than Simon's brief explanation might make it appear. Simon outlined the basic heuristic technique of goal-oriented method selection, but he did not dwell on the rest of the administrative structure. A complex problem can be solved only by breaking it into parts, solving these, remembering how they are interrelated, and synthesizing the partial results. This has been done in a number of existing programs, and their structure is very complicated. GPS will have to be supplied with an adequate "administrative" structure.

It is hard to see how such structures could emerge, in a reasonable time, from a system with much less organization. Consider the basic process of "postponement." Once a problem is split up, we must work one part and save the other(s); the postponed problems must be retained with information about their relevancies. There may be several goals, not entirely consistent with one another, and we must establish priorities or more sophisticated ways of making decisions in case of conflict. Before a self-organizing system can work on such problems, it must develop facilities for postponement. This could be done, perhaps by providing a shrewdly designed training sequence of problems; but in such a case it would be hard to justify the distinction between an evolution and a carefully assembled program. The programmed alternative would turn out to be easier and more efficient; it also would demand less organized stimulation from the environment.

To be sure, once a certain (rather high) degree of problem-solving ability is achieved, we could give a program the problem of improving its own operation. This is a goal that Simon's group has set itself for GPS. I am inclined to believe that this can be done, in a sophisticated sense, only in a system with a good deal of ability. Indeed, it is not clear yet whether GPS has enough organization to do this. GPS can invent and select improved methods within its framework; but it is not clear how it could improve the basic structural outline.

We should mention, to avoid misunderstanding, that we can construct very simple systems which can optimize their own parameters: These are the "hill-climbing" or "self-optimizing" mechanisms. Everyone invents these shortly after first considering the intelligent-machine problem. The serious difficulty is at the next step: how to improve a structure not given in terms of a natural parameter system? The question that immediately arises is whether adequate structures can be described by the system in a form that can be discovered without excessive search.

I am very optimistic about the eventual outcome of the work on machine solution of intellectual problems. Within our lifetime machines may surpass us in general intelligence. I believe that Simon and his colleagues share this view. Perhaps that is why he feels no urge to discuss here the consequences of his work for management. We can discuss the subject of management rationally when considering information retrieval, simulation of companies, linear programming, and similar topics, many of which have been treated in other lectures of this series. But the prospect of machines that are better thinkers than we are is hardly a stimulant to sober discussion. It makes us feel that the problems of future management may be the machines', not ours.

MILLER. I wish that I could find some large and significant issue where Professor Simon and I could disagree, so that we could have a good, hot argument and stir up lots of excitement and arm waving. Audiences always enjoy a good battle, and any discussant worth his salt should be willing to go out of his way to provide it. A good fight is valuable not only for the emotional refreshment that it provides, it also helps to clarify what the debaters are against, as well as what they support. One of the best ways to find out what something *is* is to find out what it *is not,* to find its contrast classes. And contrast classes often emerge most sharply and clearly under the stimulus of disagreement.

In this instance, however, I find myself stuck for something worth fighting about. Professor Simon invited me to take exception to his analysis of learning to talk, and I could. I could quibble over some of the linguistic details as he presented them to us. I might ask him to define what he means by a "phoneme" and how it differs from a sound. I know that is a good question because most linguists cannot answer it either.

I might ask him to be a little more explicit about how a child acquires the ability to imitate. Or I might ask him the $64 question: What exactly are the particular components of speech learning that he has in mind? But in the present context these problems are matters of technical detail, and quibbling about them could obscure rather than illuminate the central point that Professor Simon was making when he used the acquisition of speech as his example. His point was that learning can proceed much more rapidly when a task has been factored into (relatively) independent components. It seems to me that this observation is not only true in general, but that in particular it can be applied to a description of the acquisition of speech. So I see no reason to go into detailed criticisms of this particular learning process.

Instead of carping about the details, therefore, I want to take just a few moments to say why I, as a psychologist, find the work of Newell, Shaw, and Simon so valuable, and why I am so reluctant to do battle with them. Let me put it this way: Suppose you were a psychologist and you wanted to formulate a theory to account for some realm of human thought or human behavior. How would you proceed? In particular, what calculus would you use to express your theory?

Let's consider the alternatives that are available. There is, first of all, the natural language. This is the psychologist's favorite calculus, and I do not want to sell it short; the theories of Sigmund Freud, William James, John Dewey, C. G. Jung, and many others were grand achievements of the human understanding even though they were expressed in terms no more rigorous than the language of everyday life. Nevertheless, I think we should all agree that if a science is to grow, it must eventually develop methods and concepts that are more concise than the common language can express. When that day comes for the psychologist, where is he to turn?

He might, perhaps, turn to the differential and integral calculus, the language that first expressed the deepest secrets of the physical universe. It is true that there are numerous psychological processes that can be represented in this way — where the essence of the matter can be caught by a functional relation between two or more continuous variables. But this is a mathematical language that was not invented for these problems. The psychologists who try to use it inevitably look like children wearing big brother's hand-me-downs. The calculus, for example, does not have any way to represent a simple contingency; the idea of contingency must be introduced informally either by words or some other foreign device. But this is surely one of the central concepts we need for a comprehensive psychological theory.

In some quarters, of course, there has been considerable enthusiasm for symbolic logic as the proper language. Certainly the work of McCulloch and Pitts — and of their successors (including Professor Minsky, in spite of his comments) — suggests that logic is an excellent tool for describing neural nets. But neural nets are, by definition, neural. A psychologist can watch this application of logic with great interest and not a little envy, but he cannot pretend that it is solving his psychological problems. The situation is somewhat like that of the psychologist who is given a pile of lumber and the job of building a house from it. These neural net people keep telling him about the nature of cellulose, and it does not help him very much.

There have been a few attempts to apply logical description at the psychological level: Clark Hull's description of rote memorization in logical terms is now largely (and I think happily) forgotten. Jean Piaget's efforts to describe the thinking of children and adolescents in logical terms are more pertinent, but to anyone who studies Piaget carefully it becomes all too obvious that he is forced to stuff his logical symbols full of all kinds of significance and connotations that would make a true logician cringe and turn pale. Piaget is using a great deal more than just the raw logic. The most successful endeavor of this kind that I know of is Noam Chomsky's logical description of grammar; but whether this breakthrough in the neighboring field of linguistics can infect psychology with similar success remains an open question at the present time.

If not classical mathematics or symbolic logic, then what remains? One of the most popular languages for formal theories in psychology is the calculus of probability. Probabilistic descriptions of what I can perceive are useful, and I can even accept a probabilistic description of what I can remember, if it is phrased with sufficient delicacy. But there is something deliberately backwards about the way these probabilistic theories generally proceed. The theory generates a null hypothesis that we hope we shall be unable to disprove. As a consequence, we often hypothesize that some psychological process is random even though we know it is not, then demonstrate that certain kinds of data are insufficient to prove that the hypothesis is wrong. At the present time psychological theory is suffering from our failure to decide when a probability is an explanation and when it is an admission of ignorance. Since many of my best friends indulge in this kind of theorizing, however, I hesitate to launch a full-scale offensive. Not here, anyhow.

By a process of elimination, therefore, a psychologist who wants to make his theory both comprehensive and explicit is perhaps not driven, but is certainly nudged, in the direction of the computer program as a natural way to do it. This is a new calculus for expressing theories, and we psychologists do not yet understand how to use it most effectively; but we are slowly learning. Among the pioneers in exploring this new calculus, of course, Herb Simon is one of the most eminent. You will have to forgive me for not fighting with him. A fight is a lot of fun, but it is a rotten way to express your gratitude.

SIMON. I was very glad to have Professor Minsky point out that my account of our common field of interest was one-sided. My stress has been on the use of simulation to understand how humans think, but many of the people in the field who have contributed much to it are interested more in the other side: how to obtain good problem-solving programs. In other words, my colleagues and I have given emphasis to the word "intelligence" in our work; other research groups have given emphasis to "artificial."

The interesting thing is that up to now it has been very worth while to devote considerable effort to explorations of the sly tricks that humans use to solve problems, as a modest prelude to finding better methods of solution. By studying the human thought processes, we have learned a great deal about a whole class of problem-solving devices, which I have referred to, loosely, as heuristics. We did not have much formal knowledge of these devices before, although they certainly had been investigated by other researchers, e.g., the mathematician, Polya.

There is thus a double aim in the field: understanding human processes, and automating various kinds of complex cognitive tasks. We took the tack we did in our paper for two reasons:

First, I had my say at some length elsewhere about the automation aspects, and particularly about the implications for management.[4]

Second, the human aspects were the ones which primarily motivated the work of my colleagues and me.

I do not agree with Professor Minsky that we shall stop trying to understand the human mind as soon as we surpass the ability of humans to solve problems. The challenge to our society is not simply one of acquiring more powerful devices to do our thinking for us. We have more powerful devices now to dig dirt, pour concrete, erect buildings; and they do solve some of our problems. We do not have to work as hard as we once did, for example. They also *create* certain problems that we all could easily enumerate.

If we are to take the next step and face up to some of the hard-core problems that the human species is going to have to solve over the next few generations in order to survive, then we have to know more about ourselves than we do now. Research devoted to the study of human thinking and human cognitive processes is one way, at least, to work toward a better understanding of ourselves. I feel that we must attach a very high importance to this goal, quite apart from whether it enables us to substitute automated processes for natural ones in some applications.

I have one other comment, which actually is stimulated by both Minsky's and Miller's remarks. Professor Minsky asked whether a program like GPS could bootstrap itself, that is, apply its learning processes to improving its own program. He expressed some doubts about whether some of the proposed self-organizing nets could do this. Professor Miller pointed out quite rightfully that while I described how a child might go about learning a language in general, I cheerfully (by means of a few references to work by him and others) elided over the details of just what a phoneme was and how it might be represented. The issues raised by Minsky and Miller can be fruitfully investigated with simulation techniques.

The way to answer the query, "Can GPS bootstrap itself?," is to spend the next six months asking what changes have to be made in the program so that it will. The ultimate test of a computer simulation is whether it simulates. In many forms of theorizing, not including mathematics usually, you can get by with hand waving at the appropriate moment. In my constitutional law days, for example, I observed that whenever Chief Justice Marshall got to a delicate point in an opinion he said, "Obviously," and went on. If you write a computer program and say, "Obviously," and go on, nothing happens. The people running the computer room send back a little note reading, "Error stop."

I think what Minsky and Miller were alluding to, but were too polite to say aloud, was, "If GPS is a theory of how a machine can bootstrap itself into higher intelligence or how people learn language, then let it bootstrap itself, and let it learn language." This is an entirely appropriate obligation to impose. The real power of the simulation technique is that it provides not only a means for stating a theory but also a very sharp criterion for testing whether the statement is adequate. Not just on behalf of myself, but on behalf of the entire group of people working in the field (including the two discussants), I accept the obligation and hope that one of us will produce the requisite programs before too long.

ALEXANDER. This great solidarity in the field suggests to me at least that there may be an external threat. I do not know whether it is represented here tonight, but whatever is represented, I shall now open the meeting to questions from the audience.

123

General Discussion

BERKELEY. I should like to ask what a "hierarchy of final causes" is.

SIMON. I should have Walter Pitts answer. I think that it is just a nice phrase for expressing the fact that posing a problem for solution and setting a goal lead to the creation of subproblems, and the solution of each subproblem becomes in turn the immediate goal. If we examine in retrospect the complete path that a problem-solving organism has followed, we see that the problem has become a series of subproblems, sub-subproblems, and so on, organized in an hierarchical fashion.

One of the interesting phenomena of problem-solving behavior is the fact that subgoals often get detached and become autonomous. A large part of the theorizing about human motivations is concerned with how the subgoals are formed, how they become autonomous, and how the hierarchical structure, if it is hierarchical, becomes ramshackle and rambling in the adult human being.

MINSKY. To provide further evidence of the solidarity, George Miller and I agree that if this isn't what Pitts meant, it's what he should have meant.

ANONYMOUS. It seems to me that GPS is something like a weak form of utilitarianism. It tells us that the thing to search for is the thing that will most reduce the difference between the current state and the desired state. But how can we recognize which is the proper way to proceed? We may well be voiding our assumptions if we take a certain path. In other words, if you just turn over to the machine the problem of preparing a dinner, it may cook the cook.

SIMON. That brings us back to the missionaries and the cannibals, doesn't it? The reason that the machine does not cook the cook is that there are many side conditions in the statement of the problem, at least one of which precludes this contingency. If GPS constitutes a theory of how humans think, it must provide for side conditions; and, in fact, in the problem of the missionaries and the cannibals, it does. Before GPS applies an operator, it checks to see whether the side conditions are satisfied. One of these conditions is that there should not be a preponderance of cannibals (or, in your case, that the cook should not be cooked). If you carefully observed the young lady on television trying to solve this problem, you may have seen her begin to move a group to the other side of the river, and then stop upon realizing that she was about to cause a preponderance of cannibals. The human problem solver also follows each partial attempt by checking whether the side conditions are satisfied.

The broader answer to your question is that there is nothing about GPS which requires the statement of the goal to be simple. This statement may be an extremely complex description of a state of affairs. It will be very interesting when we get to the point where we can describe, for example, what it is that makes a painter decide that he has finished his painting and should start on a new canvas. We certainly have not had any statements of goals, so far, on this level of subtlety.

ANONYMOUS. I should like to ask how a machine built by a human being arrives at ways of solving problems that are better than human techniques.

SIMON. Testimony to the possibility of this is found in the fact that the machine already performs certain functions much better than the human: adding, subtracting, multiplying, and dividing, for example. So there certainly is no reason in principle why a machine cannot be built to do things that the builder cannot do. We have known this about steam shovels for a long time. Why should it not also be true for cognitive acts? I might ask, "How could the blind forces of evolution have created a mechanism which exercises intelligence?"

The fact is that we can draw a blueprint for a computer without being able to predict at all what the behavior of the computer will be under interaction with a specified environment. This is true of things much simpler than a computer. It is true of most laboratory research in chemistry, for example. I should like to put the burden of proof on the other side.

Why should we suppose, just because we have the ability to create a certain situation, that the behavior resulting from the situation will be very simple, very predictable, less interesting, and less complex than our own behavior?

FUTRELLE. I was wondering about Professor Simon's dichotomy between operator and object. In the speech-learning example, he dichotomized between the operation of a child's producing a sound and the object of the child's hearing the sound. It seems to me that this dichotomy would have to be imposed from the outside. Would not the child or the program have to learn somehow to distinguish between the motor action and the auditory stimulus?

SIMON. I do not think that distinguishing operator from object should be too troublesome. This differentiation already exists to a considerable extent in the organization of our nervous system. I do not want to oversimplify the afferent-efferent distinction, because there are many feedback processes complicating matters, but basically the nervous system is organized in terms of tracts which feed signals in, and tracts which take signals out to the muscles. I do not believe that we have to impose this dichotomy any more than biology has had to impose it.

MINSKY. The operators in the version of GPS that Simon described are changes in motor patterns. Since the operators cause changes in the objects, they are on a higher level than the objects; so there is certainly no possibility of confusing the two.

RATH. I believe it has been demonstrated that we can imitate processes. We also know that we can build bridges. But scientists today are not studying how we build bridges. They are studying mathematics, physics, and chemistry. I think maybe we are spending too much time playing the game of imitating processes, and not enough time studying psychology, mathematics, and logic.

SIMON. To answer this fully, we should have to discuss at some length what a theory is. In one sense a theory is always an imitation. This is particularly true of the kind of theory that purports to describe how a system moves through time, e.g., the theories of classical mechanics. I believe that the important question is not whether we are imitating, but whether in fact the imitation explains the phenomenon. The reason that we approved of Kepler's imitation of the movement of the spheres is because it told us where the spheres would be "tomorrow night" in a way which was more parsimonious and in other respects more satisfactory than earlier explanations. I should think that we should want to judge the GPS activity in the same way. I do not see that this activity is different from psychology. If it is right, it is good psychology; if it is wrong, it is bad psychology. And we all know what to do with good psychology and bad psychology.

ANONYMOUS. It often has been said that European rats solve problems by insight, whereas American rats solve problems by trial and error. Do you think GPS could become international and solve problems by insight, too?

SIMON. The reason there have been psychologists with European rats and psychologists with American rats is that it has been very difficult, up to now, to deal with complicated phenomena like insight and at the same time to abide by certain canons of scientific rigor. The psychologists who ran the American rats believed in rigor, while the psychologists who ran the European rats were interested more in the richness of behavior.

It turns out that there is actually no contradiction between insight and trial and error. It is just a matter of degree. Behavior begins to look very insightful when the amount of trial and error is relatively small and the amount of selectivity is relatively large. Our group has been able to simulate what I think is insight. GPS has had at least a modest "Aha" experience, and if I had had a little more time to discuss the planning program, I could have told you what that "Aha" was. I do not think we have to live with the contradiction anymore; we can have our insight and our rigor, too.

EMERY. Professor Minsky touched on this, and I should like to pursue it a little further. If you have a program that is self-modifying, after a number of these self-modifications will you

127

be able to trace its "thought" processes, and what relevance will these thought processes have to human thought processes?

SIMON. Presumably we do know something about the variation of an adult human being who grows up in a human culture, and we therefore can get some measure of the differences that can be produced by changes of experience. One thing we certainly should do more than we have in the past is give the computer the same series of experiences that we give a human being, say, a child learning to speak. The test of whether we get modifications of the same kind and direction in the computer and in the child is another test that the theory should have to pass, however unlikely this might seem at the moment. If it is the right theory of learning, it will learn the right thing. By "right" I mean the thing a person would learn when confronted with the same experience. This has to be our test of the theory.

BEACH. I think we would all agree that no two human brains and no two thought processes are 100 per cent alike. How does GPS take account of this fact? Does it incorporate noise patterns?

SIMON. No, not noise patterns. The program has sufficient flexibility to fit different subjects. If we had to write a completely new program for every subject, then the game would be lost. But I believe that there are enough similarities among people to make it useful to attempt a general description of their thought processes.

What we have done so far in this regard, and it is not very much, has been to try to detect the differences in our subjects' thinking which might account for differences in their protocols. For example, our most successful problem-solving subjects made much more obvious use of the planning method than did our less effective subjects. My guess is that we now could demonstrate that one of the real differences between the A students and the C students is the extent to which planning and abstracting programs are part of their problem-solving apparatus.

This is one interpersonal difference that we already have begun to detect. There are more minor differences, some of which can be accounted for by a few easy modifications of

128

certain of the parameters of the program. For example, subjects will differ in the order in which they deal with symbolic objects, and this difference is reliable from one problem to another, at least over short sequences. It may be represented by a difference in the order in which certain items are stored on lists in memory and retrieved from these lists.

We would hope, therefore, to account for individual differences in terms of changes in program particulars which leave the broad structure of GPS reasonably invariant from person to person. If it turns out that we cannot, then something is very wrong with the theory. I see no indication of this at the moment.

ALEXANDER. I cannot refrain from using my privilege as moderator to ask the final question suggested by this last response. Is GPS so general that it would apply as well to the amoeba in its swamp water as to Einstein working on relativity theory?

SIMON. We certainly have not experimented with any range of individual difference comparable with the amoeba versus Einstein. I should want to think some before I tried to describe the processes of an amoeba. But the processes of Einstein, since he was a member of our species, seem a little less mysterious. The main difference between Einstein and other people was that Einstein had been to college, had learned and thought about certain things, and had talked to certain persons. There were tremendous differences in experience between him and anyone else who existed in the year 1905. If we admit these differences in experience, then we can get by with rather modest differences between Einstein's thinking processes and those of other people. In other words, we can load much of the burden on differences in experience.

There is a fair amount of historical evidence supporting this. For example, there are not many cases of people living socially and geographically outside of very small parts of Western Europe who invented steam engines or things like that. We must either postulate that gray matter is very different in other parts of the world (which is probably wrong biologically and certainly is distasteful to most of us), or postulate that substantial differences in problem solving can be due to differences in experience. My encouraging comment would be, if you just think long enough about it, you too can invent relativity.

REFERENCES

1. A number of these undertakings are catalogued in Professor E. G. Boring's instructive and entertaining paper, "Mind and Mechanism," *Amer. Journal of Psychology*, Vol. 59, 173–192 (Apr., 1946).

2. See the *Proceedings of the 1955 Western Joint Computer Conference*, "Session on Learning Machines," The Institute of Radio Engineers, New York, 1955, pp. 85–111.

3. *Ibid.*, p. 108.

4. See Simon, H. A., *The New Science of Management Decision*, Harper & Brothers, New York, 1960.

5. For an excellent recent survey of heuristic programs, although with emphasis upon artificial intelligence rather than simulation of human thought, see Minsky, M., "Steps Toward Artificial Intelligence," *Proceedings of the IRE*, Vol. 49, 8–30 (Jan., 1961).

6. For a fuller description, see Newell, A., Shaw, J. C., and Simon, H. A., "Report on a General Problem-Solving Program," in *Information Processing*, Proceedings of the International Conference on Information Processing, UNESCO, Paris 15–20 June 1959, UNESCO, Paris, 1960, pp. 256–264.

7. See *ibid.*, pp. 261–262, for a description of a specific planning method for GPS. In our subjects, abstracting often takes the form of simply ignoring some of the problem detail at certain stages of the solution process.

8. See Newell, A., and Simon, H. A., "The Simulation of Human Thought," in *Current Trends in Psychological Theory*, University of Pittsburgh Press, Pittsburgh, 1961, pp. 152–169.

9. See, for example, Osgood, C. E., *Method and Theory in Experimental Psychology*, Oxford University Press, New York, 1953, pp. 683–690; Miller, G. A., "Speech and Language," Chap. 21 in *Handbook of Experimental Psychology*, Stevens, S. S., Ed., John Wiley & Sons, Inc., New York, 1951; and Miller, G. A., *Language and Communication*, McGraw-Hill Book Co., New York, 1951, Chap. 7.

10. We qualify the adverb "purely" when we come to consider the factorization of words into phonemes and phoneme components.

11. For a general introduction to these topics, see Miller, G. A., *Language and Communication*, Chap. 2. An excellent recent survey is Fatehchand, R., "Machine Recognition of Spoken Words," in *Advances in Computers*, Vol. 1, Alt, F. L., Ed., Academic Press, Inc., New York, 1960, pp. 193–321. See also Forgie, J. W., and C. D., "Results Obtained from a Vowel Recognition Computer Program," *The Journal of the Acoustical Society of America*, Vol. 31, 1480–1489 (Nov., 1959), and Liberman, A. M., and others, "Minimal Rules for Synthesizing Speech," *ibid.*, Vol. 31, 1490–1499 (Nov., 1959). The last three references cited illustrate, incidentally, the large role that computers are playing today in linguistic and phonetic research.

12. The full account of this learning scheme is given in Newell, A., Shaw, J. C., and Simon, H. A., "A Variety of Intelligent Learning in a General Problem Solver," in *Self-Organizing Systems*, Yovits, M. C., and Cameron, S., Eds., Pergamon Press, Inc., New York, 1960, pp. 153–187.

13. We need hardly say that this description does not commit us to any oversimplified reflex-arc picture of the peripheral and central systems. GPS is a concrete example of a system of the sort we are describing. In it, the perceptual-motor associations are represented by the table of connections between differences and operators. The use it makes of these connections, and consequently the relation of response to stimulus, is highly complex.

14. It should be observed that the body is part of the environment that is perceived. Hence, drives like hunger produce perceptual symbols just as external senses do. Or perhaps it would be better to say that the drive *is* the perceptual symbol produced by the perception of hunger.

15. Other aspects of the state-process dichotomy are discussed in Newell, A., Shaw, J. C., and Simon, H. A., "The Processes of Creative Thinking," presented before a symposium on creativity at the University of Colorado, May 14, 1958. The RAND Corporation, P–1320, Santa Monica, Calif., Sept. 16, 1958.

16. We should like to call attention to the similarity, hardly accidental, between the translation problems we have been describing and some of the most striking results of modern mathematics — the undecidability theorems. Decision problems, in the Gödel sense, can always be represented as problems of finding in language B the representation of an object that is described in language A, where there are at least some objects that have names in both languages. If the rules of correspondence between the two languages are sufficiently complicated, this will be difficult, and, as the undecidability theorems show, it may be impossible.

4

A
Library
for
2000 A.D.

4

A
Library
for
2000 A.D.

Speaker	**JOHN G. KEMENY** Chairman Department of Mathematics and Astronomy Dartmouth College
Discussants	**ROBERT M. FANO** Professor of Electrical Communications Massachusetts Institute of Technology **GILBERT W. KING** Director of Research International Business Machines Corporation
Moderator	**WILLIAM N. LOCKE** Director of Libraries and Head, Department of Modern Languages Massachusetts Institute of Technology

KEMENY. Since I am about to propose a radical reorganization of university libraries, I must first establish that some such
reorganization is inevitable. I shall argue that our university
libraries will be obsolete by 2000 A.D.

The Need

Harvard University will have a library of more than ten million volumes by 2000 A.D. Dartmouth College will purchase its
one-millionth library volume during the bicentennial celebra-
tions of the college, in 1969–1970, and if the present rate of
growth continues, the second million volumes will be purchased
in thirty-five years. At that rate of growth universities will have
a full-time occupation building new libraries in the twenty-first
century.

It is clear that the cost of building, purchasing volumes, cataloguing, and servicing these monstrous libraries will ruin our

richest universities. Even if Harvard University conceived a ten million volume collection as physically feasible, this would postpone the decision by only a few decades, since the collection of a hundred million volumes that one could predict for 2100 A.D. could not possibly be handled in a manner similar to the procedures of any existing libraries.

As our present libraries grow in size, they also become increasingly difficult to use. Library catalogues are growing into giants and are approached with fear by both students and faculty. Unless one knows the exact name of an author (including initials) or unless one knows the exact title of a book, it may become hopeless to locate it. And once a mistake is made, it is best to forget about it and start all over again. For example, many libraries have discovered that if a book is misplaced on the shelves and cannot be located after a short search, it is less costly to replace it than to try to find it.

That the very conception of the way books are made available is wrong can best be illustrated in terms of an actual example of search I recently carried on in the Dartmouth Library. Table 1 gives a factual account of the search.

TABLE 1

An Example of Search

Walk from 328 Dartmouth to Baker Library	4 minutes
Find card in catalogue	30 seconds
Walk up four flights	1 minute 30 seconds
Find that book is missing	15 seconds
Walk down four flights	1 minute
Find out that Professor S checked out book	30 seconds
Walk from Baker Library to 329 Dartmouth	5 minutes
Wait for Professor S to return from lunch	2 hours
Wait for Professor S to find book	15 minutes
Total search time	2 hours 27 minutes 45 seconds

As can be seen, there are two major bottlenecks in the search procedure. First of all, the physical running around is a very significant proportion of the time I spent in using the library. Dartmouth College's library is fully open stack; if it were not, then someone else would do a great deal of this running around, and the time consumed would be considerably longer. But even the actual catalogue look-up and the running-around time together are negligible compared with the delay caused by the fact that once a book is removed from the library it is likely to be out of circulation for at least two weeks. If Professor S borrows a book, he is likely to have it on his shelf anywhere from one week to one year, during which period he might use it for a total of less than one hour. Of course, one could require him to use the book only in the library; but if he wishes to consult it a dozen times during the coming weeks, it is most unreasonable that he should have to spend a considerable amount of time on each occurrence in locating the book. It is clear to me that as long as libraries function in the present manner, this problem is unsolvable.

I have saved for last the most acute problem of search today. How can a worker in field X find out in a reasonable amount of time what results are known concerning problem Y? For example, there are several hundred mathematics research journals published in the world, and in addition to this, hundreds of volumes of mathematics books appear each year. Relevant information for a research problem may be contained in the numbers of any one of fifty journals spreading back over the last thirty years, or in any one of a hundred books. To find half a dozen relevant items, it may be necessary to search thousands, and the odds are great that some crucial piece of information will be overlooked.

This problem is so critical that it must be solved and solved relatively rapidly, independently of the problem of the reorganization of libraries. (This is, of course, the problem of the retrieval of scientific information.) However, this problem is made more acute by the clumsiness of our libraries. If, to search through two hundred books and journals, we have to locate each one by the procedure sketched above, and we have to wait until twenty of them are returned to the library by colleagues, the problem becomes completely hopeless.

In summary, our libraries are practically obsolete today. They are certain to be obsolete by the end of the twenty-first century, and will for most purposes be useless by 2000 A.D. It is therefore appropriate to consider a radical reorganization of the entire scheme of university libraries, and it is by no means too early to begin planning today.

Statement of the Problem

If my proposals are to have serious scientific merit rather than turn into science fiction, I must impose certain restrictions on the solutions of the problem. First of all, I shall require that my library be within the capability of our technology by 2000 A.D., and I shall require that it still be useful at the end of the twenty-first century. One cannot possibly hope for more than that. No one can foresee the needs of the year 2100 A.D. or the tremendously powerful tools mankind will have available by that time. Specifically this will mean that the only devices that may be used are those that will be available within the next two or three decades, and that the library should start with some ten million volumes and have the means of expanding by a factor of 30. (At the present rate of growth, one would expect a growth by the factor of 8 within a century. I am allowing a factor of 30, since I am certain that the rate of expansion will increase. If the rate should turn out to be much more rapid even than that, then the library about to be described may become obsolete before 2100 A.D.)

Second, the library must solve the present bottleneck in making items available to research workers. The time to take out a book from the library should be of the order of magnitude of a few minutes at most.

Third, there must be a reasonable procedure for finding out where information is available. This procedure should be applicable not only to search by author or by title but to search by subject matter.

Finally, I want to put realistic financial restrictions on my library. A solution that would require that the cost of purchase, cataloguing, storage, and making information available increases the library budget of every university by a factor of 100 is not acceptable.

Basic Principles

If one accepts the statement of the problem as given above, there are a few basic principles that are easily arrived at. For example, it is clear that the library of the future will have to make heavy use of automation. There is no conceivable way in a library of several tens of millions of volumes that human effort could locate an item in a matter of minutes. I shall, therefore, proceed on the assumption that I can make free use of whatever machinery can be designed in the near future, even if this will drastically alter our conception of a library. However, I shall try not to propose the use of a machine where a human being can perform the same task more efficiently. Just as the majority of mankind resists the introduction of automation, due to very natural but irrational prejudices, the minority of mankind pioneering automation has the tendency to use machines in place of human beings whether this can be justified or not.

It is equally clear that while the physical format of books is very convenient for human handling, it is most inconvenient for machine processing. A simple calculation of the volume occupied by a hundred million books shows that even if they were solidly packed, without room for humans to move around in, they would occupy a building of impressive size. If we were to have reasonable access to the books, we presumably should need a building greater than the Empire State Building. Therefore, storage methods must miniaturize books and put them on a medium easily handled by machines, for example, some type of tape.

The very crudest estimates for a feasible library will put the cost of construction somewhere in the hundred million dollar to billion dollar range. It is not reasonable to expect that individual universities should spend sums of money of this order of magnitude. Indeed, it is difficult to see even today how one can justify the tremendous waste of effort in which each university has its own staff to order books, classify, and catalogue them, and run a variety of duplicative reference services. I shall therefore adopt as a basic principle that we are designing a single central library that will serve for research purposes both the Federal Government and the major universities of the country. I shall refer to it as the *National Research Library.*

In such a centralized library many functions will be no more costly for the entire country than the cost at any individual institution. Even where the central library will have to allow for a considerable amount of duplication, presumably the merging of one hundred university libraries will not need more than ten times the expense of an individual library. Therefore I estimate that the actual cost of a central library might be of the order of magnitude of 2 or 3 per cent of the cost of building one hundred individual libraries.

I shall further assume that it will take our universities some twenty years to decide that their libraries are rapidly becoming obsolete. This will leave them an additional two decades to complete the National Library by 2000 A.D. If each of one hundred major universities agrees to contribute one hundred thousand dollars per year from 1980 A.D. to 2000 A.D., and if the Federal Government matches these funds, we should have 0.4 billion dollars available for the construction. Since many of the universities will actually save a good deal more than one hundred thousand dollars per year, and since the Federal Government could easily contribute a larger sum of money, it is perhaps reasonable to allow up to 1 billion dollars for the planning, design, and construction of the National Research Library.

It may be appropriate to say a few words concerning the likely fate of present libraries in the twenty-first century. I shall take it for granted that our university libraries will *not* be abolished, even if their role becomes secondary. Partly this will be because they will serve a limited but useful purpose, but mainly because faculty members will be reluctant to give up personal contact with books.

Aside from purely sentimental reasons for maintaining our libraries, one can certainly make a strong case for keeping on a given campus any book that may be consulted as often as once a week. This would certainly include the present reference rooms, as well as core research libraries in all subjects. The periodical room would still serve as useful a purpose as in the past, though perhaps it would be wasteful to preserve most of the periodicals. The students would have books on reserve, though they should also be encouraged to use the National Research Library, so that they become familiar with its operation. One must also take into account that our university libraries play a major role in leisure-time reading, and the pleasure of browsing should not be taken away from either students or faculty.

All of these functions can be fulfilled comfortably with a collection of no more than a few hundred thousand volumes. I estimate this number generously, since I feel that the sentimental attachment of faculty members to books is very strong. Our present libraries should be decimated in 2000 A.D., to cut them down to such a reasonable working size. The number of volumes could then either be kept constant by removing less-often-used books and replacing them by current ones, or a very slow rate of growth could be permitted. In any case, a great deal of room would be freed under this scheme for faculty studies and reading rooms (which are now in great demand and in short supply on most campuses). One would also want to put aside part of the library as reading rooms, in the new sense to be described below.

Organization of National Research Library

We are planning a library which will start with some ten million volumes and which may grow to three hundred million volumes during the twenty-first century. I shall propose a basic division of the material in this library into *subjects* and a division of the subjects into *branches*. The fundamental unit of storage, search, and retrieval will be known as an *item*.

A rough examination of the Dewey Decimal System, which although out of date still is basically sound, suggests that present-day knowledge can be classified into one hundred major categories that I shall call *subjects*. Roughly speaking, a subject corresponds to the first two digits in the Dewey Decimal System or in a modernized version of the same. For example, mathematics is identified by the digits 55. Allowing for the increased complexity of knowledge in the twenty-first century, I shall assume that the number of subjects will be doubled during the lifetime of the library. I think that this is a realistic assumption; certainly the number of subjects must grow at a much slower rate than the number of volumes.

Each subject will function as a unit in the new library, and will have its own room and complete means of storage, search, and retrieval. The National Research Library might originally consist of a hundred large rooms, and might have to grow into a structure of two hundred rooms. This is a much more modest rate of growth than any library can foresee in the immediate future.

From now on I shall discuss only a single subject, since each subject will be organized on the same basic principles as each of the other roughly one hundred subjects. As my standard example I shall use pure mathematics; a rough estimate would show that pure mathematics and applied mathematics are each of just about the right size to be represented as one one-hundredth of a research library. According to the estimates in Table 2, a subject should grow by some 60,000 items per year in 2000 A.D. A subject that would reach that rate in forty years should today grow at some 25,000 items annually, which makes pure mathematics possible as a small subject. On the other hand, this indicates that chemistry will have to be treated as five different subjects in 2000 A.D.

A subject will be divided into a number of *branches*. The basic restriction on this division will be that most problems be classifiable as falling within a single branch. I have used as my guide in this matter the journal *Mathematical Reviews,* which publishes brief descriptions of everything that appears in print in mathematics. From the journal's subject index it is reasonable to estimate that by 2000 A.D. pure mathematics may be divided into fifty branches. I shall allow the number of branches of a given subject to grow up to one hundred. At this stage it would appear better to have the subject subdivided into two subjects.

As an estimate of the size, growth, and complexity of the central library, we may take the figures in Table 2. These figures are guesses at averages, which should be fairly reliable, at least in their orders of magnitude.

Within a given branch, material may be classified into books, and books may be subdivided into *items.* By an item I shall mean roughly a chapter of a book, or an article in a journal. By definition an item will be somewhere between one and fifty printed pages, and I should assume that most items would be ten to thirty pages in length. If publications continue in any-

TABLE 2

Size of Library

	2000 A.D.	2100 A.D.
Volumes	10^7	3×10^8
Items	3×10^8	10^{10}
Subjects	100	200
Items per subject	3×10^6	5×10^7
Items per subject in a year	6×10^4	10^6
Branches	5×10^3	15×10^3
Volumes per branch (with duplicates)	4×10^3	4×10^4
Items per branch	10^5	10^6

thing like their present form, this would seem to be the smallest reasonable unit for storage and retrieval.

At this point I should like to propose a basic modification of the manner in which items are stored. I can illustrate this in terms of a research journal in mathematics. A given volume of a research journal is likely to contain articles on a wide variety of topics in mathematics, and only a small fraction of these would be of interest to any one research worker. It would be much more sensible to collect all articles that are published in a given month which relate to a given branch, and label them as a "volume." Since items will be stored by branches, some such procedure will be essential. Of course there will be the difficulty that some articles will be relevant to several different branches, and in this case we should bind copies of the same item into several different volumes and add them to the library of all of these branches. Thus a volume will be a homogeneous collection of articles relating to a single branch. The classification of items according to branches will of course be crucial to the success of our National Library. However, this does not seem to be an unsolvable problem. For example, in mathematics, where the American Mathematical Society operates *Mathematical Reviews*, each reviewer is even now asked to suggest a classification or classifications for the article he reviews. Similarly, our library could retain experts in all fields, to write abstracts and to indicate to which branch or branches the article most appropriately belongs.

Each item could be catalogued by a code name consisting of three letters and nine digits. For example, in the code ABC–12–34567–89, the letters ABC designate the subject and the number 12 the branch. The volume within the branch is indicated by 34567 and the item within the volume by the last two digits. By consulting Table 2 we can see that this reasonably simple coding system could take care of the needs of the twenty-first century. If one visualizes retrieval of information by means of a device similar to a telephone dial, we find that we have available roughly 5×10^{11} combinations, while our maximum need is for some 10^{10} labels. This degree of "waste" is certainly necessary if the coding system is to be at all natural.

For example, an expert in probability theory would soon learn to dial MAT–17 to obtain access to his specialty, after which he could dial a seven-digit number to obtain a specific item.

The Problem of Storage

We must now face the problem of storing on a single tape several hundred thousand items belonging to a given branch. There is every reason to believe that within the next hundred years miniaturization will make it possible to store all the volumes in the library in a small box. However, our devices must be available in this century, and they must make items available quickly and inexpensively. Therefore, a page should be reduced only to a size from which it can be magnified to its normal dimensions optically. This would indicate that we should store each page on a millimeter square. This degree of miniaturization is essentially feasible today, and will certainly be practical in another two decades.

We are now in a position to store all the articles of a given branch on a tape with dimensions of roughly 2 inches by several hundred feet. Let us refer to a 1-millimeter cross section of the tape as a *line*. We shall store all the pages of a given item on a line. (We should note that a 2-inch width is exactly right to allow the storage of up to fifty pages on a single line.) Since the basic unit of storage and retrieval will be an item, it will be convenient to have copying operations done a line at a time.

If we estimate that a branch will have a maximum of 10^6 items, we must allow tapes 3300 feet in length. Since current high-speed tapes may be 2400 feet in length, the manipulation of library tapes could be handled by a device not very different from tape units now employed.

How long would it take to retrieve a given item from such a tape? The current devices can run through the entire tape, filling in or copying every bit of it, in 5 to 10 minutes. Of course this speed can easily be improved. And we must take into account that we should rarely want to copy any significant portion of the tape; we may instead employ a rapid search device to find the beginning of a volume, and then copy the relevant items from the volume at a more modest speed. We may therefore safely assume that we can build tape devices, which, given the code numbers of some twenty items in half-a-dozen different volumes, could copy the items onto another tape in less than 1 minute.

I therefore visualize a room that has about one hundred tape units for the storage of books concerned with the given subject. Typically the subject would have fifty different branches, and therefore without duplication fifty tapes would suffice. Indeed, some branches would be consulted sufficiently rarely that a single copy of its tape will make material quickly accessible, but in the more popular branches two or three duplicates of the same tape will be desirable. If we assume that each customer ties down a tape unit for 1 or 2 minutes (and we shall see below that this is a safe assumption), then we may estimate the number of duplicate tapes necessary by requiring that during the busy part of the day no more than thirty to sixty customers per copy would wish to consult the tape. Even in a central library it is safe to assume that a device that can satisfy some two hundred customers per day will suffice for many branches. And it is hard to think of branches in which more than two or three duplicate copies will be required.

Since storage will certainly be one of the major expenditures in any future library, it is worth pausing to estimate the cost of storage. In 2000 A.D. we shall have to allow approximately 10,000 tape units. Since they will be produced in such great numbers, the cost per unit should not exceed a few thousand dollars, making the expenditure for storage less than one hundred million dollars — entirely within the range of our budget. This estimate indicates that the one billion dollar figure given earlier for the total cost of the library is a very generous one, but it does show that the total cost will have to run to a few hundreds of millions of dollars. During the century the number of tape units may quadruple. This would mean an annual expenditure of between one and two million dollars, which will be a reasonable fraction of the total operating cost of a library that serves the entire country.

One of the advantages of storing items by branches will be the ease with which new items can be added. Since the numbering of volumes of a given tape is arbitrary, one may simply append new volumes at the end of the tape, assigning the next available serial number. I should propose that, although the National Research Library should operate night and day, every day, each subject be "closed down" one day a month for the addition of new material and for necessary checking and repairs. The addition of some one hundred volumes to a branch should be a very simple operation. The material could be put on a master tape during the rest of the month and transcribed onto the appropriate branch tapes on the special date. If the mathematicians of the country get used to the fact that the mathematics library is closed on the 13th of each month, this will be of very little inconvenience to them in the long run.

It will be an important safety device to keep one copy of each branch tape in a vault, to be available for the repair or replacement of parts of the tape that become damaged or "worn out." Or it may in the long run prove simpler and cheaper to replace each tape at the end of the year by a copy from the master tape. From here on I shall ignore this problem of the updating of materials and the question of repairs, since there is no essential difficulty in either.

Retrieval of Information

Let us now turn our attention to the user of the National Library. He will be located at his own academic institution, and therefore the institution must be connected to the central library by means of a multichannel cable on which pictures can be transmitted. Such devices have already been developed, and we can expect them to be in general use soon. The university will have a large number of reading units scattered around the campus, some at the university library, some in departmental reading rooms, and some in individual professors' offices. (See Figure 1.) The number of these units and the number of channels to the central library will no doubt depend on the size of the institution and on its "library budget."

The reading unit may appear similar to a microfilm reader, but it must be equipped with a tape unit capable of receiving pictures from the central library, each picture representing one page. The unit must also be equipped with some means of sending signals to the central processing unit; for the sake of simplicity I shall visualize this device as a telephone dial.

The customer turns his set on, and begins by dialing the three-letter code of the subject of interest, say MAT for pure mathematics. This connects his reading unit to the central processing unit for pure mathematics, and makes a projection unit available to him at the National Library. Next the customer dials the two-digit code number for a branch (say, 17 for probability theory) or for a catalogue (say, 00 for author cata-

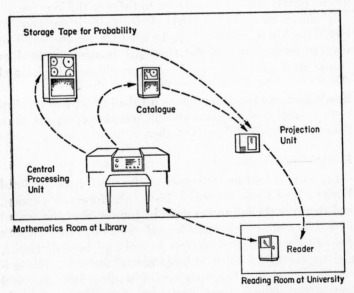

Figure 1   Mathematics Room and Reading Room for National Research Library

logue), or a special code for some other service provided by the central library.

For example, the customer might dial MAT–00–ART. This would connect him with the mathematics room, and with the author catalogue in that room. He would start looking through the author catalogue with authors whose names start with the letters ART and he could "flip through" the catalogue by pushing a button on his set which instructs the projector to advance by a page.

The idea of having library catalogues arranged by subjects is so simple and practical that it is hard for me to believe that it is not now in general use. Surely it would speed the finding of a given book, if, instead of having one gigantic catalogue, one would have it divided into a hundred segments corresponding to individual subjects. In most cases the customer would immediately find the correct subject; and even in the worst case he is unlikely to have to look in more than two or three subjects. Having to look in card files one one-hundredth the size would, I am certain, speed up the retrieval procedure considerably. Except for this modification in the arrangement of the catalogues, the author and title catalogues — which are among the more efficient features of present libraries — would not be drastically different from present files.

Once he finds the listing of the item he desires, he can dial its nine-digit code number to obtain the item itself. A slightly different code could be used if he wishes to obtain an entire book (e.g., using 00 in place of the item number). With a little skill and some thought it should take a customer less than 5 minutes from the time he turns on his set to the time that he has retrieved an item of interest from storage.

This makes it very convenient for the user who obtains an item, but what about his many colleagues who would like to look up the same item while he is perusing it? Of course we should no longer have items tied down for several weeks, only for the period that the item is actually being read; but in a library servicing a hundred universities this would still be an intolerable bottleneck. Fortunately, there is a simple way to deal with this problem: The customer is never allowed to use an item directly from the files, but only a copy of it.

When an item is requested, this is transferred from the storage tape to the projection unit, by copying one line, and from there it is sent, conveniently magnified, to the tape in the reading unit. The latter tape might be visualized as similar to a 3-minute length of Videotape. Such a tape can receive information at a speed of an item a second even without improving on today's technology, and it can hold about ten volumes (assuming that we store one page per exposure at normal camera speed). Once the items wanted are copied onto the reading tape, the customer "hangs up" and frees the storage tape and projection unit for his next user. He can then read the transcribed items at leisure. Once he has finished with these, he may either keep the tape for his personal library (a 10-volume collection of personally selected items on a 10-dollar tape!) or reuse the tape next time.

As indicated above, dialing MAT connects him with the mathematics room, and procures a projector. Next, dialing 17 connects the probability storage tape unit to the projector. As he dials the five digits of a given volume, the storage unit carries out a high-speed search, and the final two digits of code instruct it to transfer an item (or an entire volume) to the projector. While the next item is being dialed by the customer, the projection unit transmits the previous one to the reader's tape. Thus items may be obtained just as rapidly as the customer can dial seven-digit code numbers. The average customer should not tie down the storage unit for more than a minute or two. This procedure will also hold the cost of long-distance consultations to a minimum.

A similar procedure could also be used in looking up items in a catalogue. Instead of tying down the catalogue while the customer searches, relevant portions of the catalogue could be copied onto his reading tape, and he could search the catalogue at his leisure.

The reading unit could be of a relatively simple type, as shown in Figure 1. It would have to hold a short tape on which it can receive pictures at normal camera speed. It would present this tape a frame at a time, magnifying it as in an ordinary microfilm reader. It would have to be able to advance the tape a square, or move back a square, and to move to the next item, or to back up to the previous item. In addition to this, the unit would have a signaling device, say, a phone dial, for communicating with the central library. It is reasonable to expect that such units could be mass-produced at a cost that would not only allow each institution to purchase a number of these but that even individual professors might obtain private readers.

Each reading unit would be furnished with a "telephone book" containing the code names of subjects and the code numbers of the branches of each subject. To make use of this book practical, under each branch there should be a brief description of the contents of this branch, since, as we shall see later, correct identification of branches will be crucial for search purposes. As the complexity of the library grows, the division into subjects and branches will have to be revised every ten years, and thus new "telephone books" will be issued at the beginning of every decade.

Any number of additional uses of this setup suggest themselves. For example, we have already noted the possibility of a customer recording interesting items for his personal library. For a particularly important item it may be desirable to have a copy available in normal size, and thus we may wish to attach a photocopier to the reading unit. The exact extent to which these services are used will depend both on the relative costs of permanent copies versus long-distance calls, and on the frequency with which the items are needed. Unless they are used very frequently by the customer, it must be recalled that it will take him less time to obtain a new copy from the central library than to find the item in question in his personal library.

Or again, we could attach a projector to the reading device, which shows a page on a screen. Not only would this make it easier for men with visual defects to consult the library, but it would enable the mathematician to lie down on his couch while he thumbs through the latest research journals. The same device could be used in a seminar or a research conference, allowing all participants to have simultaneous access to an item from the National Research Library.

I want to emphasize that I have thought these items up during a period of a few months, and I am forced to consider subjects in which I am not an expert. However, I believe that even this crude sketch establishes the fact that a storage and retrieval system to meet all of my conditions *can* be designed by 2000 A.D. I am quite certain that a group of one hundred experts in a variety of fields, cooperating over a period of twenty years, could come up with a scheme for a central library that will be as far superior to my proposals as my proposals are to our present obsolete libraries.

For example, one of my Dartmouth colleagues suggests that instead of having the National Research Library centralized, it could be located at various major libraries, each serving as the custodian for one or more subjects. While such decentralization may be more costly to maintain, it might have many advantages. If each major library had a complete projection unit available, the local library could have on tape frequently used copies of items from all subjects, and all the catalogues, thus cutting down significantly on the demands on long-distance cables. Of course a user need not know the actual location of a subject. His request would be taken care of automatically by the usual means for routing long-distance phone calls. Thus the alternate scheme amounts to a decentralized but unified National Research Library.

This leaves us with but one major problem, namely, the problem of searching for information relevant to given scientific problems.

The Problem of Search

Let us consider the problem of finding information relevant to a research problem in a typical branch in the middle of the twenty-first century. Hopefully we manage to pinpoint the problem as belonging to a single branch. This still leaves us several hundred thousand items to search. It is in this area that the high-speed computing machine could make a significant contribution. So far we have automated our library to a considerable degree, but we have employed only machines of the simplest possible type. Only the problem of search is sufficiently complex to justify the use of a "giant brain."

Let us make our problem more precise. It is entirely reasonable to expect that for search purposes we have available a relatively brief abstract of each item in the branch. For example, this could be a coded version of a review in *Mathematical Reviews*. Or more usefully, a general scheme for the format of *Mathematical Reviews* could be agreed upon by the American Mathematical Society, and reviewers could be asked to write their reviews in this specific format. At any rate, each item is represented by one coded page, and we are to search relevant pages among several hundred thousand. Let us first consider two extreme solutions of the problem: In one the machine will play a role that is trivial, and in the other the machine will play an exceedingly complex role.

The simplest role the machine could play is that of a gigantic memory with a simple treelike pattern built into it. Experts in a given branch are asked to subdivide the branch into subbranches and divide those into topics and those into subtopics etc., making at each point some two to ten subdivisions until the partition is fine enough that any one cell has sufficiently few items in it for a research worker to examine all the abstracts in the cell. If we start with, say, 5×10^5 abstracts and wish to narrow it down to twenty abstracts in a typical problem, there must be 25,000 subdivisions of the branch. This would put a tremendous strain on the experts who are to arrive at the classification scheme, and the probability of taking the wrong fork in the search processes would almost necessarily be very high. Nevertheless, this is a possible scheme, and therefore I have carried out a small experiment to see how well it could work.

I took the two-hundred-odd articles in pure probability theory that were reviewed in one year in *Mathematical Reviews*. Starting with the division into subbranches of that journal, I introduced a division into topics, and in some cases into subtopics. If the system worked well, it would narrow the search down to two or three abstracts after only two or three questions. I must confess that I had great misgivings about this system even while I was designing it, since in some cases papers could legitimately belong to several categories, while in others it was hard to find common features for any significant number of articles.

The results of the experiment were catastrophic. In thirteen search problems, performed by three probabilists — with an assistant of mine playing the role of the machine — the abstract was located on the first try in five cases, after a small number of tries in two more instances, and not at all in six cases. It was not uncommon that the very first division, that taken from *Mathematical Reviews*, led the searcher into the wrong category. I have since learned that reviewers for *Mathematical Reviews* frequently refuse to classify papers more accurately than into branches, because of the ambiguity of the other divisions. I therefore conclude that this method of search cannot be practical on a large scale.

At the other extreme, the entire burden could be placed on the computer. The customer could furnish it with information about what type of problem he is considering, and the computer would be asked to search through the hundreds of thousands of abstracts to try to detect ones that appear to it to be relevant. It would then present the customer with all these abstracts, and the customer could choose amongst them. I feel quite certain that a scheme similar to this will be entirely practical a hundred years from now, but rough estimates seem to show that in the immediate future such a procedure is still utopian. If the scheme is not to make too many mistakes and yet be successful in narrowing down the abstracts to a couple of dozen, the computational time involved would be prohibitive.

I therefore come to the conclusion that a scheme that is to be practical in 2000 A.D. and stay practical for a few decades would have to be some sort of give-and-take between the human being and the high-speed computer. Although a complete classification scheme described above seems to be too cumbersome a system, a partial classification would certainly be practical. *Mathematical Reviews* divides each branch into something like ten subbranches. My experiment indicates that this is not completely safe, in that even at this stage of division the chances are great that the customer will be in doubt about which of two or three branches he is interested in. However, I can conceive of a series of ten questions in each branch that the computing machine might ask the consumer, and the research worker could indicate in each of the categories all those topics that might possibly be relevant to his search. It would be important to allow in each case the option of indicating that the particular method of division is irrelevant to the problem in question. I should visualize the give-and-take as follows: The machine flashes to the reading unit a list of alternatives, and the customer signals back by dialing the relevant numbers. Perhaps an answer of zero could indicate that the method of subdivision is not helpful. If even half of the questions turn out to be relevant, and in each case the possibilities are cut in third, you will have narrowed the number of abstracts down to around two thousand.

At this stage the computer would be called upon to perform a more essential role. It would search these two thousand abstracts and try to find features that many of them share. It could then ask the customer to indicate which of these features would be of interest to him. The computer could also indicate after each reply how many abstracts are still "in the running." After three or four exchanges of information the list of abstracts should have decreased to a manageable quantity.

This would appear to be a more fruitful division of labor. The experts in the branch would be asked to devise ten criteria on which items may be classified, and the reviewers would have to indicate for each criterion how the item should be classified. This is a practical procedure as long as it is not expected that in the cross-partitioning every combination (or even most combinations) should occur, or that the final output of such classification needs to be a very small number of abstracts.

It is crucial that in the search the customer be allowed to

declare that a given method of classification is irrelevant. For example one obvious criterion might be the date of publication. For some purposes only the last ten years need to be considered, a situation that would narrow the search considerably. For some other purposes the date criterion is irrelevant. For still other purposes the last thirty years would suffice. Thus the experts might suggest listing the last eighty years in ten-year intervals as eight categories, and "older" as ninth, with "irrelevant" being the tenth. Then one researcher might narrow it to a single category, another to one of three categories, while still another would ask that this criterion be ignored.

The searcher would have ample opportunity for using his skill, in trying to narrow the search, without loss of valuable information. He is also free to decide at what point the search has narrowed sufficiently for his purposes. For example, if he is trying to compile a bibliography, he is likely to want to look at a much larger number of abstracts than if he simply wants to know whether a certain theorem is known to be true.

Finally, the machine plays a significant role, but on a practical scale. Clearly the ingenuity with which it is programmed to classify the remaining abstracts into "similar" ones will make all the difference in the speed and likelihood of success of the operation. Yet we are not asking of it anything that is beyond the likely developments of the next twenty years, nor anything that would take more than a few minutes per stage.

In summary, each component seems to be playing a near optimal role: The experts in the field can suggest useful questions that will in most cases narrow the field, the customer can use these criteria optimally for his own purposes and can make the final selection from a short list of abstracts, while the computer serves partly as a memory for questions and partly as a rapid device for the rough classification of a large number of abstracts.

I should propose that the search machine also be programmed to observe its own operations and to improve its procedure as it learns from experience.

An incidental benefit of the compromise solution is that it

does not require extra hardware at the customer's end. His reading device and dialing system will be sufficient. He can dial a suitable code, and then simply answer questions presented to him on his screen by dialing all relevant numbers. Finally, when the search has narrowed sufficiently for his taste, he would signal the computer to put all the remaining abstracts on his reading tape, and he could examine them at his leisure, noting down call numbers of relevant items.

To test these ideas, I carried out a second search experiment.* Taking the probability publications of one year as my data, I designed a scheme by which each item was to be classified according to whether it had present in it one of fifty interesting features, falling into several major categories. The searcher was to indicate all features of interest to him, and our Dartmouth LGP-30 was to find all items having these features. In the experiment the coding was carried out by my assistant, who was not an expert in probability theory — a fact that no doubt had a serious effect on the outcome. Then each subject was asked to pick an item from the year's product, and to list its significant characteristics (from the list of fifty), judging from an abstract of the article.

Strictly speaking, this experiment was no more successful than its predecessor. It produced about 50 per cent success in some thirty tries. However, while the first experiment seemed to be hopeless, the second one had several promising features. For example, when it succeeded, it was too successful: It often produced only one or two abstracts. This seems to indicate that a cruder classification would have sufficed. When it failed, it usually failed because the searcher noted some one feature that the classifier did not include. In many cases this was directly due to the inexperience of the classifier, and my assistant feels that if the classification had been performed by an expert, the percentage of success would have been much greater.

It is also significant to note that failure usually resulted in no abstract being turned up at all. In many cases a repeated

* In both experiments I was ably assisted by George Cooke, a sophomore research assistant at Dartmouth.

search, omitting one criterion at a time, produced the desired abstract, without producing too many others. Thus there seems every hope that an improved search scheme along these lines would be reasonably successful.

But there are also a number of danger signals present in the outcome. It is most disturbing to note how easy it is for two experts in a given field to disagree on whether to include or exclude a significant feature. I am now convinced that any search scheme in which one "wrong" answer dooms us to failure cannot possibly work. It was also significant that the subjects were invariably eager to ask the experimenter additional questions. I do not see how some "conversation" with the machine can be avoided.

A second disturbing feature is the length of time necessary for even a simple search. Our method required about ½ minute per item. Of course, on a faster machine this can be cut by a factor of 10^3, and in the future it is likely to be cut by an additional factor of 10. But there is reason to believe that as the number of items increases by a factor of n (and the number of criteria by a factor of perhaps $\sqrt{n}$) the length of search time may increase by a factor of n^2. Since we expect a branch to have some one thousand times as many items as the number we searched, this could mean an increase by a factor of $10^6/10^4$, or 100. And search times of the order of an hour are prohibitive.

It would be easy to answer that this will no doubt be improved upon with the progress of technology, but we have already admitted that the techniques I tried were too primitive, and that slower techniques will have to be used. Thus here is one area where considerable improvement in computer design and use may be required. Of course this research will be of vast value for many other purposes, and we may expect this research to take place whether or not we decide to build a National Research Library.

This still leaves the question of what type of machine is required for search. Should it be one gigantic machine for the entire National Library, or one for each subject? If the latter is not prohibitively expensive, it would certainly be preferable.

But here I should estimate that two hundred machines with the capabilities desired would exceed our budget. I therefore suggest a single gigantic computer as more practical. The computer could operate on a single master program, with tapes giving it the suggested questions for any one branch, and having on file all the abstracts of the branch.

The machine should certainly be designed so that several customers can consult it simultaneously. This will eliminate some of the waste caused by the fact that the customer thinks at a much slower rate than the machine. Recent developments in computer design would indicate that there should be no difficulty in having one hundred or even one thousand simultaneous consultations.

If this turns out to be practical, a customer could dial INF to be put in touch with the information-search machine, and then dial the code for the subject and branch. From then on the procedure would be as indicated above.

Of all the problems discussed in this paper, this is the one requiring most study. I expect that here is an area where a group of experts could make vast improvements on the scheme I have proposed.

Conclusion

I have argued that our present libraries will be obsolete by 2000 A.D., and that the library of the twenty-first century must be designed on entirely different principles. I hope that I have answered this challenge by describing a possible library for 2000 A.D. within the reach of technological development and within a realistic budget.

I find the concept of such a library very attractive. I am basically a lazy person. I should like to sit in my office and have access to a book with no more trouble than calling a friend on the phone long-distance. Of course, I may occasionally get a busy signal, but few of us would argue that this makes the phone impractical. I have tried to argue that we should get busy signals less often than the frequency with which the book we are looking for is out of our library today. And we could arrange our calling system so that we can hold on and obtain access to a storage tape as soon as one is freed for the particular branch — an interval that should be within minutes.

I am particularly attracted to the prospect of combining this automated library with machine search. I should hope that this feature alone would justify the great central library. It is possible that, even with all this elaborate mechanization, information retrieval will become hopeless in one hundred years, but without mechanization we won't have a ghost of a chance. I look forward with delight to being able to find in 10 minutes everything relevant that has been written on a given subject, or to find that nothing relevant has been written.

I do not claim that this will save money for our universities in the long run, but I do believe that only in this way will they be able to continue operating at anything like their present library budgets. The alternative is either to abandon any degree of completeness or to increase library expenditures to fantastic sums.

And we must realize that the incidental benefits of change will be tremendous. Most important, of course, will be that all participating universities will have access to all the books of the National Research Library. The impact of this single fact on research could be so great that all my estimates for growth could prove too conservative.

But we can also visualize an endless list of auxiliary services, tied to the central library. For example, a search service could be established for the convenience of industries needing quick and thorough information on past research in a given field. When one considers the hundreds of organizations now offering partial services along this line, it is not inconceivable that this service alone could bring in enough income to finance the National Research Library.

But I am more interested in the variety of new services that could be made available to university staffs. It is a research worker's dream to think of a system that would provide as the result of a single call all the items published in his branch during the past month. All it would take is a special marker at the head of the items added during the past month. Then one could dial a special code, say MAT–17–99999, to obtain a transcript of all these items. Or alternatively, one could be furnished with abstracts of all such items. It is the only way that I can conceive of mathematicians keeping up with their specialty in 2000 A.D. And think of the needless duplication resulting from lag of information that would be eliminated!

Again, it is reasonable to assume that machine translation will be available by 2000 A.D.; hence the reader should have the option of obtaining an item in the original language or in translation.

Equally promising is a scheme for compiling a bibliography for a research project. The potential user would furnish a list of relevant articles, and a brief description of the project. The central machine would scan the bibliography of each article, examine its entries for relevance, and look up the bibliographies of the new relevant items, etc. This procedure, a familiar one to research workers, would condense weeks of work into minutes. Even if it produces a number of irrelevant items, it would be very valuable for research purposes.

And, no doubt, the reader will think of some pet projects of his own that will become possible in a National Research Library.

It is also safe to predict that the effect of such a library on the very nature of research will be immense. I don't dare to explore this subject too far, for fear of sounding fantastic, but I do want to raise one possibility. Isn't it conceivable that the nature of publications will change? Why should we continue to publish hundreds of journals in each subject, when the simple act of depositing an item in the National Library would accomplish more? We can visualize a time when a research article in mathematics is simply submitted to the "mathematics editorial board" at the National Library, where it would receive the customary referees' treatment. Once it is accepted, it is filed into the National Collection, together with an abstract of the accepted format, on the next 13th of a month. Any library or individual would have access to it after that, and could obtain a copy of it by the procedure described earlier. The time of "publication" could be cut to about three months from the present two years, and the cost would return to normal proportions.

My purpose has not been to say the last word on this subject. After all I have suggested a time requirement of twenty years and an expenditure of one billion dollars for the design and building of the Library. I have tried to show only that even after so brief a period of thought one can design something vastly superior to our present libraries, and hence I hope to have established the possibility of a National Research Library for the twenty-first century. My fondest desire is that others should go far beyond my modest beginnings, and that someone may be persuaded — sometime during the next two decades — to do something about this vital problem.

Panel Discussion

.FANO. Professor Kemeny's estimate of the magnitude of the problem that libraries and library users will face in the future is unfortunately very realistic. One might say that the volume of printed matter, like entropy, always increases. As a matter of fact, the rate of generation of scientific literature has already reached the point where some discoveries have to be made twice: the second time, when the paper in which the original research was reported is discovered by the scientific community.

I have no major objections to Professor Kemeny's outline of a National Research Library from which copies of any desired item can be obtained automatically by dialing the appropriate number. I certainly agree that such a solution is economically possible as well as technically feasible. Incidentally, it would require a change of the present copyright law. On the other hand, I doubt very much that such a centralized library can become a reality until some efficient and effective method is developed for identifying automatically the items pertinent to any particular literature search. As far as I know, no acceptable solution to this literature-retrieval problem is yet in sight. I should like to make a few comments on the nature of this problem, and on Professor Kemeny's approach to it.

I strongly agree with Professor Kemeny's statement that some sort of give-and-take between the customer and the library machine is necessary. I do not see how the object of the search can be adequately specified otherwise. As a matter of fact, such give-and-take is necessary even between scientists in order to pinpoint a specialized topic.

On the other hand, I do not share Professor Kemeny's optimism with regard to the possibility of devising an acceptable search procedure based on the classification of items according to subject matter or any other predetermined features. As a matter of fact, I am rather skeptical even about his proposed division of the literature into subjects and branches. Today's research activities often cross the boundaries between traditional fields such as mathematics, physics, and electrical engineering. Certainly, I could not limit my own literature searches to electrical engineering. I believe that the difficulties already experienced by Professor Kemeny in his attempts to classify items are not accidental. It seems to me that human knowledge cannot be classified with sufficient precision for literature-search purposes, and that even if it could be classified at any given time, the classification would change too fast to be of any real use. As a matter of fact, the acceptance by the scientific community of the terminology required to classify a new area of research often lags by years behind the research; and the most interesting period of literature search is when the field is new. Furthermore, even if a satisfactory classification could be made, the specialized scientific manpower required to classify and reclassify documents would be prohibitive.

In searching for a more promising approach, we may inquire about the strategies that we have found helpful in our own literature searches. I can only speak for myself, but I do not think that I am too different from other people in this respect. Personally, I usually start from some paper with which I am familiar, and trace through the chain of references from paper to paper. Unfortunately, such a search can lead only into the past and not into the future. That is, by this method I can find papers written before the one with which I am familiar, but not papers written after it. On the other hand, if a library machine were provided with the list of references cited in each item, it could provide forward as well as backward references. That is, it could give a list of the papers that refer to any one particular paper. Then one could search the literature both backward and forward in time, thereby reducing considerably the possibility of missing an important chain of papers. I feel that the danger of missing an important chain is more critical and more difficult to avoid than that of finding too many papers.

The idea of a backward and forward search is not new. It has been suggested independently by various people, but it has not been implemented yet in a library, at least to my knowledge. However, I understand that Dr. Kessler of Lincoln Laboratory has performed some experiments along these lines on ten years of the *Physical Review*. If he is in the audience, I hope that he will comment on his work during the general discussion period.

Another important element in my own literature searches has been the suggestions made by colleagues and librarians. In other words, I feel that the library experiences of other people have been very helpful to me. Clearly, a library machine could make available to each customer the benefit of the experience of preceding customers. At the very least, the library machine could maintain a running statistic of the items simultaneously selected by previous customers as pertinent to some topic. The topic does not have to be named for this purpose. One may even conceive of the machine's maintaining a list of the literature items consulted by each individual customer; or, if the number of customers is too large, by a selected group of customers, say, a group of scientific leaders. For instance, because of my interest in information theory, I should like to know which papers Claude Shannon has consulted.

There are many ways in which data such as those mentioned above could be used by a library machine in answering customers' queries. For instance, the customer might specify his query to the machine by listing items which are pertinent to his query and also items which are not pertinent to it. This would be a way of defining his problem. Usually, however, this definition would not be sufficient. Therefore, the library machine might suggest sequentially a test list of items for the purpose of pinpointing more precisely the query, and request the customer to specify which of the items suggested are pertinent to it. This assumes that each item could be presented on a screen very quickly from a central library. After receiving the answers, the machine would provide a list of items that appear to be strongly interrelated statistically on the basis of cross references, selections by previous customers, and perhaps other data.

The point that I wish to make is that one can conceive of literature-retrieval procedures that do not require the classification or characterization of items according to any *preconceived* scheme. As a matter of fact, I should be inclined to say that the topic and character of a paper is often best specified by the list of other papers which the scientific community considers to be closely related to it. I believe that scientists are more likely to agree on whether or not two papers are closely related than on whether the same two papers should be classified under the same preconceived heading. All a scientist would be asked is whether he thinks that the two papers are related, not why. There is a tremendous difference. For instance, it is evident to any of us when two persons look alike, yet it may be very difficult to pin down why they look alike. I think the same is true of papers.

If any retrieval system based on cross references and previous customer selections could be made to operate, it would have the great advantage that the data to be supplied to the machine could be collected by clerical means without the use of specialists. This fact alone has such tremendous economic and manpower implications that we cannot afford to overlook the possibility that a system of this type could be designed.

The final point that I would like to make is that the retrieval of literature is only part of the general literature problem. Even if we can find the papers that are pertinent to our search, even if we can obtain copies of them quickly and whenever we wish, we are still confronted by a very serious difficulty. A tremendous amount of time and energy is consumed in reading badly written papers, redundant papers, and papers using different or confusing terminology. I believe that there is a need for better and more timely books to supplant these papers.

In concluding, may I express the hope that Professor Kemeny's interest in the problem of literature retrieval will be a continuing one. This problem urgently needs the attention of people with his imagination and mathematical competence if it is to be solved in the near future.

KING. When I reflect that in twenty-three years we shall have 1984, I find it difficult to extrapolate through this discontinuity to the year 2000 A.D. Dr. Kemeny made the assumption that there will be an exponential increase in the number of books and articles produced in the decades ahead. If we accept that assumption, at least we should try to make the extrapolation self-consistent. Dr. Kemeny indicated that his prediction applies to books on science and technology as much as to books in other fields. Now these books must be about something. They will not simply contain permutations of our current knowledge. Since some, in fact, may be about automatic libraries, we might expect sizable technological changes by 2000 A.D. The power of data-processing machines, for example, historically has increased by a factor of 10 every year or so. But Dr. Kemeny has not extrapolated the contents of books the way he has their numbers. Therefore, not only can he say that present libraries are obsolete, but also that *his* library is obsolete.

The numbers quoted by Dr. Kemeny are already out of date. The National Bureau of Standards has demonstrated how photographic material can be reduced by a factor of 1000 linearly, which is a factor of 1,000,000 in area. Enough work has been done along these lines to show that all volumes of the Library of Congress could be stored in a 1-cubic-yard box. Of course, the question is what to do with it once you have it there, and this question is still largely unanswered.

The density of storage has increased so much recently that "tapes" referred to by Dr. Kemeny are giving way to discs or three-dimensional storage devices, to which much more rapid access is possible. Times of access are not minutes but milliseconds now. Exhaustive scanning of, say, 10^6 items, referred to by Dr. Kemeny as taking 10 minutes, will in a very few years take but a few milliseconds, judging from the nanosecond circuits now in being. These figures are important because sophisticated search will require hundreds or thousands of individual look-ups in executing a path to the desired information.

In the history of data processing, the cost of unit operation has also decreased by an order of magnitude every three or four years. At the present time, automatic libraries, although quite feasible technically, are apparently too expensive to be built; but judging from history, there is every reason to believe the cost will be reduced to an acceptable level by the time details of the system have been worked out. Dr. Kemeny's estimate of a range of one hundred million to one billion dollars may be as many orders of magnitude high as his estimates of the technology are low.

The real difficulty, as Dr. Kemeny emphasizes, lies in the theory, and the need for a solution to the problem of search. Something new must be conceived before the real facilities of a library can be exploited automatically. Indexing, at least by the classical methods assumed by Dr. Kemeny, has demonstrably failed. Knowledge cannot be organized for any reasonable period of time by a tree, such as the Decimal Classification. On the contrary, new ideas, which are really the object of information retrieval, result from the inverse of a tree, namely the combination of ideas. Cross referencing, not dissection, is the essence of a library.

Index headings are single words on which the whole intellectual content of a document is mapped, obviously with loss of information. Similarly, abstracts are really rejection filters preventing the reader from being exposed to the detail he really wants. It is evident that for some time indexes and abstacts are the only tools at hand to search with, and will be features of automatic libraries in the near future. But one hopes that by 2000 A.D. we shall know very much more about the way people search, or want to search, a library. The systems will adapt themselves to the basic psychology of being informed rather than to librarians' conventions. The electronic equivalent of browsing and exhaustive scan are definite possibilities.

In conclusion, one might ask whether the human race has to succumb to ever-growing libraries and automation. Perhaps we could solve this problem in other ways. For example, by removing books from libraries. Some of us used to use Crelle's *Rechnungtafeln* for multiplication, where every product of four-digit numbers was listed. But with the advent of cheap desk calculators we reconstruct the product each time. Here is one book that can be removed from a working library. This is an *extreme* position, but a few basic books well constructed could replace a great many of our present publications. In general, the dying arts of writing reviews and treatises could keep the growth of scientific and technical literature under control, at least with the aid of a relatively modest automatic library.

KEMENY. I shall consider the two sets of comments in the order in which they came. I agree with Professor Fano's comments, in general, and feel that he brought up some excellent points which I had not covered. However, I do disagree with him on one point. I very much doubt that we can avoid the use of experts. I too was tempted by the idea of tracing through bibliographic references in doing literature search. But there is a certain amount of evidence to indicate that this might turn up the entire library. An illustration is found in Professor Fano's analogy of two persons who look alike. If we start out with a particular person, and take all people who bear a definite resemblance to him, and in turn consider all people who very definitely look like each of these, and continue in this way, then with enough patience I think we shall discover that all human beings are included eventually.

I am not so pessimistic as Professor Fano about the possibility of getting experts to classify and abstract; at least my experience with *Mathematical Reviews* indicates otherwise. Outstanding mathematicians do abstracts of essentially everything that is written in mathematics. They receive two kinds of compensation: one is free copies of *Mathematical Reviews*, a very modest reimbursement; the other is the opportunity to say nasty things about the papers of other mathematicians.

I find it more difficult to reply to the comments made by Dr. King. I suppose it is to be expected that an expert in hardware will find problems of hardware easy and problems of coding more difficult. For a mathematician, the coding problems seem rather trivial, whereas considerations of hardware availability seem more mysterious.

General Discussion

KESSLER.* The research to which Professor Fano referred is not only in its infancy, it is almost embryonic. I am therefore a little reluctant to quote results.

I agree with Dr. Fano that a retrieval system based on a rigid classification scheme, although possibly applicable to a small personal library, would be completely inappropriate for a library exceeding a certain critical size. It was as a result of this conviction that we began working along lines other than rigid classification. What we did was to place about ten years of the *Physical Review* on tape, recording the title, author, and bibliography of each article in those years. We have been performing three experiments on the information assembled.

The first experiment is designed to study whether two papers may be said to be alike on the basis of their bibliographic

* Dr. Kessler was invited by the moderator to comment on his research work, which Professor Fano had cited.

structure. If two papers have identical bibliographies, then they probably have something in common. But complete identity is never found. We are thus faced with the questions of what is likeness and what is a suitable measure for likeness. These questions lead to logical and programming problems, our current concern.

The second experiment deals with the tracing of bibliographies into the past. Sometimes the tracing-back process produces an unlimited number of articles. But sometimes it does close in upon itself, and a focusing takes place on a group of what we might call seminal papers. For the case of certain subjects in solid-state physics, we asked experts to list the ten papers in their field which they considered particularly interesting and important. There were definite indications that the tracing-back process did pick up some of the papers suggested by the experts, but I must emphasize that these results are very preliminary.

The third experiment is concerned with the possibility that Dr. Fano mentioned of tracing bibliographies into the future. We take a paper and ask who used it. I feel that this is a very effective way to classify a paper — not in terms of its subject matter, but in terms of who found it useful and why. This experiment turned up the most surprising result of all. Most of the papers in our sampling from *Physical Review*, a much-used journal, were not referred to at all within the first five to ten years after their publication. In fact, two of my own papers fell into this category.

McCarthy. I should like to consider the question of costs in somewhat greater detail. I shall base my estimates on present technology, not because I am uninterested in 2000 A.D., but simply because I am more interested in the possibilities for 1965.

The first cost that I feel is relevant is the cost of information transfer. A long-distance cross-country telephone call costs two dollars for 3 minutes. The call is carried over a telephone line which theoretically can transmit 2500 bits per second. The telephone company also rents dataphones that transmit up to

1200 bits per second. This is not bad, until we ask ourselves what we can use on the other end to receive bits sent at this rate. There are currently two possibilities: a video system or a typewriter. The video system is unsatisfactory because it takes too long to display a page, while the typewriter is too slow a receiver and leads to an excessive cost of transmission. This difficulty in present technology will have to be overcome before anything approaching Professor Kemeny's library can be realized.

A second cost that is also very pertinent and important right now is the cost of converting the present library to automatic media. The Library of Congress has approximately twelve million books. If we very conservatively assume that it would cost an average of two hundred dollars to have a secretary or printer convert each book, then the total initial conversion cost would be two billion dollars. We can hope that if we wait a few years we shall have a character-sensing machine that will be able to copy books for much less; and I think this not unlikely. But I did want to bring out what I feel are the present obstacles.

With regard to the possibilities for the near future, it is clear that we cannot expect to put the Library of Congress into machine form by 1965. But my calculations indicate that we could, for example, put *Mathematical Reviews* into machine form by 1965. Furthermore, if we had a time-sharing computer system available, we could do as much searching of these reviews by 1965 as could be programmed by then.

My last comment is that some of the people who have been working in the information field, and I do not include myself among them, may feel offended by the absence of mention of their efforts. No mention has been made of the efforts to code by descriptors as a way of getting around the tree-structure difficulties. Nor has there been any mention of the work done on literature search by computers. One example that comes to mind is the U.S. Naval Ordnance Test Station at China Lake, California, which claims to be very satisfied with its IBM 704 system, using magnetic tapes, for searching the literature on rockets.

BUCKLAND. I always find talks like Dr. Kemeny's very interesting, but discussing 2000 A.D. also leaves me with a somewhat anxious feeling. I have a hard enough time getting from 1961 to 1962. I think that I can point out three difficulties connected with the suggested approaches, based on my own experience.

First, any number of people have talked about reduction to a 1-millimeter-square photographic image. This can be done, but the difficulty is in doing it cheaply. Second, the time-sharing concept of operating a computer in the give-and-take manner suggested is not the same thing as two people sitting at a computer debugging a program. It is a much faster and more demanding type of man-machine interaction. Finally, I think there are many mistaken ideas about abstracts. It does not follow that abstracts are easier to read because they are short. They are not necessarily the answer to the search problem.

GYFTOPOULOS. I should like to question the assumption that we need such a big monster as the National Library. I often am concerned about the ratio of knowledge to amount of material published each year. It seems to me that the purpose of science is to summarize knowledge about our universe in as few words as possible. I therefore would like to ask the speaker whether he feels that something should be done to reduce the volume of printed matter.

KEMENY. Surely that would be a desirable solution. But if you are proposing to set up an authorized agency that will agree to publish only one out of a hundred articles that are now being published, I think that you are proposing a task much more gigantic than the National Research Library that I suggest.

There have been some very interesting points made in the discussion, and I should like to comment on them briefly, if I may. In reply to Mr. Buckland, I am told by physicists (who claim they know) that 1-millimeter-square reproduction is going to be practical very soon, if it is not already. Also, I am sure that time sharing on machines, in a much more drastic sense than we now know, is in the works. There is no reason, eventually, why any number of people cannot use a machine simultaneously, just by the correct synchronization of requests.

I was a little troubled by Mr. Buckland's remark on abstracts. Perhaps fields differ greatly, but I do not know what mathematicians would do without abstracts. It is obviously shorter to read a three-paragraph abstract than it is to read a thirty-page paper. The abstract clearly is not going to replace the paper. The ultimate object of a literature search is to retrieve all *papers* relevant to a particular problem or subject. But it seems to me that the intermediate step of eliminating the irrelevant papers by sifting through abstracts is a method of search that we use even today. In mathematics, anyway, it is an invaluable method.

I should like to point out that Buckland and McCarthy took positions at opposite extremes with respect to abstracts. Buckland suggested that abstracts really were of no use at all in search procedures, while McCarthy implied that we should build our entire retrieval system just for the purpose of searching abstracts. My own sympathies lie in the latter direction.

McCarthy's point on the difficulty of getting books into the library was very well taken. I should have mentioned this. Since typing or transcribing onto tape by electronic means implies a cost of several billion dollars, I took it for granted that photocopying would be the only practical method. This was part of the motivation for the storage-and-retrieval system that I described.

KING. I should like to remark on the possibility of having less to store by using the machine to reconstruct knowledge. There has been some work on theorem-proving machines which indicates that, starting with the right axioms, the reconstruction of results in geometry is possible. So you might be able to reconstruct a great deal of that kind of literature.

On the issue of abstracts, I agree with Dr. Kemeny that much depends on the field, as well as on the type of person you are. But we have conducted experiments in which one group of persons was given abstracts to read, while a second group of persons was given the full articles, with time enough to read only 10 per cent of the article. Later questioning has shown that the second group comprehended slightly more than the first. Perhaps this would not be true in mathematics.

FANO. I should like to correct a misconception that arose earlier. In speaking about forming a bibliography by tracing through chains of references backward and forward, I did not mean that all the items found should be included. Obviously, such a procedure would be unsatisfactory, as Dr. Kemeny has pointed out. Instead, only those items should be included which are strongly interrelated to one another on the basis of cross references and use by readers.

I should like also to emphasize the problem of deciding what data a machine must have available in order to be capable of providing satisfactory answers to search queries. For instance, I believe that storing the entire documents in machine-operable form is not sufficient, and probably not necessary. The pertinence of a paper to a particular problem may well depend on characteristics of a mathematical approach or a block diagram which we cannot expect a machine to determine, at least in the near future. Often I must *study* a paper, rather than just read it, in order to determine whether it is pertinent to my problem.

MOOERS. One important fact that has not been brought out is that here we are in 1961, and many of the techniques that could be applied have been around for twenty years or longer. For instance, the Armed Services Technical Information Agency (ASTIA) has shaken the library world with a great accomplishment of electronic computers. A major part of this accomplishment could be achieved with descriptors. Descriptors and similar instruments were discussed in 1920. And the collator, basic to the ASTIA technique, also has been on the scene for a long time.

To address a comment specifically to the speaker, I am very much against the idea of a National Research Library. It appears to me that this idea brings with it the danger of a national bottleneck. A national cooperative library would be far more desirable and could include the many kinds of local documentary material in paper form which would never be copied and transmitted. It is easy to overlook the immense problems of paper storage and handling associated with specialized collections. A cooperative library system, instead of consolidating these collections at a central point, would maintain them at their original locations and make generally available notice of where they are.

With respect to the search problem, it was formulated around 1946 or 1947, largely because of the efforts of the American Chemical Society. An M.I.T. man, J. W. Perry, did a great deal to stimulate interest in the problem and encourage developments. It can safely be said that our techniques for searching at the present time are far better than we are prepared to use. Even with current resources, even with the services of ASTIA, for example, we certainly can get more information in paper form than can be easily assimilated.

BAUMANN. First I should like to comment on Professor McCarthy's remarks about output to individual users. At the recent meeting of the Institute of Radio Engineers, the Sony Company of Japan exhibited a little video tape recorder which can be manufactured for about ten thousand dollars now, and probably for one thousand dollars some time in the future. This machine could not only play back information recorded at the full transmission rate of the telephone line, but could also be made to exhibit one frame of the information for any length of time.

Second, I should like to comment on a method of search which Professor Fano suggested but did not cover fully. It seems to me that a person desiring information should sit down and write an abstract of the information that he wants. Then use could be made of simple statistical techniques, similar to those developed by Luhn of IBM, based on frequency of word occurrences. This would be a first-class approach, even with scanning rates that are currently attainable. Staying with the 1965 picture and using about one hundred photoreceptors in parallel working at around 10 megacycles, we can envision a scanning time for the Library of Congress of approximately 3 hours.

Thus if we had a machine capable of searching through abstracts and making statistical analyses of word frequencies, we should have at most a 3-hour delay in obtaining all possible information in the Library of Congress. Maybe some people are so impetuous that they must have their answer immediately upon asking for it, but I should just as soon take a coffee break while waiting for mine.

KEMENY. The problem is not just to scan. While you are having your coffee break, someone has to digest the tremendous amount of information generated. The time required to figure out what it is that you have scanned is an order of magnitude greater than the time required simply to peruse it.

KING. I agree with Dr. Kemeny.

WEGNER. I feel that the library of 2000 A.D. should be part of a larger computer system. The individual could submit his research problem to the computer and have it solved for him via the give-and-take process. The computer then would be able to invent its own classification scheme and would play a more active role in the development of the library than Professor Kemeny suggested. This would be a completely computer-oriented approach. In this connection, I should like to bring attention to Dr. King's Freudian slip in his mention of 1984. In fact he is looking forward to the day when IBM will be "Big Brother."

ABRAHAMS. I should like to raise a question about a basic limitation that I think Mr. Wegner recognized. Will the human being who is searching for information be able to absorb all that he receives? As the amount of relevant information increases, it may be expected that the person will absorb a smaller and smaller proportion. The aim should be more than finding out what is relevant. It should be finding out what is good among that which is relevant.

A second and associated problem is that if we have a central library, then no matter which type of retrieval system is used, the system will have a bias. The system has to be organized so that it will lead to the selection of certain kinds of things. This is especially true of a retrieval system based on what people have looked at before.

FANO. We can readily think of many learning phenomena that may occur in a library machine which makes use of the experiences of previous users, some desirable and some undesirable. For instance, items may effectively disappear from the library through nonuse. We can conceive also of situations in which a machine, by combining the experiences of various people, may discover a significant relation between papers that nobody had yet appreciated. Clearly much experimentation will be necessary before a satisfactory learning library machine can be designed.

Incidentally, I feel that there has been a serious imbalance in the information-retrieval field between theoretical and experimental work, perhaps because of the high cost of experimentation.

FREDKIN. I am hopeful that we shall still have some traditional libraries in the year 2000 A.D. If books were to be replaced by telephone dials and television sets, I should miss having a place to walk down to occasionally to take out a book. I think that books are very well engineered devices. They are easy to use, and I cannot conceive of a better way right now to store information. I am sure that there are better ways, but it is important that in looking for them we not commit ourselves to some fancy, cumbersome system for retrieving and viewing information. I think that we have enough television already.

LOCKE. As a librarian, I cannot resist the temptation of closing the session at this point. Thank you Dr. Kemeny, Dr. Fano, and Dr. King.

REFERENCES

Juhasz, S., Ed., *Proceedings of 2nd Annual Conference, National Federation of Science Abstracting and Indexing Services*, NFSAIS, Washington, D. C., 1959.

Luhn, H. P., "A Statistical Approach to Mechanized Encoding and Searching of Literary Information," *IBM Journal of Research and Development*, Vol. 1, 309–317 (Oct., 1957).

References

Luhn, H. P., "The Automatic Creation of Literature Abstracts," *ibid.*, Vol. 2, 159–165 (Apr., 1958).

Luhn, H. P., *Selective Dissemination of New Scientific Information with the Aid of Electronic Processing Equipment*, IBM Advanced Systems Development Division Report, Yorktown Heights, N.Y., Nov. 30, 1959.

Maron, M. E., and Kuhns, J. L., "On Relevance, Probabilistic Indexing and Information Retrieval," *Journal of the Assoc. for Computing Machinery*, Vol. 7, 216–244 (July, 1960).

Mooers, C. N., "The Next Twenty Years in Information Retrieval: Some Goals and Predictions," *Proceedings of the Western Joint Computer Conference*, San Francisco, 1959, The Institute of Radio Engineers, New York, 1959, pp. 81–86; also *American Documentation*, Vol 11, 229–236 (July, 1960).

Mooers, C. N., "Some Mathematical Fundamentals of the Use of Symbols in Information Retrieval," in *Information Processing*, Proceedings of the International Conference on Information Processing, UNESCO, Paris 15–20 June 1959, UNESCO, Paris, 1960, pp. 315–321.

Newman, S. M., *Problems in Mechanizing the Search in Examining Patent Applications*, U.S. Patent Office, Office of Research and Development, Washington, D. C., 1956.

Perry, J. W., Kent, A., and Berry, M. M., *Machine Literature Searching*, Western Reserve University Press and Interscience Publishers, Inc., New York, 1956.

Ray, L. C., and Kirsch, R. A., "Finding Chemical Records by Digital Computers," *Science*, Vol. 126, 814–819 (Oct., 1957).

Taube, M., and Wooster, H., Eds., *Information Storage and Retrieval*, Columbia University Press, New York, 1958. Contains further bibliography.

5

The Computer in the University

5

The
Computer
in the
University

Speaker	**Alan J. Perlis** Director of the Computation Center Carnegie Institute of Technology
Discussants	**Peter Elias** Head, Department of Electrical Engineering Professor of Electrical Engineering Massachusetts Institute of Technology **J. C. R. Licklider** Vice President Bolt Beranek & Newman Inc.
Moderator	**Donald G. Marquis** Professor of Industrial Management Massachusetts Institute of Technology

PERLIS. There are currently over one hundred computers installed in American universities. Probably two dozen or more will be added this year. In 1955 the number was less than twenty-five. Of course, the number of computers employed in industry has increased by more than this factor of 5, and those in government have increased at an even greater rate. Nevertheless, considering the costs involved in obtaining, maintaining, and expanding these machines, the universities have done very well in acquiring hardware with their limited funds.

Actually, much of the credit for the scope of the computer collection in universities today is due to intelligent planning by IBM and to the stubborn efforts of some Washington patriots at the National Science Foundation who took advantage of a period of national dismay to arrange for funds so that universities not only could have computers, but could have good ones, i.e., computers having large storage and high processing speed.[1] Of course, the NSF and IBM decisions were not made in a vacuum. People in NSF and IBM had before them considerable evidence of the intelligent and farsighted use to which some universities could put computers. Certainly, M.I.T., from the Bush analyzer to Whirlwind to the present computer-rich environment, has provided abundant evidence that universities could indeed do wonders with these machines.

How Universities Are Using Their Computers

Now that computers are generally available at universities, it is time to assess their real purpose there. The basic purpose, at present, is to do computations associated with and supported by university research programs, largely government financed. Some of this research makes marginal use of the computer, e.g., computation of data arising during the performance of the research. Some uses require the computer's full-time participation, e.g., simulation studies and certain numerical analysis research. Some research, started in the former category, ends in the latter. Less often encountered is the reverse trend. Sad to state, some uses occur merely because the computer is available, and seem to have no higher purpose than that.

Some of this research is quite important and its consequences ramified. Some uses invent computation techniques that will probably have a more profound effect than the original research objective. With only a few users does the computer itself (or, more precisely, the insight it takes to use it) invest a deeper interpretation of the development being studied.

Testifying to the growing involvement of computers in graduate research, one notes the increasingly large percentage of M.S. and Ph.D. theses in psychology, the physical sciences, and engineering that contain reference to tables and approximate solutions to equations produced on a machine; also to codes, often specified in the heady symbolism of a language like FORTRAN, whose execution has produced these important results.

Most university computation centers produce annual reports

that document the diversity of applications successfully carried out or in progress on their computers during the year. The list, and some of the results, are quite impressive. They testify to the value of a computer as a research instrument in the university. In a few years it is not unlikely that the computer may have settled immutably into our thought as an absolutely essential part of any university research program in the physical, psychological, and economic sciences.

As a consequence of the prolonged contact of research students with the computer, interest in numerical analysis has increased, and courses are now available in this subject in all universities possessing computers, and in many which do not. Most of these courses are on classical numerical analysis. Few require or encourage continual contact with the computer. This is partly because the time required to teach programming to the students would seriously reduce the contact hours available for learning numerical analysis; and it is partly because the machine time is just not available, either in length of period or frequency.

This lack of contact is a serious delinquency, not because numerical analysis cannot be taught, appreciated, or learned without a computer; but rather because with the student programming continuously it is possible to (1) reduce for him the programming composition effort to that required of any mode of communication in which we are expected eventually to be fluent (such as writing in English), and (2) reveal the important developments of the subject through real problems in which the students are personally involved. These real problems illustrate the developments as no blackboard or textbook example can. The instructor's direct administrative involvement with these problem efforts can be reduced greatly by having the exercises graded by the computer. I shall say more of this possibility later.

Through such a course the engineering and science student acquires a feeling for, as distinct from a catalogue of facts about, such things as infinite sequences, and convergence rates from successive approximation schemes; the value of an axiomatic approach to finite dimensional vector spaces (shown to be an aid in the concise description of processes for solving systems of linear equations and characteristic-value problems); the importance of constructive existence theorems in differential equations; the relationship between random processes in nature and numerical methods for solving their representation in mathematical form as it arises, for example, in partial differential equations; and the importance of heuristic, as distinct from analytically justifiable, approaches in practical numerical analysis, e.g., a very beautiful method of estimating error in numerical quadrature, due to Lanczos,[2] which avoids high-order derivatives or their equivalent, but which has no precise analytical justification.

Finally, the student, through his programming, becomes aware of the importance of representation itself as he describes computational processes that are strongly dependent on the way information is organized and supplied to the process, e.g., in Chebychev approximation. Among the linguistic representations with which he becomes acutely acquainted are those languages (complex but unambiguous) for specifying algorithms for the machine — the so-called problem-oriented computer languages. At Carnegie Tech the two-term senior-level numerical analysis course requires each student to program and run about twenty numerical solutions of diverse problems in a year, not nearly as many as would be desired, however.

Whereas numerical analysis has fitted naturally into the educational program of the engineer and scientist, computer programming per se has not. Generally, programming has meant either dilute numerical analysis, machine code learning, or logical design of computers, and sometimes fantastic mixtures of all three. In many schools the intellectual content of "programming" is considered so devoid of university material that only because of its practical utility is it taught, and then, often, only in after-hour short courses given without credit, or inspiration, or perspective. Such courses are often summed up with a triumphant exercise in coding, e.g., use of Simpson's rule to obtain approximations for π. These courses are taught as though a computer were merely another shop tool.

In the past three to four years some economics departments have begun the systematic exploitation of the computer as part of their research and educational programs. Some of those research projects are primarily analysis of data; others utilize the computer to simulate organizations, their actions, and policies; others study mathematical models of economic practice. The models are often combinatorial, and it is amazing to see the same students who have great difficulty with the calculus manipulate scheduling models represented as graphs — and glibly program clever algorithms that compute values for the graph properties.

One of the most important applications to economics education is the development of the management game as an educational tool. The injection of the game into the educational process has stimulated the student's appreciation of the decision-making problem in management. There are, of course, many kinds of management games and diverse opinions about their role in education. A faculty whose members are fluent in programming, because it has been made simple for them to learn and practice to be so, will see more clearly, in a fundamentally different way from the novice, the ramifications of a complex, dynamic game played with a computer. If the computer is made available to the students as a matter of course, both students and faculty will see in it a really powerful educational tool. The Carnegie Tech Management Game[3] has become not a (marginal) laboratory exercise but a pivot for management education. Indeed, the authors of the game believe that it will develop, through actual practice, the following skills in the student:

"1. An ability to abstract, organize, and use information from a complex and diffuse environment.
2. An ability to forecast and to plan.
3. An ability to combine the role of generalist and specialist.
4. An ability to work effectively with other people."

The game involves a good deal of information transfer and sharpens the ability of the player to analyze in a realistic time framework large amounts of information. Eventually the player himself will be able to program, or to call upon subprograms that will process the data he gathers from the game-dominated universe. Thus the computer will serve as both the environmental source and analyzer of information. Having a functioning "doll's house" available, the faculty, without fear of by-passing the very important practical examples, can donate their wisdom to emphasizing important theory and economic relationships that, when coupled with student drill, give the proper balance to an education.

Educating the Student

The preceding uses have several common features. With the exception of the cited economics applications, they are characterized by extensions of previously used methods to computers; and they are accomplished by people already well trained in their field or specialty who have received most of their training without computer contact. It is, however, the thesis of this paper that the programming and using of computers deserve an early appearance in the university curriculum for the educated man. Indeed, such training should appear not only early but also often during university training.

The question might be asked about the way students are educated to use the computer in a university today. Three frequently used methods are the following:

1. When an application makes it necessary. When an application arises, the student is trained, through example, to recognize and utilize the computer for this and similar applications. Clearly, extensions of method will occur to the student, but he is not likely to produce major thematic reorganizations of theory and material motivated through computer experience.
2. When the student's mathematical maturity permits the absorption of a catalogue of numerical techniques that are

of general utility in computer applications. This is the standard intent of the numerical analysis course, usually offered in the junior or senior year to science and engineering majors.

3. Self-education when the student thinks he cannot do his assignments without use of the computer.

I wish to remark that the first method suffers from a dependence on instructors who for the most part, even at this time, are themselves inexperienced with computers; it also suffers from the deficiencies of any piecemeal education on how to use any device or theory. The importance that the Ford Foundation places on computer education of engineers is evidenced by the healthy programs it supports at Michigan[4] and M.I.T.; and much of this support is directed toward the computer education of engineering faculties — still largely delinquent in understanding computation and dreadfully unprepared to teach it. The second method suffers from identifying the domain of computer application too closely with the standard problems and techniques of numerical analysis. The third method suffers because it possibly illustrates that universities and their carefully nurtured degree programs are not in any case necessary to our society in solving its problems.

Some universities have used a fourth approach. A credit course involving the use of some automatic programming language is provided. Fluency in "conversation" with this language and clear understanding of the language's grammar are the intents of such a course. Here, too, the approach suffers from limited and even misguided pedagogic objectives; and the result is a student well conversant in, say, ALGOL 60, but still very likely uneducated as to the scope of computation.

These approaches all fall far short of what is urgently needed. Whatever appreciation of computers they invoke comes too late in the educational program and is inevitably too parochial. It is thus important to state quite clearly when the computer and the student should first meet and what should be the nature of their first acquaintance. As others have stated in other con-

187

texts, the product of a university education should receive training directed to the development of sensitivity, rationality, and an intelligent table look-up procedure.

Sensitivity, as the poet MacLeish so aptly has said, is a feeling for the meaning or relevance of facts. Rationality is fluency in the definition, manipulation, and communication of convenient structures, experience and ability in choosing representations for the study of models, and self-assurance in the ability to work with the large systems that are unfortunately necessary for modeling and solving the important problems of our times. Table look-up, of course, refers to the mechanism for gaining access to a catalogue of facts and problems that give meaning and physical reference to each man's concept of, and role in, society. While the computer may conceivably play a small role in the development of human sensitivity, it is quite critical to the other two developments. Indeed, no other mechanical instrument combines so well the theoretical and practical balance necessary to these two developments.

First Course in Computers

Consequently, it is felt that the first student contact with the computer should be at the earliest time possible: in the student's freshman year. This contact should be analytical and not purely descriptive, and each student during this first course should program and run or have run for him a large number of problems on the computer. At least in engineering and science programs, this course should share with mathematics and English the responsibility of developing an operational literacy, while physics and chemistry develop the background toward which this literacy is to be applied. In a liberal arts program the course could be delayed until the sophomore year, but certainly deserves inclusion in such a program because of the universal relevance of the computer to our times.

One must admit that an optimum content for the freshman course is not yet known. Few such courses have been offered. What is said here is based on limited experience at Carnegie Tech and on an academic, admittedly rather arrogant intuition concerning the importance of machines. The Carnegie course occupies two semesters. It was offered to forty-six students in the fall term, and to two hundred additional freshmen this spring term. It is felt essential that each student do about twenty problems on the computer per semester. The grading of 5000 programs in a 16-week period is a task well beyond the endurance limits of most instructor cadres, so the computer has been programmed to accomplish this task itself as well as to maintain, as a matter of course, the grades of the students.

During the first term the students wrote programs in a symbolic machine code, the Carnegie TASS system; and during the current term they are writing their codes in GATE, the Carnegie Algebraic Language system. Coding in machine language, they are taught mechanical algorithms of code analysis that enable them to do manually what the GATE translator does automatically. In particular, they are becoming adept in decoding complex logical relations to produce branching codes and in manual decoding of complex formula evaluations by mechanical processes. The intent is to reveal, through these examples, how analysis of some intuitively performed human tasks leads to mechanical algorithms accomplishable by a machine.

The processes are given at two levels: first a description using "informal" bookkeeping methods and tabular languages, and later a quite precise description using completely formal rules and representations in a formal programming language. The need for a formal system arises naturally, and the concept appears intuitively reasonable.

In the course of analyzing these complex formulas, the students are given processes represented by flow charts as *definitions* of certain functions: e.g., the square root (Newton's method), the logarithm, and the exponential. For the latter two functions, the computations are not those in common use as subroutines on machines but have the advantage of being definitions that use only arithmetic operations and square root. It is proved analytically *from the flow chart* that each of these processes actually is the function claimed and that the process in the computer is of necessity only a "rational" approximation.

To do this, the student is given some elementary theorems on limits of sequences and the Weierstrass development of real numbers from nested sets of decreasing intervals. These concepts are illustrated through computation exercises right on the machine. The logarithm process yields for any $x \geq 1$ a sequence $\ln(\delta, x)$ for which $\lim \ln(\delta, x) = \ln x$. It is shown in Figure 1.

Using Figure 1 and flow-chart operations, a proof is constructed that for $x, y \geq 1, \ln(xy) = \ln x + \ln y$, and for $0 < y < 1, \ln(1/y) = -\ln y$. This provides the computation for all $y > 0$. Unfortunately the proof process is not itself mechanical.

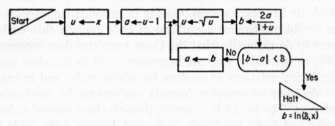

Figure 1   Flow Chart of the Logarithm Process

The construction of proofs of properties of functions from flow-chart definitions has obvious limitations in analysis but has much merit in a programming course, since the constructions are derived from specific algorithms that the students manipulate themselves. Using Newton's method, it is possible to show that if $a \geq 0, \ln x = a$ has one solution. The initial estimate is $x_0 = 1$, and

$$x_{n+1} = x_n (1 + a - \ln x_n) \qquad \text{for } n = 0, 1, 2, \cdots$$

It is then shown that $\{x_n\}$ is monotone increasing and bounded from above, while $\ln x_n \leq a$. To the student it follows simply that when $x = \lim_{n \to \infty} x_n, \ln x = a$.

Thus the definitions of these processes (the square root, the logarithmic, and the exponential) are chained. A purpose in using these definitions is to reveal one of the important principles of programming: the definition of complex processes by rational construction from simpler processes already given. I seek to make a point here. In a first course in programming it is the elements of programming that must be developed, illustrated, and emphasized. Only in subsequent contacts with the computer should a "practical" encyclopedia of numerical techniques, identified as such, be given. A well-organized set of problems for such an elementary programming course, as far as I know, does not yet exist.[5]

Elements of Programming

What then should the student be taught about programming? What are the fundamentals? The following list is admittedly incomplete but represents some fundamentals that in my opinion the student should acquire in this introductory course.

Parametrization. Every program contains at least one parameter, and binding it is necessary before the program can be run on a machine. Furthermore, within limits, the more parameters present, the more powerful the program, i.e., the more tasks it can accomplish by binding the parameters. There are numerous examples that are used: nth root instead of square root, ordering n numbers instead of 100 numbers, the number of ways of making x "cents" from coins of denomination d_1, $d_2, \ldots, d_k$. However, the student is cautioned that the empty computer is the most flexible program possible but requires a great deal of parameter binding prior to each run.

Iteration. Most programs contain cycles of operation so that the same instructions can be utilized on varying data. Teaching the student to think in terms of cycles or repetitive processes is most important.

Recursion. Instruction sequences may utilize themselves as subfunctions of their own operation. Recursion permits many processes to be programmed from the outside in. Many processes are most naturally thought of in this way, e.g., differentiation, statement scanning, game playing, etc. These examples illustrate to the student the indeterminate delay that often arises in execution of a chain of operations when it is incomplete at the time encountered.

Definitions. The development and cataloguing of highly useful code sequences. These may then be substituted into code for an occurrence of their name with variations among substitution instances induced by controlling parameters. These code sequences may, of course, contain definitions of other code sequences so that complex schemata may be generated.

A Priori Attention to Eventualities Regardless of Likelihood. The development of a mechanical attitude toward mechanical processing requires that processing of even unlikely cases be provided for. The programming of the solution of a quadratic equation and the analysis of the general second-degree equation in two variables to select conic sections are good examples where many students fail to provide for eventualities. The willingness to program through a tedious collection of tests on special cases must be fostered.

Representation. The data organization in each problem may have a "natural" representation for one phase of a computation and a different one for another. Transformations between representations must always balance in the student's mind the ease of processing versus the work involved in transformation. For example, the students were asked to compute the squares a knight might move to in j moves from a given position on a chessboard. The checking of admissible positions is most easily conceived of using an 8×8 matrix; the exhaustive check of all moves is naturally realized by a simply indexed search over a 64-position vector. (The students should decide which representation to use; or indeed, when and how often to translate during the running of a program.)

Mechanical Language. Each process, before it is run on a machine, must be described in some specific computer language. The nature of such languages is best illustrated by cataloguing their properties as they simplify the coding of certain types of problems. Here the student becomes acquainted with the inherent limitations and advantages of mechanical syntax, and also the ease with which he can adapt this syntax to his variable needs.

The student learns that often the instinctive way he chooses to describe a process is not satisfactory on a machine. But he also learns that there are ways by which he can produce such descriptions in a form acceptable to a computer, and that they really are not strange. With training, he tends to discover ever more naturally these mechanical descriptions for mechanical processes.

Simulation. It is important for the student to realize that a process possibly not even associated with, and operating external to, a computer may to varying degrees of approximation be imitated on a computer, e.g., game playing, learning, and simple process control.

Proof. The student should, through examples, develop proofs that certain algorithms he constructs actually do the task for which they are designed. Unfortunately he can only be guided by example and by appeal to a catalogue of useful proof devices; no universal proof method exists. Proving that an algorithm, claiming to be the Gauss elimination process, actually solves a system of linear equations is the most instructive pedagogic device that I have yet come across to explain the tactics used in this method of solving linear equations, the significance of zero determinants, and the uniqueness of solutions.

Grading and Guiding the Student

In a course such as the one described it is important that the student be quickly graded on his progress and guided past his mistakes. The computer can grade his progress in a generally satisfactory way. However, the identification of mistakes in programming and the isolation of the source of a student's misunderstanding in the course material are tasks that are incredibly complex, and no good automatic solution is currently available. The Carnegie computer grading program is really quite simple and works somewhat as follows:

1. The instructor writes a class problem program to include the generation of k sets of data and answers. Each data-and-answer set is identified by an index $1 < j < k$. The information is stored from within the program in a magnetic-disc memory, put there by the teaching administration routine.

2. Upon loading, a student solution program is supplied a set of data; its answers, when obtained, are compared with those associated with the class problem. Satisfactory agreement (up to a variable tolerance) of the answers over the k sets of data results in a pass grade.

3. Should the agreement be unsatisfactory, as specified by these tolerances, the index j and some diagnostic information are made available to the student. The grading may then be suspended or continued through additional data sets, depending on the problem. When the student fails to work a problem, he must try again.

4. The grading program keeps a record of the student's performance. He may, of course, work problems at any rate that he chooses. Half-right answers are not tolerated; the student is never in doubt about where he stands. He either got it right, or he did not. Therefore he cannot continue through the course in a partial fog, assuming knowledge rather than acquiring it.

While not yet in the current program, the diagnostic information can be used to control the grading program so that the student is *forced* to follow some corrective problem sequence if his errors persist in subsequent trials. The corrective problem sequence may itself be produced from within the computer. Both explanatory text and problem statements may be individually printed for each student on a high-speed printer. Thus texts are printed only when necessary. Their storage on a computer disc file would total about 50,000 computer words. (I shall say a little more later about the figures and costs of Carnegie's computing system, to shed some light on this matter.) More importantly, the grading program can maintain important counts of the frequency of use of text branches so that sensible improvements can be made in the organization of the net of problems and solutions.

Since in this first course the concepts of computer programming are new, it is these that must be taught. Discussion of the programming languages employed must be subordinated. Indeed, the language is learned as a convenient set of signs for describing these important processes. In the course of learning the techniques, the student is taught the syntax by the highly mechanical routine of the teaching machine, but it is the problem he programs that really regulates his fluency with computers.

The first and most critical stage of the computer's role in the university, it seems, is clear. It is to train entering students in the theory of computation through the development of the concepts of programming. To do this, the computer plays a partner's role with the teacher in sequencing the student through a set of problems and language definitions representative of computation principles.

At the completion of this first course, the student should now be able, for example, to recast his learning of, say, the calculus, so as to be able, himself, to devise mechanical methods for a computer to differentiate elementary expressions. The separation between the introduction and consequence of definitions and the mechanical manipulation that the student does so much of should be easy for him to make. The *concept* of the teaching program for calculus should appear natural and so should the planning procedure for accomplishing it. To be sure, the maturity in relating mathematical developments, e.g., that of algebra and calculus in the integration of rational functions, is still not yet developed; but such as it is, the maturity will be applied to an intellect already attuned to the rationale of process definition and synthesis.

To such students the following problem would be a challenge:

Devise an algorithm and write a computer program to generate, upon request, a sequence of integrals involving trigonometric functions that could serve as solvable drill problems for future students in this course. The members of the sequence should, in a sense for you to determine, increase in difficulty of integration.

It would be difficult for most, and for some unfeasible; but for almost all the basic approach would be obvious.

I do not of course mean to imply, here, that calculus should be learned only through the development of those processes, and certainly not only from their execution; but the recognition that mechanical processes are there and, given the effort, can be designed and constructed will increase the student's perception of what is important and relevant, of what is basic and what is derived.

I should expect students, later in their education (in a course in complex variables), to give serious thought to the properties of an algorithm that would perform on a computer the formal evaluation of certain definite integrals by contour integration using the calculus of residues. The algorithm, of necessity, will be recognized as only a partial one. Parametrized, it will be a proof that certain *classes* of integrals can be so treated. The student's limited success with the algorithm will not cause him to lose interest in such use of a computer, but rather prepare him for what I regard as the ultimate role of the machine.

The Ultimate Role

I should certainly expect students to attack with interest the problem of creating within the computer a technician for doing mechanical analysis. This I consider to be the ultimate use of the computer in education — the role of technical aid to match that already acquired of teaching aid; an aid in mathematical manipulation and in obtaining proofs. Such a technical aid could help a student perform tiresome manipulations (e.g., those required by many of the problems in Whittaker and Watson).

I envisage it as a fundamental task of the university computing center to develop the programming language in whose terms such a technical aid may be programmed. This programming language will require more flexible notational abilities than any now extant. But it is the university laboratory that must develop the language.

It goes without saying that the university computer or computers on which this educational program is to be accomplished must possess certain salient features: high speed multiprogramming ability, multiple input-output facilities that are many in number and low in price, high-speed printers, and large random-access storage units. The computer should be economical to use, so that the burden of its upkeep will not require it to be used less as an educational instrument than as a device for contract research computing.

The remote input-output consoles are critical for the success of this program. Past use has emphasized automatic computing, that is, *a priori* directed machine control of the entire computing process. Naturally, as computing power increases, there is an accompanying tendency to increase the automation of problem solving both in scope and depth in a given situation, for example, automatic error analysis in the solution of ordinary differential equations. One reason for this is that the expense attached to modern, large-scale computer operations does not make it feasible for the problem solver to be "in the computer loop" when his program is run.

In the educational program it is essential that the student be able to function in the computer loop without at the same time causing an exorbitant increase in everyone else's computer cost. Indeed, we may regard this as one of the prime intentions of the educational computer system being described. However, though the student is in the operating loop, it is specified that he must not control the loop; i.e., he enters when permitted and leaves when told.

Thus it is reasonable to consider that the computing load consists of a pattern of running codes some of which are monitored from an array of consoles. The rate at which characters enter from the console will be absurdly low, being about two or three characters a second (by the hunt-and-peck method). Consequently, input from the console will be by a code organized to maximize information transmitted per character, and may be quite different from the standard problem-solving languages we now use. The computer will require about 150 microseconds to process each character at transmit time. Thus, in a message, about 300 microseconds every second will be devoted to maintaining records about input data (per console). The input information will naturally be processed as a group only after a terminal signal is received. The ultimate university computer must therefore possess this satellite facility so that many students may have simultaneous access to the computer.

I should like to cite some cost figures that may put things in perspective. Suppose, as part of its computing system, a university has one or more high-speed (600-line per minute) printers, costing $12,000 a year per printer. Suppose it also has 1000 students taking three courses each, and each student receives (upon application) an average of three texts in each of his courses. Suppose the texts contain 100 pages of 40 lines each. How much does it cost to have the computer provide the students with their texts? The cost per year is about $500 for printing time, that is, $500 for all 1000 students.

Suppose the university wishes to store a text in its computer. A magnetic-disc file on some machines (not all) costs around $20,000 a year. The capacity of such a disc file is about 2×10^7 characters. If the university stores a text in this memory, it utilizes on the order of 5×10^4 characters, and the (opportunity) cost of the memory is $50 per year.

Suppose the university employs a secretary, who can type at the rather fantastic rate of 200 characters a minute, to enter a text into the computer from a console; then the computer will require, say, up to 500 microseconds per character to accept this information and some programming time to store it away. The total time necessary to read in a text of 50,000 characters will be of the order of 1 minute of the machine's precious computing time, assuming that it is doing other work simultaneously.

This implies that the computer is not as ferociously expensive an instrument for education as it might seem at first glance. Once the cost of the machine itself is within reason, it is not at all out of the question to consider a computer that serves *only* for educational purposes and not as a horse for contract research. At a purchase cost of the order of, say, $300,000 or $400,000, the university can operate a computer for the education of its students quite economically. Indeed, the idea of keeping texts on the computer is one that we at Carnegie intend to exploit with our new machine for courses in programming and the calculus.

Given then the appropriate computer, the capability of developing programming systems, the proper freshman course, and possibly a good follow-up program, the computer will achieve its ultimate role as handmaiden to scholarly university activities. The professor can then relinquish the role of drill sergeant and assume the role of philosopher-teacher.

Panel Discussion

Elias. Professor Perlis' pretty picture of a happy symbiosis between students and computers is appealing, and so of course is his proposal to make use of the computer to do both the numerical and the symbolic detail work in mathematics. I have little doubt that much of what he has described will come to pass. There are a number of distinguishable elements that he has artistically composed to form the picture, and I should like to spend my time in distinguishing them and setting up some attempt at priority and purpose among them. They have different impacts on the use of computers in the university.

If the computers, together with sufficiently ingenious languages and programming systems, are capable of doing everything that Professor Perlis describes — and I believe they are (and more) — then they should be ingenious enough to do it without the human symbiote being obliged to perform the mechanical chores which are a large part of current programming effort, and which are a large part of what must now be taught in the introductory course that he proposes. Adequate communication between man and machine, which is a necessary prerequisite to the most interesting parts of the program, is not attained so long as it is necessary for people to learn things that are of no intrinsic interest merely to communicate.

If the notations in use in mathematics, we discover, are not the notations we should be using, if they are not as explicit, as unambiguous, or as convenient as they should be, then by all means they should be modified for the sake of the people who work with them year after year. However, if we find a notation that is well adapted to the particular class of problems in which we are interested, then it seems to me that the burden of adjusting to this notation (if it is a burden, one would expect it to be reasonably matched to both the partners) should be on the machine.

Of course, this does not mean that the human should make no contribution in learning things which he does not now learn, in order to communicate better with his partner. But the things he should learn are those things that we have discovered (in the course of learning about programming, perhaps) to be more generally interesting than we had previously suspected: for example, logic and recursive function theory, the meaning of a proof, meaning of an algorithm. However, I think it is quite possible to justify learning these topics, computer or no computer. That is, I don't think this is a matter of matching people to machines. I think it is simply a matter of being able to talk intelligently about a class of interesting problems that we have discovered.

It can be argued, of course, that there is some educational value in making people adjust to the machine. It can be argued that some practice in numerical integration will make the calculus more comprehensible and teach what a limit really means. In fact, Perlis has argued this, and to a certain extent it is undoubtedly true. It is undoubtedly true that someone who has gone through a numerical integration operation has learned something about the calculus in the process. If it is sufficiently true, if such a discussion improves the learning and understanding of the calculus sufficiently, then we should do it whether or not we are interested in training students in programming and numerical analysis. We should do it because we want to teach the calculus well. And if it is sufficiently true to be worth something, but not necessarily the amount of time it takes to do numerical analysis with the desk calculator, then perhaps it becomes worth while when we have high-speed digital computers available.

On the other hand, it may very well be true that although it is worth something, in the rather intense intellectual competition of four years of undergraduate life, nowadays, it is not worth enough for all students. There may be more useful things to learn about the calculus than this, or more effective ways to spend one's time while learning the calculus.

If this is the case, if there is not enough educational value in numerical integration to justify it for the sake of teaching the calculus, then the programming systems should be expanded so as to include an error analysis automatically when doing numerical integration, providing answers along with estimates of validity without bothering the student with the details of where the estimates come from. Those are appropriate topics for a course in numerical analysis, which I do *not* believe every student interested in science or engineering should be *obliged* to take.

It may be argued that students of science and engineering should not have to use techniques they do not understand, that a programming language that is very far from the language which the machine uses insulates the students from knowledge about the nature of a computer, and that this is bad; that these students are capable by background of understanding every step, and there is no reason why they should not.

Well, of course, this again is a matter of intellectual competition. There are a great many things that these students are capable of learning, but they cannot learn them all in four years. It is also a bit artificial, since even if you teach students the primitive machine code and let them follow the transfers from register to register, they are still being insulated from the facts of life. They do not know what a flip-flop is in circuit terms, let alone the necessary solid-state physics which would let them understand how one of the transistors in the flip-flop works. Yet these are things the science and engineering undergraduates are perfectly capable of learning.

To require of every economist who wants the solution to a set of simultaneous equations that he first learn solid-state physics, so that he can learn machine language coding, so that he can learn programming, so that he can learn numerical analysis, so that he can learn how to put his economic problem in programming terms, seems absurd; and the omission of the first three steps leaves the sequence at least half as absurd as it was. Only an electrical engineer might reasonably be expected to learn about computers from the ground up, as it were, and he certainly does not start at the beginning with solid-state physics before his freshman programming course.

So I should argue that there is no basic reason for forcing everyone to understand in detail how a computer operates. There is reason for teaching the people the languages they will need in order to state the problems they are interested in solving, but presumably only to the extent that those are the languages which are well matched to the problems and not well matched to the computer, although I do not think this difference is ultimately very great. I assume that as we learn more about organizing computers and designing languages, the languages which are matched to the appropriate kinds of problems will also be matched to the appropriate kinds of computer organizations, and will not be too remote from the way the computer functions.

My area of disagreement with Perlis is really not very great. I join him in looking forward to the ultimate symbiosis where students will be interacting with computers and where everyone at a university will be making use of computers in a variety of ways. I agree that we should have freshman and sophomore courses available in the elements of programming. He would like to make such courses compulsory, and I should not. But this is not a major point. The evidence seems to be that about a third of the science and engineering students will elect these courses if given a chance. The fraction might be as large in economics and psychology and will grow with time, so that there will be a large enough audience to make the careful development of such subjects worth while in any case. The audience should even be large enough to make special subjects in mathematics oriented toward computers worth while, so that experimentation with the impact of the computer on other subject matter should not require universal adoption of a programming course.

Perhaps our most serious difference is in predicting the ultimate state of affairs when time-shared computers are available on every campus and good symbolic processing languages are in use. By that stage it sounds to me as though Perlis would have programming assume a large role in the curriculum, while I should hope that it would have disappeared from the curricula of all but a moderate group of specialists.

I have a feeling that if over the next ten years we train a third of our undergraduates at M.I.T. in programming, this will generate enough worthwhile languages for us to be able to stop, and that succeeding undergraduates will face the console with such a natural keyboard and such a natural language that there will be very little left, if anything, to the teaching of programming. We shall continue, of course, to have a group of students who are interested and specialize in numerical analysis per se or programming per se. But I hope this does not continue to have to be a major concern for the large majority of people doing any kind of scientific or engineering work.

I think if we stop short of that, if it continues to demand as much effort to learn how to speak to the machine as it costs us to teach students a course for a couple of semesters, then we have failed. I do not see anything built into the situation which requires as much as that.

LICKLIDER. Pete [Elias], I think the first apes who tried to talk with one another decided that learning language was a dreadful bore. They hoped that a few apes would work the

203

thing out so the rest could avoid the bother. But some people write poetry in the language we speak. Perhaps better poetry will be written in the language of digital computers of the future than has ever been written in English.

Let me explain myself. I am just a psychologist who has had the rare and wonderful opportunity of some contact with computers and some associations with computing people. All I can bring to you, I think, is a little more enthusiasm than my two colleagues here have brought with them.

With most of Perlis' concepts and ideas I agree enthusiastically. The aim of my discussion therefore will not be to separate what he has said into that with which I agree and that with which I disagree. The only exception is that you [Perlis] said that the computer would not do anything toward the creation of sensitivity, and with that I disagree wholeheartedly.

PERLIS. I disagree with it too.

LICKLIDER. Thank you. All I want to do is to urge that some of these concepts and ideas be extended a bit beyond the realm of numerical analysis and the teaching of calculus and the grading of problems that M.I.T. professors feel called upon to assign to their students. (I am sure that when they no longer have to grade these problems they will stop giving them, because the only earthly good the problems do is provide work for the grading staff.)

As Professor Perlis implied, there are under discussion two digital computers and two roles of the digital computer in the university. First, there is the digital computer that we have, a fabulous mechanism for calculating solutions to preformulated problems, especially long, hard, deep numerical problems. Typically, it lives behind a glass wall. It has a tighter appointment schedule, and a more resolute appointment buffer, than a dean. If you pose to it a poor problem, it labors as willingly and rapidly and accurately as if your problem had been epochal, but if you submit to it a question in which you have misplaced a comma, it insults you grossly and refuses to hear your apology before next Tuesday, at which time you may have three minutes — and your commas had better be properly placed. The role of this (present) digital computer in the university is largely, as I see it, to let imaginative, creative people catch a glimpse of the role a different digital computer *could* play.

Professor Perlis devoted some of his attention to the glimpse he has caught of the second digital computer and its role. He put his finger on what, in my opinion, is the critical key when he said that it must be large and it must be fast. Professor Perlis also said that it must be employed *simultaneously by many users* at remote stations. Let me amplify that requirement by saying that each user must be able to work on his own problem, at any time, as though he had a slower machine with almost as large a memory. He must be able to use his own programs and, in addition, the very large collection of compilers, interpreters, utility programs, tables, *and data* stored permanently in the central computer. With the aid of the compilers and interpreters (that maybe someone else has worked out, Pete) he must be able to interact with the computer in a way that is reasonably natural to the human scholar. In any event, he must not have so to clutter his mind with codes and formats that he cannot think about his substantive problem.

A computer system of this second type is technically and economically feasible. This is, however, not the time to discuss computer system designs and costs. (Let me say only that, in the heads of computer people I know here in Cambridge — e.g., John McCarthy and Marvin Minsky of M.I.T., Wesley Clark of the Lincoln Laboratory, and my young colleague Edward Fredkin — there are advanced leads to solution for all the foreseen technical problems, and that, because of the efficient use of memory and processors, the economic prospect is favorable.) The question to discuss now, it seems to me, is the role in the university of this second digital computer, this "approachable," multiprogrammed, multiuser computer.

Although the first immediate concern of the university may properly be with the education of students, the education of students may not be the best focus within which initially to examine the computer's role. It may be better to consider first the whole domain of creative intellectual processes (which is,

I think, the proper domain of the university) and to ask what role the computer may play in those processes.

Let me report, briefly, that preliminary analysis of technical and scientific creative activity suggests that such activity consists of short intervals of insight, invention, and decision making interspersed among long intervals of "staff operations." Most of the researcher's time, most of the scholar's time, most of the student's time is spent in getting into position to take a step, and only a small part of it is spent in taking the step. No one knows what it would do to a creative brain to think creatively continuously. Perhaps the brain, like the heart, must devote most of its time to rest between beats. But I doubt that this is true. I hope it is not, because a computer of the sort that Perlis is pointing toward (not really at, but toward) can give us our first look at unfettered thought. It can allow a decision maker to do almost nothing but decision making, instead of processing data to get into position to make the decision.

When we have this computer, after the several necessary years of programming, language developing, computer designing, and so forth, I think it will participate in almost every intellectual transaction that goes on in the university. Right now, of course, the computer solves preformulated problems mainly of a numerical nature. In due course it will be part of the formulation of problems; part of real-time thinking, problem solving, doing of research, conducting of experiments, getting into the literature and finding references you want. It will be part of this for, I think, all the people. First it will be so for the professors; eventually it will be so for the students, also.

As part of its contribution to the intellectual process, the computer will explore consequences of assumptions. It will present complex systems of facts and relations from new points of view, "cutting the cake another way" in a fraction of a second. It will test proposed plans of action through simulation. It will mediate and facilitate communication among human beings. It will revolutionize their access to information. It will even obtain for them the aid and services of other digital computers. At first the computer will be, in Perlis' term, a "handmaiden to scholarly university activities." In not many years, however, it will be regarded less as a handmaiden than as a partner.

Through its contribution to formulative thinking, which will be, I think, as significant as its solution of formulated problems, the computer will help us understand the structure of ideas, the nature of intellectual processes. Essential to this function is the development of procedures for computing with nonnumerical symbols. ("Computer" and "computing" do not seem to be the proper words, but their meanings may change as the nonnumerical part of digital information processing continues to grow in importance.) Although one cannot see clearly and deeply into this region of the future from the present point of view, he can be convinced that "information processing," which now connotes to many "a technology devoted to reducing data and increasing costs," will one day be the field of a basic and important science. Planning, management communication, mathematics and logic, and perhaps even psychology and philosophy will draw heavily from and contribute heavily to that science. One of the most important present functions of the digital computer in the university should be to catalyze the development of that science.

The area of investigation that seems to me to offer the most direct path toward understanding of intellectual processes is the area called "artificial intelligence," the area concerned with the development of self-organizing and/or intelligent automata. Let me not speculate now upon the outcome of such investigation. Let me say only that, in my opinion, very great advances in thought will be made in this area, just as soon as the necessary computer facilities, i.e., multiprogrammed, multiuser computers with fast processors and large memories, are developed and installed in universities. As the recent review by Minsky shows, there are many promising lines to be followed. What is holding up progress is the fact that universities have the first kind of digital computer and not the second. An important specific function of the (second) digital computer in the university is to make it feasible for creative people with diverse capabilities to work cooperatively on artificial-intelligence problems.

Professor Perlis talked about simulation and about management games. He indicated that, already, the management game at Carnegie Tech is a pivotal part of a course of instruction. Simulation, of course, has already opened a whole new approach to the study of large dynamic and stochastic systems. It is easy to extrapolate a few years to the point at which most of the major researches in management, economics, and psychology will take place as much "in the computer" as "with its aid." The computer will be making possible a kind of intellectual activity, and a degree of understanding in important fields, that we cannot possibly accomplish with human brain power alone.

The impact of the digital computer upon university education, it seems to me, will stem mainly from the changes the computer will produce in intellectual activities generally. The pedagogical responsibility of the university is not to lecture or assign problems or grade them. It is to create a situation within which most bright students will automatically learn. The multi-user digital computer opens new horizons for anyone eager to create such situations.

In a small and preliminary way, with only a small computer, a computer typewriter, and a few nights of programming, some of us have already created "motivational traps" for our children, and we are sure that a computer teaching machine can be made more attractive than television. The youngsters love real-time interaction with a thing like a computer. It can tell them immediately, "No, that was wrong"; it can calculate and post a score as it goes along; with the aid of a simple random process, it can look up in a table a suitable compliment or a suitable sarcastic remark such as "Oh, oh, you're slipping." The youngsters will sit there and punch the keys for hours learning spelling and language vocabulary.

This is just a touch of what can be done. The device can be carried on into high-school subjects, college subjects, and research. We can look forward to the time when any student from grade school through graduate school who doesn't get two hours a day at the console will be considered intellectually deprived — and will not like it.

The conclusion at which I arrive is that the present problem is not to assess the role of today's digital computer in today's university. It is to get to work on tomorrow's computer and tomorrow's university. It will not suffice to wait until the computer industry develops the computer the university needs; for commercial, industrial, and military requirements are not leading to development of such a computer on anything like the time scale that is feasible. Moreover, having such a computer is much less than half the battle. The task of preparing the programs required to make it "go critical" is great. But it is a task that universities can and should handle, for it is itself an intellectual enterprise of high order.

In short, I feel that the university has a role in (broadly defined) digital computing that must be conjugate with the role of the digital computer in the university. If the two roles are fulfilled, both the university and the computer will be considerably changed — enhanced. I am eagerly confident that universities, including this one (M.I.T.), in particular, will fulfill their role.

PERLIS. Perhaps I may have been misunderstood as to the purpose of my proposed first course in programming. It is not to teach people how to program a specific computer, nor is it to teach some new languages. The purpose of a course in programming is to teach people how to construct and analyze processes. I know of no course that the student gets in his first year in a university which has this as its sole purpose.

The course in calculus that is taught in most universities today is so covered by a mass of techniques that are completely and totally associated with the task at hand that the fundamental processes are recognized only with difficulty by many students. In physics one tries to get insight into the basic physical laws in the first course; but one is talking about physics. In chemistry the course is divided up into perhaps two parts.

You learn the factual nature of the relationships of the elements, their atomic weights, their valences, and so on. You learn how to balance equations. You also learn about the basic chemical laws: the law of mass action, the concept of equilibrium, the electrochemical series. But you are talking about chemistry, and in many students' minds the logic is never separable from the chemistry. In English you are concerned with grammar. You learn to express yourself precisely; you learn how to write; and you learn how to write only in English.

A course in programming, on the other hand, if it is taught properly, is concerned with abstraction: the abstraction of constructing, analyzing, and describing processes. It is not the particular problem content of numerical analysis or analyzing a statement which is important. Rather, it is possible to skip from problem area to problem area and still stabilize on the concept of process design and analysis. Thus in a programming course, much more than in any of these other courses, it is possible for the student to abstract ideas from the particular examples given. And I repeat: I know of no freshman course, currently, that has this objective.

I personally feel that the ability to analyze and construct processes is a very important ability, one which the student has to acquire sooner or later. I believe that he does acquire it in a rather diluted way during four years of an engineering or science program. I consider it also important to a liberal arts program.

This, to me, is the whole importance of a course in programming. It is a simulation. The point is not to teach the students how to use ALGOL, or how to program the 704. These are of little direct value. The point is to make the students construct complex processes out of simpler ones (and this is always present in programming) in the hope that the basic concepts and abilities will rub off. A properly designed programming course will develop these abilities better than any other course. I do not have a proof that this is true. I only have very little evidence of it. But this is why I think the course should be taught.

General Discussion

MCCARTHY. I should like to comment on this concept of giving a problem to the machine. I think this reveals a misunderstanding about the relationship between mathematical notation and computer programs. Unfortunately, one does not give problems to machines; one does not state a problem; one states a procedure for solving the problem. This distinction is very important. For example, the problem of finding a number that satisfies the cubic equation

$$x^3 + 9x + 7 = 0$$

is precisely stated. I have precisely stated it. There is nothing more to be said about it. But the question of solving the problem, once it is stated, is still a significant issue.

Programming is the art of stating procedures. Prior to the development of digital computers, one did not have to state procedures precisely, and no languages were developed for stating procedures precisely. Now we have a tool that will carry out any procedure, provided we can state this procedure sufficiently well. It is utopian to suppose that either English or some combination of English and mathematics will turn out to be the appropriate language for stating procedures.

One can say, "All right, if mathematics is not the language for stating procedures, what is mathematics?" The answer is that mathematics is a language for stating certain classes of facts, and a fact is different from a problem; a fact is also different from a procedure. One would suppose that appropriate languages for describing procedures will contain components which have a lot in common with mathematics and which contain a certain amount of mathematics; but they will also contain other things which are yet to be developed.

I should like to make one remark about the teaching of programming to freshmen (since I have done this). The liberal arts value of the programming course is evident, but it is still

211

overdiluted by bookkeeping. I believe that removing this excessive dilution will be a fairly gradual process.

ELIAS. I should like to reply, really using John McCarthy as an excuse, to Licklider. I did not mean to imply that people will not learn how to communicate effectively with the machine, and that what people learn in school will not be different from what they now learn, and will not be necessary for that effective communication. But I should be very disappointed if it turned out, by the time you had gotten rid of the bookkeeping, that discussing procedures, discussing algorithms as well as proofs, discussing logic as well as mathematics (if this is the appropriate language) were not an interesting and valuable thing to do for its own sake. I should be disappointed if it turned out that we had to do an appreciable amount of this for the sole purpose of communicating with machines. I hope that there is more content to this area of research than that.

MARQUIS. Dr. Minsky, your name has come into the discussion. Have you any comments?

MINSKY. I shall make one that is parallel to Licklider's. Let me start this way. Nobody in the world has really had the experience of using a time-shared computer, although there are people who should be leaping to their feet to deny this.

There have been a few experiences in the form of a couple of typewriters connected to a small computer. And there have been a few experiences of individuals operating a very large computer all by themselves: namely, individuals of great power or prestige, or those who are very quick to fill the vacuum of an IBM 704 sitting on the production line, waiting to be shipped out. These individuals have had the experience of operating a very large machine for their own amusement for long intervals of time. But in the few cases where this happened, the individuals concerned were still enmeshed in bookkeeping, in the sense that adequate programs for time sharing did not exist.

What I really mean is that nobody yet has written and used the type of monitor system necessary for administering a great number of complicated programs conveniently, just by calling their names and by binding a few of the parameters to which Perlis referred.

Educational value aside, a time-sharing computer system may be of immense personal value to the mature adult who wants to get on with his work and get something done. Licklider pointed this out in his discussion. The reason, as Licklider also has mentioned on occasion (but apparently did not dare to mention here), is that nowadays one gets about twenty minutes of real thinking done on a good day when not too many students come in to interrupt him.

We do not know what it would be like to be working in a mathematical area in which we are not too familiar (as I am not too familiar with analysis) and be able to say, "I want the Laplace transform of that," and have it appear on the scope; and then say, "I should like that variable to be Gaussian distributed," and have the appropriate convolution operations occur instantaneously. It would take the machine a long time, but it should happen well within one human reaction time, which is an unpleasantly large number of microseconds.

We could have this. Somebody has got to provide the facility and put it into the hands of the scientists who are going to do the ugly but rather interesting job of programming to make it work. But nobody has ever tried it. The tools are all here, and a few million dollars is all it would take.

LICKLIDER. I want to say that although nobody really has tried time sharing yet, enough people have gotten to sit with a big computer for a couple of hours to feel morally certain of the possibilities. I hope you will not mind if I illustrate this. One of my friends has a sign on his wall which says, "Put your clothes back on, lady, I'm a computer man."

The point is that once you get anywhere near something like the man-machine system which Minsky envisages, you know you really want it. And it is not as though the job of programming or designing hardware to obtain such a system will be objectionable. In fact, I have not had much of an introduction to this, but already I see computer programming as a way into the structure of ideas and into the understanding of

213

intellectual processes that is just a *new thing* in this world. Any psychologist is crazy to keep on working with people if he has access to a computer.

Seriously, the man-machine symbiosis gives us a much better way than we ever have had before for saying what we are trying to say and then finding out whether it is indeed correct.

PERLIS. I should like to say a word about the imminence of the time-sharing concept. Marvin [Minsky] said that no one has tried it yet; and this is quite true. The necessary equipment has not existed previously; but now it is really very imminent. The figures that I cited for the computer that we are getting at Carnegie Tech are based on fact, not fancy. We are going to have remote consoles with the machine as a matter of course: not by our own special request, but by the manufacturer's foresight.

It is still not a perfect machine. It has some severe limitations that probably are going to cause a great deal of trouble to everybody who tries to use it. But the concept of the multiple use of a computer by a large university staff working simultaneously and remotely is being adopted; and we shall soon find out whether people are really good enough to make use of their own consoles in their own offices.

I have a suspicion that very few people are going to be good enough for some time to come, no matter what programming tools we provide. I suspect that many people take refuge in bookkeeping, regardless of their professional level in life. It is a form of intellectual security, a safeguard. Introducing a console, with all of its power, will cause some anguish to many people; but I hope not to freshmen, because they are the adventurous ones.

We do not now know what will happen when freshmen in a technical university have been thoroughly educated in the computer by the end of their first year. We shall have to wait four or five years to get enough evidence, but I do not think that we shall have to wait longer than that.

FORRESTER. I wish to point out that the man-machine concepts of "human reaction time" and "immediate access" are relative terms that depend on the nature of the application. Students who use the computer to analyze nonlinear systems of 200 variables or more require from 24 to 48 hours from the time they receive an answer to determine what the answer has taught them and to decide which question to ask next. At this level of complexity, the "human reaction time" already is so long relative to the computer's speed of operation that the user effectively has "immediate access."

OETTINGER. Concerning Elias' question of whether anything of substance will be left once the machine is withdrawn, I feel that Perlis' remarks about processes contain the answer, although Perlis' emphasis on the calculus and the teaching of the calculus obscures the importance of the computer in the understanding of nonnumerical processes such as those involved in the analysis of human language, and those involved in the study of psychology and history. I agree with Perlis that in the long run, program and language development will be more than insignificant "busy work" for computer people, and I believe developments are leading to notational systems that will make the understanding of processes as essential to the educated man as is the understanding of mathematical concepts.

ELIAS. I agree that we very likely shall discover things that will be worth learning for their own sake and will have very significant intellectual content. On the other hand, let me point out as a pedagogical matter that we discovered some things in mathematics with a significant intellectual content from which, as Professor Perlis pointed out, we have managed to insulate our engineering freshmen.

What a proof is about is a valuable concept; and what an algorithm is about is also. But currently we teach the calculus to our students without getting the first concept across, and we may teach programming to our students for quite a while without getting the second concept across. Unless we are more careful than we have been over the last century in teaching mathematics, it is very likely that students will never see the second concept at all.

SLAGLE. I share the more optimistic viewpoints that have

been stated, but feel that the direct role of the computer in pedagogy has been somewhat neglected in the discussion.

LICKLIDER. I should like to pick up this thought about the pedagogical use of computers. The main thing, I think, that has come out of the study of teaching machines (à la Fred Skinner at Harvard), is that the only way to get knowledge and wisdom into the human brain is to put it in through a very extensive process.

Let me explain. You can take a field of mathematics and axiomatize it and get it down to a static nutshell: a beautiful kernel, a thing that a mathematician thinks is just lovely. And maybe you can get somebody to memorize it; but if he does so, he has not learned a thing. The only way to get it into the person is to blow it up into 50,000 operations and teach it from many points of view, using many examples. Finally it gets down into his brain in a little kernel: a beautiful pearl of knowledge.

This process is just killing us. We don't have enough teachers to handle it. University professors leave universities because of it. Computing machines, as Perlis pointed out, can do this kind of thing rapidly, economically, patiently, and without the frustration and the unhappiness. I think the computer offers a real match to the problem of getting knowledge into human skulls.

KAILATH. In Japan they say the highest form of abuse is the one that is not uttered but merely implied. Similarly, I like to think that the greatest value of computers for undergraduate education accrues when computers are not used but merely implied.

Several advantages of computers in undergraduate education have been put forward. One advantage supposedly is that the discipline of programming a computer develops certain basic skills of thought and understanding. A second advantage is that there is heuristic value in thinking up algorithms and methods to get the computer to do what you want it to do. I think the first advantage, the discipline of programming, is not worth the effort. For one thing, computers think in the crudest, most elementary terms, whereas human beings have remarkable brains by comparison. The really important advantage, to my mind, is the heuristic value of computers. Computers can enable people, such as those working in artificial intelligence, to acquire a closer appreciation of how the mind works. Eventually, however, we should be able to do away with computers and rely on inspired heuristic analogies drawn from better understanding of the process of thinking.

PERLIS. Yes and no. One should not (and I probably am more guilty of this than many) oversimplify the role of a computer. There also happen to be in our society today problems which actually require computation, and these problems are quite important to us.

REFERENCES

1. "Report on a Conference of University Computing Center Directors," *Communications of the Assoc. for Computing Machinery*, Vol. 3, 519–521 (Oct., 1960).

2. Lanczos, C., *Applied Analysis*, Prentice-Hall, Inc., Englewood Cliffs, N.J., 1956, p. 404.

3. Cohen, K. J., Cyert, R. M., Dill, W. R., and others, "The Carnegie Tech Management Game," *The Journal of Business*, Vol. 33, 303–321 (Oct., 1960).

4. "Conference Report on the Use of Computers in Engineering Classroom Instruction," *Communications of the Assoc. for Computing Machinery*, Vol. 3, 522–527 (Oct., 1960).

5. Professor Perlis has offered to make available, upon direct request to him, a set of problems used in the computer course at Carnegie.

6

**Time-Sharing
Computer
Systems**

6

Time-Sharing Computer Systems

Speaker	**JOHN MCCARTHY** Associate Professor of Communications Sciences Massachusetts Institute of Technology
Discussants	**JOHN W. MAUCHLY** President Mauchly Associates Inc. **GENE M. AMDAHL** Manager, Advanced Systems Design IBM Data Systems Division
Moderator	**EMANUEL R. PIORE** Vice President for Research and Engineering International Business Machines Corporation

McCarthy. I am going to discuss the important trend in computer design toward time-sharing computer systems. By a time-sharing computer system I shall mean one that interacts with many simultaneous users through a number of remote consoles. Such a system will look to each user like a large private computer. The new applications that time sharing will make possible will be of as much additional benefit to science and management as resulted from the introduction of the stored-program digital computer.

First I shall discuss the uses of a large private computer, and then I shall discuss how the same effect can be achieved through time sharing. I shall also touch upon the requirements that time-sharing systems impose upon computer design. Some part of what I am going to say arose in connection with the work of the Long Range Computer Study Group here at M.I.T. The material I shall present on computer-system design was developed jointly with Marvin Minsky. I also want to acknowledge the stimulating effect of discussions with Professor Herbert M. Teager and Dr. F. J. Corbató, who are developing time-sharing systems for the IBM 7090 at the M.I.T. Computation Center.

Some of the ideas concerning time-sharing systems go back quite a way. The first paper on the subject that I know of was written by Christopher Strachey and was delivered at the Paris International Conference on Information Processing.[1] A more recent paper is by Licklider.[2] The subject was also touched on in the lectures by Kemeny and Perlis. In 1945 Vannevar Bush discussed a system for personal information retrieval called Memex, which probably requires a computer system of the kind that I am going to discuss for its realization.[3]

A *Private Computer*

Why should anyone want a private computer? The reason has to do with the interaction between user and computer. In theoretical terms, a communication channel can be characterized not only by its one-way capacity, but also by its two-way capacity, a concept that is a little harder to define formally. Two-way capacity is the number of messages per second which the channel can interchange, given that the content of the leaving message depends on the content of the entering message. The advantage of a private computer is that it makes possible a large two-way communication capacity.

What the user wants is a computer that he can have continuously at his beck and call for long periods of time. Of course, computer applications differ in the amount of interaction required between user and machine (interaction can be measured by how often messages have to be exchanged between user and machine in order to complete the task). The earliest applications of computers were those in which there was little two-way interaction. Programs could be run for long periods of time without any user involvement. For instance, in the computation of mathematical tables (one of the earliest applications), you knew the tables that you wanted to compute, so you designed the machine and wrote the program and then let the thing go. Eventually the computer and the program and, unfortunately, also the tables became simultaneously obsolete.

There are still many applications that require long periods of straight computing, even with present computers. Examples are numerical weather prediction, which is still a very substantial task and promises to become even more so as models become more sophisticated, and calculations of the distribution of energy in nuclear reactors. In my remarks, however, I shall concentrate on applications, present and potential, that require frequent interaction between user and machine.

Debugging

One such application is programming. This application forces itself upon the user and requires more frequent interaction between man and machine than is presently available. Even people who are trying to program for conventional applications find themselves suffering from the lack of two-way interaction. If a program is at all complicated (and weather prediction programs are complicated), it will be built up from subprograms that require extensive testing singly and in combination. Scores of runs may be necessary to find and correct all the errors in an extensive program. Nevertheless, the amount of computer time consumed in a single run may be quite small. In fact, neglecting input-output time, only a few milliseconds may be required to detect an error in a straight-line program. Some errors, like misprints, can be corrected very quickly once the machine detects them; a programmer will get very annoyed if he has to wait a day in order to fix a misplaced comma. Other errors are more complicated, and the user may have to study his results for a day or two before he finds the trouble.

Two Present Systems of Computer Operation

There are two common ways of operating a computer for debugging programs. Both are used at M.I.T.: one by users of the TX–0 computer, and the other by the users of the IBM 709 computer at the Computation Center.

The TX–0 is a small computer that is operated very informally. Users sign up a week in advance for blocks of time of from one to several hours. During his block of time the user has a complete monopoly of the computer. He tests his program, makes necessary corrections, retests his program, and continues to make corrections. While the user is thinking about his results, the computer stands idle. If the source of trouble is hard to find, the user can waste his remaining allotment of time for the week. On the other hand, if the trouble is trivial, he can fix it immediately and continue. The TX–0 has about forty users, of whom approximately twenty-five are active in a typical week. If the TX–0 were a much larger computer, and if it were operated in the same manner as at present, the number of users who could be accommodated would still be about the same.

The IBM 709 at the M.I.T. Computation Center is a larger computer and is operated according to a different principle. Users prepare their programs and data on punched cards and deposit them in a file in a run preparation room. Machine operators transfer the programs from the punched cards to magnetic tape in batches. The programs are processed one after another by the computer, and the results of the computation are written on tape; these tapes are printed on a tape-to-printer machine, and the results are placed in the user's file. The advantage of this system is that there is no delay between individual users, and the machine is not idle while the user is thinking. By the nature of the system, a delay of two or three hours is implied between the time the cards for a job are submitted and the time that results come back. Since the Computation Center is overcrowded, however, the delay usually is more like one or two days; it is at its worst at thesis time, the end of the school year. Because the machine never waits while the user thinks, the computer can do from 125 to 160 jobs a day. The overcrowding results from the approximately 500 programmers who desire active use of the computer.

224

Neither the TX–0 system nor the 709 system is completely satisfactory. The TX–0 system is unsatisfactory because the user has to sign up well in advance and cannot go on whenever he is ready; in addition, he does not have time to think. The 709 system is unsatisfactory because of the delays in getting results back. Programming is feasible in both systems. However, the intellectual depth of projects that can be undertaken is limited by the time required to debug even relatively simple procedures. This has a very bad effect on student theses. When an ambitious student proposes to undertake something substantial, his adviser often must say, "I don't believe you can finish in time for a thesis." I have several students this semester who are in this kind of trouble. From the user's point of view the solution clearly is to have a private computer.

Man-Machine Interaction

What I have said so far has been about problems in programming that are more or less independent of what the programs are about. Now I should like to discuss applications that have an essential dependence on rapid interaction between man and machine. This topic is more speculative because these applications are undeveloped for lack of suitable machines. The first application that I should like to discuss is computing with symbolic expressions, a field in which I have worked. It is entirely feasible to have a computer manipulate formulas in the manner of a mathematician or a scientist doing theoretical work. For example, there are programs for symbolic differentiation, integration, solution of equations, simplification of algebraic expressions, the solution of differential equations, and a number of other processes. However, one rarely makes a two-hour run with symbolic calculations. If one has an integral to evaluate, even if an integration program is available, it is much easier to ask somebody (if you are not good at this sort of thing yourself) than it is to get out the program and apply it. This leads me to believe that some of the applications of symbolic calculation depend on having what is essentially a private computer, so that when you decide that you have a symbolic calculation to make, you can simply type in what you want done.

Another very important application is the use of the computer as a teacher. There has been a considerable amount of work done on teaching machines. These machines are generally of a rather simple character. A fixed sequence of questions is presented to the student, who tries to answer. When he gets the right answer, he goes on to the next question. The advantages over conventional methods are that the student can work at his own pace, and immediate reinforcement is provided for a correct answer (according to many psychologists this is very important). Present teaching machines, however, give the questions in a fixed order that does not depend on the student's answers to earlier questions. These machines cannot react to an answer other than by fitting it into one of a number of predefined categories, and furthermore, they are very limited in the amount of information (in convenient form) which they can provide the teacher on the student's progress.

Using a computer as a teacher can overcome these limitations. The decision of which information to give or which question to ask can depend on previous performance in whatever way the instructor wants. New questions can be generated to cover points where the student requires additional work. With a large class of students, each one progressing at his own pace, the instructor can be given reports identifying students who require additional help or who are doing so well as to deserve special attention and recognition. It will not be easy, however, to program a computer to take full advantage of all this flexibility.

A third application is to provide the services envisaged in Professor Kemeny's lecture in this series on "A Library for 2000 A.D." It seems that except for the incorporation of a large mass of documents, Professor Kemeny's library, and then some, can be realized, not by the year 2000, but by the year 1965.

The last specific application that I shall mention concerns interaction with laboratory apparatus in real time. The parts of laboratory apparatus that serve merely to transform information are at present very expensive to construct and tedious to debug. For a great many purposes they can be replaced conveniently by two-way connections to a computer.

I have mentioned some specific applications of a computer which require considerably more two-way interaction capability than we have at present. I could add to this by saying some more general things about the possible role of a computer as an intellectual servant. A computer can carry out any intellectual process that we can program or describe precisely. Our ability to describe processes precisely, however, is still very limited, as those of us who work on artificial-intelligence problems will certainly agree. Nevertheless, some processes of scientific research already can be reduced to routine form, and if we had a computer with which efficient two-way interaction were possible, we should be able to extend greatly our scientific capability. As our ability to understand intellectual processes expands, we shall be able to apply the computer to more and more tasks.

Advantages of a Large Computer

I should now like to discuss the question of a large computer, where by large computer I mean one with very large primary storage and very large secondary storage. The amount of secondary storage available has a simple meaning. It determines what fraction of the computer culture, so to speak, is directly accessible to the users of the computer. The implications of having a large primary storage are more subtle.

The limitations on what it has been possible to do with computers so far depend partly on the computers themselves, but even more on our ability to program. Each computer has an order code that is closely connected with the way the computer was designed, and the computer is able to obey programs that are written in this order code (also known at the *machine's language*). As you undoubtedly know, this does not mean that the user must necessarily describe his procedure in machine language. One of the intellectual procedures that the computer can be programmed to perform is the translation of procedures

227

into machine language from *source* languages in which it is more convenient to write the procedures. A number of convenient source languages have been devised, and compilers and interpreters have been written which enable a computer to obey a program written in these languages. Among these are FORTRAN, which was developed by IBM for describing numerical procedures; ALGOL, which is a proposed international standard language for describing numerical procedures; COBOL, which is a proposed United States standard language for describing file maintenance and other business data processing procedures; APT, a language that was devised at M.I.T. for programming the numerical control of machine tools; and LISP, a language that our group devised for describing computations with symbolic expressions.

Before computers there really was little need for convenient ways of formally describing procedures, and not much progress was made in developing such ways. At present, programming languages are developing rapidly, and there even has been work on constructing a mathematical theory of computation. Nevertheless, programming difficulties still cause most of the delay in preparing computers to carry out complicated procedures. If we are going to have the interaction ability that I described earlier, then we must have complex programming systems for translating procedures from source languages into machine language. If the user, sitting at his console, is going to be able to have symbolic computations performed for him, these procedures have to be at his beck and call. Ideally, the whole existing programming culture, including elaborate programming systems, should be present and readily accessible.

The main reason for needing a large primary memory is that the procedures which we can program are getting ever more elaborate. In fact, the frontier in computation is complication. An indication of this is the program for symbolic integration developed by Jim Slagle here at M.I.T. which barely fitted in the 32,768-word memory of the IBM 709. Much of the time required for developing this program was consumed in making the fit.[4] Now, symbolic integration is one of the simpler math-

228

ematical processes and occurs as a minor component in more interesting symbolic computations. We shall soon be writing programs that require an order of magnitude more memory space.

Time Sharing

I should like to go on now to consider how the private computer can be achieved. It is done by time sharing a large computer. Each user has a console that is connected to the computer by a wired channel such as a telephone line. The consoles are of two kinds, one cheap and the other better but more expensive. The cheap console is simply an electric typewriter that is used for both input and output.

Consider the operation of such a system as it appears to the user of the typewriter console. When the user wants service, he simply starts typing in a message requesting the service. The computer is always ready to pay attention to any key that he may strike, just as the telephone system is always ready for you to lift the receiver off the hook. As soon as the key is depressed on the typewriter, a signal is sent to the computer. The effect of the signal is to make the computer interrupt the program after the current instruction has been executed and jump temporarily to a program that determines what the typewriter wants. Most characters are at the beginning or middle of a message, so all the computer usually has to do is store the character or bring out a new character in case of output. If more than one typewriter requests attention simultaneously, a queue is formed. A very large number of typewriters can be handled without the computer taking more than a small amount of time away from whatever other tasks it is doing. In fact, a computer of the speed of the IBM 7090 could handle three thousand typewriters simultaneously.

Eventually a message will be completed, and the computer will have to take some kind of action other than merely storing characters. The following are examples of the kinds of action that may be required. First, the message may be a request for information from primary or secondary storage to be typed out.

Second, the message may be an expression to be integrated. Third, the message may be a statement in a program that, if formed according to the rules of the programming language, is to be added to a list of statements waiting to be translated when the program is complete. Fourth, the message may be a command to allocate an area in primary storage, or to transfer certain information from the user's files to primary storage for later action, or to transfer information from primary storage to the user's files. Fifth, the message may be a request to run a program taken from the typewriter, from the user's files, and from public subroutines. This fifth example takes the most computer time; the other examples involve specific, minor items that the computer can handle quickly.

At any moment some of the typewriters will be inactive, some will be in the middle of entering messages into the computer, some will be in the process of typing out characters, and some will be in a status of wanting programs run. There are several ways to handle the situation of a number of programs that simultaneously want to be run. I am going to discuss only the simplest way: the round-robin system. Each program is run for a definite period of time, which I shall call one quantum. If the program is not completed in this quantum, a time clock interruption occurs, and control passes to the next program in the round robin. When the round robin is completed, control returns to the first program, and so on.

How long should the quantum of time be? One answer is that the amount of time for the complete round robin should be just less than a human reaction time, say, one-tenth of a second. If this is so, then a user whose run requires less than one quantum of computer time will appear to get instantaneous service. The round-robin system is susceptible to various modifications. For example, very long programs may be postponed to slack hours in order to save memory space, and programs of very high priority can be given more than one quantum per round. A stop button would be an important part of the typewriter console, since it is very easy for a user to initiate an output that is much longer than he cares to have. There must be some way of saying, "No, stop, and pay attention to me again."

There has been extensive experience with the use of computers with typewriters as their main input-output device. The main limitation of a typewriter is that it takes too long to produce ouput. For example, the report of an assembly or compilation may take as much as twenty minutes to produce. In our system this can be improved a little bit by having high-speed printing facilities available in the computation center, so that if a user will tolerate having his output later, he can have it printed at the center and sent to him.

The more expensive console that I mentioned can include a cathode-ray-tube unit on which the computer can display pictures and text. Such a unit requires some kind of temporary storage like a tape loop or drum to avoid the computer's spending excessive time maintaining the display. Another device that has been found very useful is a light pen. This simply consists of a photocell that the user can hold against the face of the cathode-ray tube to designate a point for the computer. Other analog or digital input-output connections are desirable if the computer is connected to laboratory apparatus.

This is one example of a time-sharing system. There are a large number of users. Each user has his own console, gets service from the computer whenever he desires it, and has the computer maintain his files for him.

Computer Requirements for Time Sharing

Time sharing is technically feasible on a small computer, but the full advantages of rapid man-machine interaction require elaborate programming languages and elaborate program control. Because programs may be called on by many users and may do only relatively short pieces of work between human interactions, it is uneconomical to have to shuttle them back and forth continually to and from secondary storage. Therefore, there is a requirement for a large primary memory. How large, we are not sure. The amount of permanent program that we should want to have continuously available might be some

100,000 words, given the present state of programming services, and this suggests something on the order of one million words of directly addressable core memory for a time-sharing system. The development of new programming services could increase this requirement considerably.

What are the other requirements for a time-sharing system? Present order codes of the computer appear adequate, and the main features of present single-address computers require no important variables. Some new features will be needed, however.

One requirement is for an interruption system to handle errors as well as input and output. An interruption system works in the following way. Upon a special condition, such as an erroneous instruction to divide by zero or an input-output unit requesting attention, the next instruction in sequence is not executed. Instead, the computer takes its next instruction from a specified location, determined by the condition that caused the interruption. The program to which control is transferred deals with the condition, and if the interruption is not due to a program error, returns control after it is done to the place where the interruption arose.

Another requirement is for completely nonstop operation. If the computer were to stop with ten or fifteen people typing, it would be very difficult to retrieve the situation. The operator would not know what the computer was doing or for whom. Almost all present computers either have certain instructions that can cause a stop, or have hang-up features when certain input-output signals are absent. A proper computer ought not to rely on anyone or anything for signals on schedule. It certainly should not rely on the users to program correctly, nor should it rely on input-output units to provide signals. In the case of a tape unit which fails to provide a signal saying that a character is ready, the computer could wait a prescribed time; if the signal were not forthcoming, it could interrupt to print out a complaint to the operators.

Another requirement has to do with erroneous programs that must be prevented from damaging other programs. This is best handled by means of boundary registers and input-output interlocks. When the computer is executing a program, it must interrupt if the program attempts any memory references outside its allotted region, and it must also interrupt if the program attempts to use any instructions that activate input-output units. Input-output units should be activated only by system subroutines. Also, programs that get into endless loops must be prevented from wasting computer time. This can be accomplished by an alarm clock that interrupts a program after a quantum of time has been consumed and causes the user to be informed if his use becomes excessive.

An intricate problem arises from the fact that when a program ceases to be active it leaves an odd-sized hole in memory. It should be possible to move other programs down to fill the holes so as to provide contiguous blocks of space for new programs and data. This is facilitated by having a relocation register whose contents are added to addresses after they leave the central processing unit and before they get to memory. Another problem derives from the possibility that a system routine, such as a compiler, which is executing a program for one user, may be interrupted after a quantum of time to do another job for a different user. In order that this be feasible without confusion, it is necessary that system routines use temporary storage in blocks belonging to the user and not to themselves. Thus when program control returns to the first user, his temporary storage block is unaltered, and the system routine can take up where it left off.

The final requirement is for secondary storage large enough to maintain the users' files so that users need not have separate card or tape input-output units. For an institution like M.I.T., if only programs and data are stored (and not the M.I.T. library), then something like fifty million computer words appear adequate.

These computer requirements for time-sharing systems are not especially subtle, but the computers coming out nowadays seem to have a tendency to neglect many of them. For one thing, new computers usually are not able to address a very large memory. Their order codes generally do not provide for memories beyond a certain size.

Multisequence Computers

I want to discuss certain economic considerations that apply to computers with very large memories. A million-word memory with reasonable speed of operation may cost six million dollars. Central processing units, on the other hand, are cheaper, so we have the situation of a very large and expensive memory coupled with a much cheaper central processing unit. Is it not possible to use this large memory more efficiently and to speed up the whole system by spending more money on the central processing unit? One example of a computer that attempts to obtain a higher speed than a straightforward design would allow, is the IBM STRETCH with 2-microsecond memory. The extra speed is achieved by means of a look-ahead mechanism that simultaneously picks up several instructions and, if possible, the data needed by these instructions. Unfortunately, it appears that the effective operation of such a look-ahead system requires that the machine designers anticipate how the machine is to be used. A failure to anticipate means that the computer will not be as fast as the designers hoped.

Some of us have worked on another scheme for obtaining higher speed in a computer system. The idea is to build a system of several separate central processing units and several separate memories, in general more memories than processing units. The central processing units all have the same order code and each has the ability to address the whole memory. Boundary registers ensure that a processing unit does not transgress the limits of memory set for it at a given time. When different processors address different memory boxes, simultaneous memory references occur, but when two processors request the same memory box, a device called the arbiter simply holds up one of them for one unit of time.

We propose that successive addresses be in separate memory boxes. Based on this concept, it is interesting to note what happens when two or more processors attempt to obey the

234

same program at the same time. This can happen when the program is a system routine, such as a compiler, that the processors are running for different users. Since the processors are working for different users, they will have different temporary storage areas, as I explained before, and there will not be any conflict there. However, there might be a conflict in getting instructions. Suppose, for example, that two processors ask for the same memory box. Then one of them is held up by the arbiter and hence falls a step behind the other one. As long as the processors execute instructions from successive addresses, they will not have any further conflicts. As soon as one of the processors executes a jump instruction, however, there is a certain probability that there will again be a conflict and that one processor will be delayed.

In a time-sharing system a processor executes a quantum of program for a user and then continues in the round robin to pick up the next user in line. Unless the number of users is a multiple of the number of processors, the next time a user's turn comes around, a different processor executes his program. Thus we see that there is no particular relationship between the number of users and the number of processors, nor is there any assignment of particular processors to particular users. The number of processors in a balanced system depends on the relative costs of processors and memory, and on the size of memory required.

Serial Processors

The relative cost of computer subsystems suggested an interesting system to Ed Fredkin. It seems that 5-microsecond cycle memory is now available at a reasonable price. Logical hardware, however, also at a reasonable price, is feasible at 10 megacycles per second. This means that the time required for one unit of logic is of the order of one-fiftieth of the memory cycle. Fredkin's idea is to use a serial processor in such a system. This is a processor in which the arithmetic registers are delay lines and the arithmetic is performed serially. Thus, in an addition the bits in the word stream serially through the adder. A serial processor is much cheaper than the parallel processors currently used in large computer systems.

Computing as a Public Utility

In concluding I should like to say a word on management and the computer of the future. At present, computers are bought by individual companies or other institutions and are used only by the owning institution. If computers of the kind I have advocated become the computers of the future, then computation may someday be organized as a public utility, just as the telephone system is a public utility. We can envisage computing service companies whose subscribers are connected to them by telephone lines. Each subscriber needs to pay only for the capacity that he actually uses, but he has access to all programming languages characteristic of a very large system.

The system could develop commercially in fairly interesting ways. Certain subscribers might offer services to other subscribers. One example is weather prediction. A weather-predicting company that is a subscriber to a central computer predicts the weather but keeps the predictions in its private files. If you subscribe to its service, your programs can gain access to these files. You may even have weather-predicting programs run for your benefit to answer your own particular questions. Other possible services include those specifically connected with computing, such as programming services. Some subscribers perhaps might rent the use of their compilers. Other subscribers might furnish economic predictions. The computing utility could become the basis for a new and important industry.

Panel Discussion

MAUCHLY. Some people like a debate, but since in general I agree with what McCarthy has said, I cannot start one. Instead I wish to observe that if we are going to talk about future trends in computers, a look at the past could be helpful. For instance, the first electronic computer of large-scale, digital type had some features that are just now appearing in other computers. This computer, the Eniac, was able to read, write, and compute all at the same time. This was accomplished by a combination of equipment which we then described as the largest IBM plugboard in the world. The Eniac used an IBM card reader and an IBM card punch. The programming was not stored as is customary nowadays, but was set up by cables, patch cords, switches, and similar things. As cumbersome as it sounds, the computer could operate rather fast. How did we do that? By making the computer operate in parallel fashion. The Eniac was capable of something that is now coming back into vogue: multiprogramming. The main difference today is that we get much more capacity at a lesser cost. The departure from a parallel computer, which was able to do many separate problems simultaneously at rather high speeds, was made in an effort to achieve something more economical, similar to the motivation for the serial processor described at the end of McCarthy's talk. The more we learn about how to make hardware perform faster, the more we return to our efforts to perform larger and larger calculations at cheaper and cheaper rates. We appear to be traversing the full circle back to doing many things in parallel. If that represents a trend, it seems to be a circular one. Perhaps all we can deduce from this is that we tend to go around in circles.

There is another subject that I want to touch on here, and that is the subject of teaching machines. Perhaps this is not a new idea, but it seems to me that what we would really like to have is a learning-teaching machine. Almost any good teacher claims, and usually claims truthfully, that in the process of teaching he learns something. Yet practically all of the teaching machines that I have heard discussed so far are ones that are fixed-program. In other words, data from the student may feed back to the program of the teaching device but govern only the device's specific responses to the student. If the same student were to go through the same stupid answers (we'll say) a second time, the teaching machine might well respond in the same way as before. For a human teacher this would be exceedingly narrow. If a class does not understand a concept the first time, having it explained one way, then the teacher should go at it another way. One of the challenges of the future is that of making the teaching machines learn.

My last comment is really a comment to machine designers. We all now expect computers to talk to each other by telephone. The data phone is an existing thing — not a promise, but a reality. Someone mentioned to me earlier this evening that a computer at the recent Western Joint Computer Conference was operated by remote control through such a data link. Here again you might say we have traversed the full circle, but now it is a helical circle. We are making progress, however. It was at the September 1940 meeting of the American Mathematical Society at Dartmouth College that Dr. George Stibitz of Bell Telephone Laboratories demonstrated a computer that was operated from the Dartmouth academic halls although it was located at the Bell Laboratories. The strange thing to me is that in spite of the fact that everybody has seen telephone communication between computers coming, including the telephone company, you see very little in any present-day computer specifications about the ability of a computer either to place a telephone call or answer a telephone call. To my mind, this is a singular omission. It was easy to predict that computers should have this facility, and it is not a very hard one to provide.

AMDAHL. I am with Dr. Mauchly in being primarily in agreement with Professor McCarthy. I do have some reservations, however, about whether every individual user will desire to operate his own console. Not everyone wishes to operate his own typewriter, for example. I feel that, before it will win common acceptance, the language employed for communication between user and computer will have to become much more universal and efficient, yet be redundant enough to permit varied problem formulation. I believe that typewriter consoles should have larger character fonts to permit ready expression within this language. Some inventions in the areas of keyboards and print mechanisms to permit character font expansion economically and reliably would be very welcome for computer consoles.

With respect to time-sharing computer systems, Dr. John Cocke of IBM envisages a novel and interesting design for a multiple-usage computer that differs considerably in concept from the one proposed by Professor McCarthy. This is a computer that is one, yet many. It employs a large drum or disc type of storage for the main memory. Also on this disc or drum are arithmetic and address registers for a large number of separate computing units. As the drum or disc turns, these arithmetic and address registers are processed sequentially by a central processor; each one is processed for the execution of a single instruction. Concurrent with the sequential processing, memory references of all computing units are made as the appropriate address angles are passed. Since the time of latency for a memory reference never exceeds the time of latency for the computing unit requesting it, the drum or disc appears to be random-access memory to each computing unit. The central processor employed for the sequential simulation of the computing units does require a high-speed random-access memory adequate to hold all memory reference data for one drum or disc revolution. It could also hold all the individual arithmetic and address registers.

This computer concept is suitable for a large number of low-speed computers all time sharing a central processing unit. It could permit an extremely large and an effectively random-access memory at a very reasonable cost. It does have the disadvantage, however, of not readily permitting the allocation of more than the capacity of a single computing unit to any one problem. This allocation can be performed only for a problem whose formulation permits simultaneous multiple processing of portions of itself.

Professor McCarthy made no allusion to improved order codes for his large private computer. It is my belief that it will soon be possible to design computers whose internal language will be much closer to the programming language employed than is the case with present-day computers. I think it unlikely that they will reach a one-to-one correspondence, but a higher degree of correspondence would permit much more efficient use of the computer. This is particularly true for programs that are prepared almost entirely to fit the mathematical and physical concepts of the individual user rather than the computing hardware. Compiling programs can be used to transform the user's formulation into a more efficient one for computer processing. For debugging purposes, however, the user would also require a pseudo-inverse transformation to relieve him of considerations of the computer's internal properties.

I stated that computers might soon have order codes more closely related to programming languages. A modest approach to this appears in a logic-processing computer delivered to the Rome Air Development Center in late 1960 or early 1961 by the Aeronutronic Division of the Ford Motor Company. I designed this logic processor in the spring of 1958 in response to the need for evaluating logic equations directly without recourse to a general-purpose computer for prior assembly and compiling. I have since generalized the concepts somewhat so that numeric evaluation of algebraic equations is handled in a completely equivalent fashion. As an algebraic equation is read, the arithmetic operations and the still incomplete set of associated operands are stacked in sequence, and action is deferred until the keystone operand for the locally inner parenthetical expression is sensed. At this time the stacked operands and operations are executed in reverse sequence to the stacking. When the lowest limit of parenthetical enclosure, consistent with the present position in the equation, has been reached, reading of the equation continues as before. Recognition of the equality sign causes the final levels of the deferred operands and operations to be executed, and the final value of the equation is computed.

Such a computer organization is actually quite simple in both concept and hardware. It is only a small step in the direction of designing a problem-oriented order code, but it is significant that one common subset of a mathematical language has yielded so simply. In my opinion, the invention of further computing techniques that are appropriate to other subsets requires only time and directed effort.

I have some final remarks to make relative to the requirements of the time-sharing and multiprocessing concept favored by Professor McCarthy. In the requirement for relocatability, he suggests that when a program ceases to be active it leaves an odd-sized hole in memory. He also suggests that it must be possible to move other programs down to fill this hole so as to leave a contiguous block of space for new programs and data. It is possible to generalize relocation more completely so that such program and data transfers need not be performed. Rather, the new program and associated data can be fitted into a selection of available odd-sized holes and be processed from this non-contiguous storage. Incidentally, the same feature could provide memory protection automatically. The newly announced Burroughs B–5000 has this capability, if I interpret its description properly. In such a time-sharing computer, progression through a large number of users' programs would soon make memory allocation look like an unplanned patchwork quilt. It would appear completely orderly, however, to each and every active program.

In the multiprocessor-multimemory system suggested, the use of more than one processor depends on the effective memory traffic rate that can be achieved. The possible speed of processors appears to be increasing to the point where several 2-microsecond memories could be exercised quite effectively by a single processor. To achieve this, the complexity of the processor must be greater than that of a processor connected to a single higher-speed memory. It is doubtful, however, that this increase in complexity would be as great as that of several slower processors with a memory-reference arbiter serving them. The single higher-speed central processor also has the advantage of being able to provide the maximum computing capacity to a single active program without requiring this active program to admit to simultaneous processing of parts of itself. The single processor does have a disadvantage, however. If the processor malfunctions, the entire computing capacity vanishes, not just a given fraction of the capacity. Of course, acquiring the ability to shift computing tasks from a malfunctioning unit to the remaining good units would require a great deal of system-program planning.

McCARTHY. What I have to say in reply will deal mainly with Dr. Amdahl's comments. I agree that we need larger character fonts and input-output devices more flexible than typewriters. Even with present typewriters, however, a great deal can be done, and input-output does not seem to be the main limiting factor at present. With regard to John Cocke's computer, I guess I do not fully understand what the relationship is between the capability of such a computer and the capability of the kind of computer that I described. It sounds like less computer for a lot less money.

With respect to the matter of making order codes more like the problem-oriented languages, I disagree with Dr. Amdahl's point of view. It is true that order codes will be improved, but it seems to me that this improvement is not going to reduce by an order of magnitude the time required for a given calculation. I think that reduction by a factor of 2 is as much as can be expected. My reason for believing this has to do with the time consumed by the basic arithmetic operations themselves, and by memory references for instructions and data. When we first started programming the LISP system for symbolic expressions, we were very enthusiastic about the possible advantages to be gained from new instructions. It turns out that new instructions could do things faster, but not much faster. The way we saw this was by comparing the total memory references that the computer made with the effective or unavoidable memory references. We arrived at an efficiency of about one-sixth for the case of the IBM 709 computer. That is, one-sixth of the memory references were references to actual working data. (Adding references to instructions to references to data would have improved the efficiency figure.) It seemed to us that if we had had the instructions we wanted, we could have doubled the efficiency. And if we have any say about the order codes of subsequent computers, we certainly shall attempt to achieve this. But I doubt that any larger improvement than this is to be expected, either from order codes resembling problem-oriented languages or from order codes allowing programs which look like algebraic expressions.

Another question on which I disagree somewhat with Dr. Amdahl is whether we have to move programs down to fill odd-sized blocks, or whether we can leave them as they are. The artificial-intelligence group at M.I.T. happens to be the proprietors of a list-type programming system that does not move blocks down but manages to get along very well with odd-sized blocks. This works very well for certain kinds of calculation. However, some rather ridiculous results have been obtained by using the system where it is not suited. An example is matrix calculation. It is true that a matrix can be represented by a list of lists, where the individual lists run all through storage, but addresses must be computed for matrix calculation. If you determine that you want the seventeenth element in a matrix, it unfortunately takes much longer to count seventeen steps down a list (however you do it) than it does to proceed directly to register $A + 17$. From our experience in using un-ordered systems, we have come to realize that there are certain important classes of calculations in which it is preferable to retain the numerical method of addressing.

My final comment concerns the question of a single high-speed processor versus several processors. It should be understood that the answer to this question depends very much on the current state of technology. For example, if some discovery makes very high speed memory feasible, so that the ratio of memory speed to logical speed becomes larger than it is at present, then a very straightforward computer design would be appropriate. But if the speed of logical operations remains much higher than the speed of memory, a single processor has to look very far ahead in the program to achieve efficiency. The STRETCH computer, for example, achieves its speed by looking up to four instructions ahead. Even this is accomplished with considerable difficulty and some inefficiency. With the present ratio of speed of memory to speed of logic, it might be necessary to accomplish as many as ten or twenty memory references simultaneously. This would require the computer to have still greater powers of foresight.

Amdahl said that the disadvantage of using several processors is that in order to apply all the capacity to a single problem, you have to do some tricky programming; and even then you may not succeed. For a computer that is used by many people, this does not seem to be a serious limitation.

General Discussion

ANONYMOUS. Professor McCarthy, you stated that the memory is relatively more expensive than the central processing unit. But looking at your system organization, the only time sharing you seem to be doing is on the central processing unit and not on the memory. Would you care to comment on that?

McCARTHY. If you have a very large memory, say on the order of a million memory words, it will consist of a number of boxes containing something like 16,000 words each. I did intend that these boxes be operated simultaneously, so that the memory *would* be time shared, at least in this sense.

ANONYMOUS. But this is not the same kind of time sharing as with your central processing unit. The same processor works on all programs, but the same word of memory is assigned only to one specific program. To infer your memory requirements, you multiply the number of programmers by the average size of a program. To infer the requirements for your central processing unit, you multiply by the average execution time of a program. These are very different things.

McCARTHY. Are you suggesting that different users share the same memory register? This is possible only by making rapid transfers to and from secondary storage, a procedure that does not seem desirable. By the way, the memory used by system programs *is* time shared. Although there are many processors in the system I described, there is only one set of system programs. One of the flashiest features of the system is that different processors can be executing the same system program at the same time.

ANONYMOUS. Professor McCarthy, are you familiar with the real-time computer of Remington Rand? If so, I want to ask to what degree you think this computer already meets the requirements that you stated. One of its features that you did not mention as being desirable is its ability to accept voice commands. This reduces both the knowledge of special codes which the operator has to have and also the probability of error in input. The Remington Rand computer was designed especially for time sharing and is in use in the Capital Airlines system.

McCARTHY. I am not familiar with this computer, but I will say one thing nevertheless. It does not have enough memory. As for voice commands, I am in favor of voice input to computers, but as for reducing the amount of information the user has to have, this is not as obvious a virtue as it may seem. To tell the truth, the amount of information one has to acquire in order to program is disgracefully small as it is, compared with the amount of information one has to acquire in order to do well in other fields. What is more important is to extend our ability to use computers, make them do things that we cannot now make them do. As we develop the art of computation, the amount that a user will have to know in order to use computers with full effectiveness should increase rather than decrease.

STEVENS. You have been talking about a central computer and regional consoles. How about the possibility of regional computers and merely a central arbitrator?

McCARTHY. This question reminds me of the polymorphic computers put forward by Ramo-Wooldridge. I think that such systems are difficult to program, do not make enough memory available to individual users in a straightforward way, and do not allow as efficient sharing of system programs as the multiprocessor system I described.

REYNOLDS. Don't you think that if good input-output programs were available you could use secondary storage much more effectively and not need such large primary storage? Do you think the large primary storage is really worth the cost that it would incur?

McCarthy. This is a difficult question. Certainly for many purposes a cheaper system could keep the user's program in secondary storage and bring it in as part of each active quantum. Several comments can be made on this possibility. First, very large primary storage is not so terribly expensive and probably will become cheaper. Second, when we get into the new applications of teaching machines, symbolic calculation, and so forth, requests for individual actions are on the average going to require relatively little computation. Thus the cost of bringing in a large program from secondary storage to do a small job is going to loom larger than it does at present. Finally, certain problems now being contemplated do require very large, directly accessible storage.

Piore. I am going to ask Dr. Mauchly to make any observations that he would care to make at this point.

Mauchly. We have confined our attention so far tonight to the development of the digital computer, but the analog computer also has had considerable development over the same span of years, especially in the engineering fields. One of the things that impresses me about the garden variety of analog computer, if it is at all general purpose and not specifically conceived to do just one job like process control, is that it is very often set up with patch cords, cables, switches, and so forth. Thus problem-setup time is of importance. Even before analog computers went electronic, we had right here at M.I.T. one of the large examples of the trend toward automatic setup: a differential analyzer of the mechanical variety which was set up from punched paper tape. The trend toward automatic setup continues, but there is evidence of an even more alarming (or encouraging) trend. Instead of fighting over the problem of whether a particular calculation should be done by analog methods or digital methods, there is a trend toward combining the two to produce some sort of hybrid unit, with both analog and digital computers cooperating to solve the same problem. It seems to me that for the kind of situation which Professor McCarthy envisages, a combination like this might be very effective, provided that the analog part could be set up from the remote consoles.

PIORE.   Gene [Amdahl], have you any comments?

AMDAHL.   I should like to pursue Dr. Mauchly's idea a little further. In addition to attaching an analog computer to the system, one might also attach other kinds of digital computers that are individually designed to be particularly good at certain functions. In symbol-manipulating programs, for example, certain features of a digital computer might be heavily used, while other features are not used at all. For instance, the floating-point capabilities may not be used. One readily can imagine a system in which several simple computers, each one slanted toward a particular task, are attached to the same memory. Different portions of the same program then would be executed on different computers. This would be sort of an extension of the GAMMA 60 computer system.

PIORE.   John [McCarthy], do you want to have a final word before we close the meeting?

McCARTHY.   Well, it is difficult to find a final word that is somehow worthy of the honor of closing the meeting. All I was going to do was quibble a little more on the last point that was made. The idea of having specialized computers for specialized tasks in order to save money on the hardware seems like a good one, but if we have to program the assignment of different parts of a task to different processors, we had better be sure that the money saved on hardware is not spent on programming.

REFERENCES

1. Strachey, C., "Time Sharing in Large, Fast Computers," in *Information Processing*, Proceedings of the International Conference on Information Processing, UNESCO, Paris 15–20 June 1959, UNESCO, Paris, 1960, pp. 336–341.

2. Licklider, J. C. R., "Man-Computer Symbiosis," *IRE Transactions on Human Factors in Electronics*, Vol. HFE–1, 4–11 (Mar., 1960).

247

References

3. Bush, Vannevar, "As We May Think," *Atlantic Monthly*, Vol. 176, 101–108 (July, 1945).
4. Slagle, J., "A Heuristic Program that Solves Symbolic Integration Problems in Freshman Calculus, Symbolic Automatic Integrator (SAINT)," Ph.D. thesis, Department of Mathematics, Massachusetts Institute of Technology, May, 1961.

7

A New Concept in Programming

7

A
New Concept
in
Programming

Speaker	**GEORGE W. BROWN** Professor of Business Administration Professor of Engineering, and Director, Western Data Processing Center University of California at Los Angeles
Discussants	**GRACE M. HOPPER** Director, Research — Systems and Programming Remington Rand Division Sperry Rand Corporation
	DAVID SAYRE Corporate Director of Programming International Business Machines Corporation
Moderator	**PHILIP M. MORSE** Professor of Physics Director of the Computation Center, and Director of the Operations Research Center Massachusetts Institute of Technology

BROWN. It is no secret to people attending this series that the complexity of processes being considered for programming is almost without limit. Military information and command systems, business data processing, simulation, and artificial intelligence all may yield extremely complex structures. To program these complex structures may require hundreds of thousands or even millions of machine instructions. I should like to discuss parallelism and the implications of parallelism, both in the programming and modeling of these complex processes. By parallelism I mean the doing of things simultaneously, rather than in series. The programming effort must be apportioned to teams of people who can work reasonably independently on subsections of the total program. And the model may have to reflect a multiplicity of external demands inherent in the process. For example, a military command system typically has a number of recognizably different needs, any one of which may request service at some time.

In addition, there may be parallelism in the structure of the computer. I think we all remember the cartoonist's picture (some cartoonists still use it) which shows a large room-size cabinet with lights and dials and switches. That is a computing machine to the cartoonist; but no major computing system today is anything like this monolithic image. Today's computer system may have twenty to forty separate boxes, each one of modest size. The boxes are of various kinds and are mysteriously interconnected. Within such a computing system there is considerable specialization of function.

The simple-minded, traditional picture of the monolithic machine is about sixteen years old. The picture includes a processing unit with a large repertoire of operations which does all kinds of arithmetic and logic; a memory unit which stores data, intermediate results, and instructions, all in the same form; and finally, some rather vague and unimportant set of input-output devices. The picture is hopelessly inadequate as a description of any computing system today, yet it dominates current programming and operating approaches. If you observe almost any computing system in operation, you find that, of the many boxes, relatively few are in operation at any particular time. You also find that portions of the system work very hard and very fast when they are working, but they do not work a high enough percentage of the time. To use the engineers' description, their duty cycle is very low.

In principle, the time sharing of equipment by diverse tasks, coupled with the specialization of processing elements in parallel, could permit a far more efficient utilization of the equipment than is currently obtainable. And here the analogy of a job shop is not a bad one. A job shop has at any given time a large number of different tasks to do, generally by means of a mix of machines, some of which are duplicated many times over. The amount and type of machinery are chosen to balance with expected work loads. Time sharing of the machines permits a reasonable match and produces reasonable duty cycles on the most expensive equipment.

I do not think that it is stretching the analogy too far to say that modern computing equipment is already like a job shop and could be much more like one if we had an effective way of utilizing parallelism. The parallelism is of two kinds: One is in work load, and the other is in elements. I hope to sketch for you an approach that depends on two conceptions for dealing with these requirements of parallelism: conceptions of a programming process and of an operation process. First, I want a method for the logical description of problem requirements which is free, at least above a certain minimal level, from the kind of overspecification of sequence constraints that characterizes present programming. Second, I want a processor which will make dynamic assignments of subtasks to the various processing units, as they become available, in accordance with logical specifications and priority requirements. Now I assert that there are tools currently available for this approach. I have no hesitation in saying that the approach is inevitable and in its broad outlines will be just about like what I am going to describe.*

In this paper I outline the elements of computer programs and processors which would allow program execution to be free from arbitrary sequencing constraints unrelated to underlying logical requirements. An approach of this nature would permit flexible operation of complex data-processing systems that exhibit parallelism in structure and are capable, in principle, of dealing with task assignments in parallel.

The Problem

The brief modern history of computing technology has been characterized by a series of mismatches: first, between various portions of the computer anatomy, and second, between the computer hardware and programming and operating technology. The earliest electronic computer consisted of a relatively rapid arithmetic and control unit, with memory of limited capacity, and with minimal input and output facilities connecting directly to the arithmetic registers of the machine. This early computer literally operated one step at a time on programs laboriously written one step at a time, usually in machine language

* This first portion of Professor Brown's presentation is based on an extemporaneous introduction to his prepared paper. The prepared paper now follows.

and without programming aids of even the most elementary kind. Storage limitations as well as input-output limitations made programming aids unthinkable.

In a period of approximately fifteen years, high-speed memories have grown relatively large, auxiliary memory devices of enormous capacity have been added, and luxurious input-output and peripheral equipment of great versatility has been developed, with the result that under many circumstances the typical large system may be limited now by its arithmetic unit. (Of course, it is still possible to exhibit applications in which the limitation rests in the input-output equipment.) Accompanying the hardware development, an impressive array of programming aids has been adopted (often reluctantly). These aids range from the mnemonic use of alphabetic characters to represent instruction codes, to the symbolic designation of memory cells to permit automatic assignment of actual memory addresses by an assembly program, to the most elaborate compilers and source languages. Automatic operator systems with sophisticated loading, debugging, and monitoring facilities also have been developed.

Despite these achievements, it is fair to say that computer programming still shows more than vestigial traces of its ancestry. This is particularly evident in the requirement for sequencing decisions which is imposed upon the programmer. Almost every problem of any magnitude has subsections whose actual order of execution is immaterial logically; but existing practice demands that the programmer arbitrarily make sequencing decisions. The final program, whatever the source language, has these arbitrary sequencing decisions congealed and, indeed, thoroughly concealed in it.

If we look to the near future, machine systems will bear little resemblance to their ancestors of a few years ago. Communication links will connect portions of systems at great distances from one another, there will be multiple remote interrogation stations, and the diversity of memory and auxiliary equipment will increase. Arrangements of arithmetic, control, and logical processing devices of either general or special nature may become highly complex. It is not appropriate to view such arrangements as single machines, surrounded vaguely by input-output equipment. Most actual operations with large systems involve the input-output equipment deeply in the operations themselves. The logical structure of these systems no longer is adequately represented by the older image of a one-step-at-a-time machine, and programs conceived for such machines make it impossible to get efficient equipment utilization. This fact is testified to by the operation of many large computing systems. Often only a few of the magnetic tape units are in operation at any one time, and there are frequent intervals when the arithmetic unit idly waits for tapes to rewind or for some other operation to take place. In an absolute sense, it does not appear that anything like reasonable efficiency is attained. The more complex the system, the more striking is the phenomenon.

There is little doubt that full realization of the inherent power of complex systems is seriously impeded by difficulties associated with the prevailing programming philosophies. Given a complex program, whether prepared by a single individual or by a group effort, it is effectively impossible to predict with any reliability the detailed course of the program, the times and durations of activity of the various units in the system, or the pattern of storage requirements as a function of time. Indeed these factors may depend critically on the input data. As a result, compiling a complex program in advance as a large, fixed unit removes flexibility and introduces inefficiencies in operation over and above those attributable to mismatch between the problem requirements and the machine configuration. Operating on two or more different programs in parallel might reduce the over-all mismatch between tasks and facilities, but it is difficult to see how to proceed in this direction beyond elementary buffering of inputs and outputs as long as any one of the rigid units of program may make arbitrary demands on any portion of the machine at almost any time.

This difficulty is related to the problem of translating programs prepared for one machine into programs for a different machine. A program written in machine language may fabricate instructions during execution. If an attempt is made to translate the program in advance, the fabricated instructions, absent from the original program, will not be translated. As a result, translation often is accomplished by "simulator" programs that translate in dynamic fashion one instruction at a time as the program unfolds. This interpretive approach is usually extremely slow, and is unsatisfactory as a general solution to the problem. Here again the fundamental obstacle is the fact that programs are in general unpredictable before execution.

The problem is one of attaining more efficient utilization of machine elements, either by time sharing or by specializing processing elements in parallel. Nekora[1] distinguishes between multiprogramming, "the execution of several programs by transferring control among them," and multiprocessing, "the simultaneous sharing of memory by different processors." Both are needed and generate, from the point of view of this paper, identical requirements for effective operation. In a discussion of multiprogramming, Ryle[2] formulates ten design requirements, of which the last is that "the job of the programmer must not be made more complex or difficult." In the light of our earlier discussion, we cannot disagree with this requirement, as long as it is not interpreted to mean that the system must not interfere with the programmer's sacred right to call upon any part of the machine configuration at any time and without notice. At least one attempt at multiprogramming has adopted such an interpretation, with the consequence that the effort has reduced to an attempt to schedule time sharing in advance on the basis of programmer estimates of running time. On the face of it, such an approach does not offer much. The dependence upon estimates violates Ryle's requirement, and there is not even any assurance that these estimates will be realistic.

A Proposed Approach

A solution to multiprogramming and multiprocessing may be found in a further separation between the functions of programmer and operating system. This could be accomplished by reducing the substantial amount of logical overspecification currently forced upon, and indulged in by, the programmer. By withholding the superfluous sequencing controls imposed in present programs, which are not necessary to the logic of the task, sufficient flexibility will be made available to an operating program so that time sharing can be scheduled dynamically as tasks proceed, using very simple rules of assignment.

Duly noting (and discounting) the usual screams of anguish from programmers, it should be recognized that what the programmer is asked to relinquish is not the right to program an operation but rather the unrestrained right to specify implicitly exactly when it will be executed. The programmer will be required not to do more work but to do less; he will be asked to confine himself to the problem of defining unambiguously what he wants to occur, and to give up at least some of the problem of determining in advance when it will occur; he will be asked to furnish certain structural information that is available to him during the analysis of his problem rather than to conceal it within his program. Programmers, conditioned perhaps by the programming needs of the early years (hence the screams), exhibit a compulsion to overspecify and to overcontrol. Compulsive overspecification of sequence controls must be given up, and the machine must be made to perform the logically trivial bookkeeping and assignment tasks.

The approach suggested has a number of by-products of considerable importance. Allowing the programmer to stay closer to his problem and allowing him to delegate the unessential decisions to the machine will simplify his job and reduce the frequency of logical errors. The programs submitted by programmers will be in a more appropriate form for coordinating group effort on complex problems; modification by sections will be easier; the number of recompilations caused by program alteration will be reduced; and programs will be less dependent upon exact machine configurations. There might also be a considerable reduction in the amount of reprogramming necessitated by the substitution of one machine for another.

Two Levels of Logic

The approach advanced here presupposes two levels of logic in the finished program. Program sections of the lower level are designated *atomic processes*. They may be specified in any programming language which the system is equipped for, subject to the limitation that the absolute locations of input, output, and program (at execution time) must be either at the disposal of, or known to, the executive program. In order to make the necessary assignments, the executive program must have available to it information on the types of units and storage required by every atomic process. While no real restriction is thus imposed or intended, it is clear that atomic processes must be specialized enough to allow the executive program some flexibility, yet general enough to deserve the effort of the executive program. Unnecessary absolute assignments clearly ought to be avoided in the specification of the atomic processes. Atomic processes may reside in the system library or may be written ad hoc by the programmers.

The upper level of logic consists of statements of a particular language used to define processes. Whereas the atomic processes may be essentially anything, and hence their language must be machine-dependent, the language of process definition might reasonably be standard for all digital computing equipment. The logic of the upper level simply specifies the structure of a program, ultimately in terms of atomic processes. One requirement imposed on the language of the upper level is that the effective logical result of any statement, as far as the programmer is concerned, be independent of its serial position with respect to other statements. Relative positions may or may not affect the priorities of execution, depending on the system design and the scheduling requirements imposed.

Tasks are described in terms of suitable process and input definitions. The executive program examines these definitions to specify *atomic tasks* (by specifying the inputs for the corresponding atomic processes) and to assign atomic tasks to units.

258

Completion of an atomic task causes further task definition by the executive program. Tasks may be added or canceled at any time.

The system proposed does not distinguish between tasks of different origin; it therefore identifies the problem of parallel jobs as equivalent to the problem of providing for the efficient execution of a single job. The executive program is essentially an interpreter of the upper-level language that assigns tasks specified in the lower-level languages. Thus, if one views the atomic processes as having been compiled previously, the executive program is an interpretive routine that assigns subroutines dynamically. It contains assignment tables and other bookkeeping devices of the type normally present in compilers. The interpretive character at the upper level makes possible the monitoring functions described and provides the efficiency desired. It seems reasonable to expect that the simplest of queuing rules, coupled with the abilities to determine when a unit is available and when a task may be assignable, will give relatively good performance. To estimate performance gains under a range of conditions, McKenney[3] simulated a system of the sort described.

The Upper-Level Language

Turning to the upper-level language, it may be observed that algebraic languages, such as FORTRAN or ALGOL, permit the construction of certain expressions without necessarily implying the whole computational sequence. Thus an algebraic statement of the form $z = a(b + c)$, where a, b, and c are themselves composite expressions, carries no logical implication about the sequence in which a, b, and c are to be calculated. Whatever the sequence, z may be computed after the factors a and $b + c$ are made available. Even though the statement allows certain options, the compiler will normally specify a particular sequence that then will be fixed. If this were the only obstacle to the use of such languages, it could be removed by proper separation of the functions of the compiler and of the executive program.

259

Unfortunately, the existing statement languages require complete specification of statement sequence, so that statements are assumed to be executed in turn. Programmers make nontrivial use of this property, as in the process of using a storage cell both for a completed result and for temporary storage during a calculation, simply by using the same symbol in different parts of the program. Constructions such as $n = n + 1$, for example, must be properly placed within a program. The logical specification is therefore not invariant under permutation of statements. Analysis of such programs to determine which positions are movable or not is difficult to contemplate. Apparently what is required is a statement language exhibiting functional dependencies, with sequence constraints determined implicitly by the dependencies and with the statement sequence excluded from any role in specifying the logical relations. Statement sequence, however, might play a proper role in assigning priorities for execution.

An adaptation of McCarthy's[4] formalism for defining functions recursively fulfills our requirements for the upper-level language. We share McCarthy's belief that this formalism has advantages as a programming language. To adapt his approach to the recursive definition of symbolic expressions, atomic processes must be treated as an unlimited set of primitives in terms of which all processes to be executed are defined. In what follows, conventional functional notation will be used to denote processes relating output to input. The functions represented need not be single-valued.

Following McCarthy, we use conditional expressions of the form

$$(p_1 \rightarrow e_1, \cdots, p_n \rightarrow e_n)$$

where the p's are propositional expressions and the e's are expressions of any kind. We examine the p's from left to right and set the expression equal to the e corresponding to the first p encountered with truth value T, provided no undefined p is encountered earlier. The conditional expression is undefined if no such p is found, or if the e that is designated is undefined.

Taking a Square Root

Consider McCarthy's example of the Newtonian algorithm for obtaining an approximate square root of a number a, given initial approximation x, and error limit e:

$$\text{sqrt } (a, x, e) = (|x^2 - a| < e \rightarrow x, T \rightarrow \text{sqrt } (a, \tfrac{1}{2}(x + \tfrac{a}{x}), e))$$

T stands for the truth value T and serves, in the conditional expression, to provide an alternative if the predicate $|x^2 - a| < e$ is not true. This usage corresponds to the "If . . . else . . ." of ALGOL. Actually, the expression might as well be abbreviated by dropping "$T \rightarrow$." We might now write this as

$$\text{sqrt } (a, x, e) = (P(x, a, e) \rightarrow x, \text{sqrt } (a, f(x, a), e))$$

where P stands for an atomic process such that $P(x, a, e) = T$ when $|x^2 - a| < e$, and f stands for an atomic process such that $f(x, a) = \tfrac{1}{2}(x + \tfrac{a}{x})$. Note that it is assumed that the executive program knows how to identify x, a, and e for the execution of P and f, and knows how to get at the truth value of $P(x, a, e)$.

Suppose now that a task is assigned in terms of the process sqrt and the input data elements corresponding to a, x, and e; denote the task by sqrt (A, X, E), distinguishing the indicated data elements from the bound variables appearing in the process description. The first atomic task assigned then would be $P(X, A, E)$. Without logical error the executive program could also assign $f(X, A)$ at the same time, which corresponds to looking ahead and possibly computing something that may not ultimately be required. We shall assume, however, that the executive program does not normally proceed beyond the first undefined antecedent in a conditional expression. With such a rule no unnecessary processing will be performed. Options may be permitted the executive program in such instances; also there exist alternate process descriptions that get around the rule if desired.

If $P(X, A, E)$ has truth value F, the executive program now replaces the task sqrt (A, X, E) by the alternate process sqrt $(a, f(x, a), e)$ applied to (A, X, E), that is, by the task sqrt $(A, f(X, A), E)$. Following this the task $P(f(X, A), A, E)$ will be assigned. The next atomic task to be assigned is $f(X, A)$, followed by $P(X', A, E)$, where X' is the output of $f(X, A)$. It is seen, therefore, that the executive program modifies the assigned tasks according to the execution of assigned atomic tasks, while retaining access to the original process definition for sqrt, which enters again and again. The rule suggested in the previous paragraph is simply that expressions of the form $(p \rightarrow e_1, e_2)$ will cause no assignments beyond the arrow as long as p is undefined. The truth value T will cause assignment of the task corresponding to e_1, while F will cause assignment of the task corresponding to e_2. The initial sequence of assignment is $(p \rightarrow e_1, e_2)$, from which the assignment of p is derived, thence, as described.

This informal description of the executive process may also indicate how the executive program can tell when storage space may be released for items no longer required. For this purpose we require a look beyond the conditional arrows, even though assignments are not yet made there. Abbreviating sqrt by $(p \rightarrow e_1, e_2)$, we see that X is required for p, e_1, or e_2; A is required for p or e_2; and E is required for p or e_2. Evaluation of p as T eliminates e_2 from further consideration, with the result that A and E can be released. Evaluation of p as F causes assignment of e_2 and elimination of e_1 as a candidate, with the result that X, A, E are now required only for e_2. Assignment of e_2 leads to evaluation of $X' = f(X, A)$, after which X is no longer required and may be dropped by the executive program.

It can now be observed that the executive program processes lists of symbols of data items, expands and contracts these lists, notes which items are defined, proceeds in one direction to find tasks defining the undefined items, and proceeds in the other direction to determine where an item to be defined is or may be required. The executive program should also be able to interpret the propositional connectives $\wedge$ ("and"), $\vee$ ("or"), and $\sim$ ("not"). We suggest that the definitions given by Mc-Carthy, which are noncommutative under certain conditions, should not be used here. To be consistent with the philosophy of this paper, we should expect $p \wedge q$ to be false if either is false and $p \vee q$ to be true if either is true, even when the other constituent expression is undefined. The executive program may assign p and q simultaneously, or may defer assignment of one pending determination of the other. If it is desired to impose a particular sequence of evaluation, this may be achieved by use of the conditional expressions proposed by McCarthy as definitions. It would seem appropriate to leave the flexibility of assignment to the executive program through use of the connectives.

A Second Example

The next example will illustrate the manner in which the executive routine might make use of the latitude inherent in the problem structure. Suppose the transformation F operates on the pair (x, y) to produce $(ax - by, bx + ay)$, with parameters a, b. Suppose that the result of applying F twice in succession is required, using the same parameters each time, with $x = X$, $y = Y$, and $(a, b) = (\sin C, \cos C)$; X, Y, and C being given. Taking as atomic processes $g(x, y) = xy$, $f_1(x, y) = x - y$, $f_2(x, y) = x + y$, and $h(\theta) = (\sin \theta, \cos \theta)$, we might describe this task as follows:

$$\left\{ \begin{array}{l} Z = F(F(X, Y, h(C)), h(C)) \\ \quad F(x, y, a, b) = (f_1(g(a, x), g(b, y)), f_2(g(b, x), g(a, y))) \end{array} \right.$$

In list form the top line may be written

$$Z = F(A, L, M)$$
$$A = F(B, L, M)$$
$$(L, M) = h(C)$$
$$B = (X, Y)$$

and the bottom line may be written

$$F(x, y, a, b) = (s, t)$$
$$s = f_1(u_1, v_1)$$
$$t = f_2(u_2, v_2)$$
$$u_1 = g(a, x)$$
$$v_1 = g(b, y)$$
$$u_2 = g(b, x)$$
$$v_2 = g(a, y)$$

Clearly execution of both $F(B, L, M)$ and $F(A, L, M)$ will require interpretation according to the second list in order to assign atomic tasks whenever possible. Assuming only that this interpretation takes place fast enough to keep up with the execution of atomic tasks, in whatever sequence they may be completed, we can observe that at the outset only the atomic task $h(C)$ is assignable, yielding L and M. After completion of $h(C)$ the four atomic tasks $g(L, X)$, $g(M, Y)$, $g(M, X)$, and $g(L, Y)$ become assignable, coming from the task $F(B, L, M)$.

We may now observe that $A_1 = f_1(g(L, X), g(M, Y))$ will be assignable as soon as both $g(L, X)$ and $g(M, Y)$ are completed, and that $A_2 = f_2(g(M, X), g(L, Y))$ will be assignable as soon as both $g(M, X)$ and $g(L, Y)$ are completed. In turn, completion of A_1 makes $g(L, A_1)$ and $g(M, A_1)$ assignable, and completion of A_2 makes $g(L, A_2)$ and $g(M, A_2)$ assignable, as part of the calculation of $F(A, L, M)$. Note therefore that it is possible for the calculation to proceed as far as $g(L, A_1)$ and $g(M, A_1)$ before completion of $g(M, X)$ or $g(L, Y)$.

The flow diagram of Figure 1 displays the logical structure. It is clear that considerable freedom exists to make assignments consistent with this logical structure, in contrast to the customary restriction to a single arbitrary sequence specified by the programmer. It is important also to observe that the process of problem specification is simplified by expressing the logical structure directly in terms of the relationships involved, without need to expand the structure to its form during calculation. It may further be observed that the executive program will take

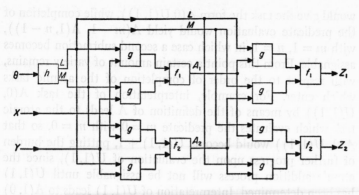

Figure 1   Flow Diagram of Logical Structure

care of the red tape usually associated with initializing the various subroutines at the appropriate times, thus eliminating a common source of programming error. The system proposed therefore provides most of the advantages associated with common algebraic programming languages, without suffering from the customary limitations and restrictions.

Ackerman's Function

An interesting example is given by the following recursive definition of Ackerman's function, $A(m, n)$:

$$A(m, n) = (m = 0 \rightarrow n + 1, A(m - 1, U(m, n)))$$
$$U(m, n) = (n = 0 \rightarrow 1, A(m, n - 1))$$

Here A is defined (for nonnegative integers) in terms of itself and of U, whereas U is defined in terms of A. We shall analyze the task $A(1, 1)$ from the point of view of an executive program, taking as atomic processes the evaluation of the predicate $m = 0$, the addition of 1, or the subtraction of 1.

At the outset the task $A(1, 1)$ causes assignment of the predicate $m = 0$ with $m = 1$. Since the result is F, the task $A(1, 1)$ now becomes the task $A(m - 1, U(m, n))$ with $m = 1$, $n = 1$. The atomic subtraction task is now assigned, together with the task $U(1, 1)$, which causes assignment (again) of the predicate $m = 0$ and $m = 1$. Completion of the subtraction

265

would give the task the form $A(0\ U(1, 1))$, while completion of the predicate evaluation would yield $A(m - 1, A(1, n - 1))$, with $m = 1$, $n = 1$, in which case a second subtraction becomes assignable. From this point a certain amount of variety remains, with respect to the order of completion of the atomic tasks which enter. For example, interpretation of the task $A(0, U(1, 1))$ by means of the definition of A leads to the atomic task which evaluates the predicate $m = 0$ with $m = 0$, so that $A(0, U(1, 1))$ would become $U(1, 1) + 1$, putting the burden of further progress upon the evaluation of $U(1, 1)$, since the atomic addition process will not be assignable until $U(1, 1)$ has been determined. Interpretation of $U(1, 1)$ leads to $A(1, 0)$ where again the leading predicate may or may not be evaluated before completion of the subtraction. $A(1, 0)$ becomes $A(0, U(1, 0))$, so that finally the computation $(1 + 1) + 1$ will have to be performed, causing two consecutive assignments of the atomic task that adds 1.

A Complication

A very simple example will illustrate a possible practical complication in the operation of the executive routine. While the complication in question may be handled in a number of ways, further study is required before the problem can be disposed of completely. Suppose the function $F(x, n)$ is to be defined as the nth iterate of the function $f(x)$, perhaps by the definition $F(x, n) = (n = 0 \rightarrow x, F(f(x), n - 1))$. Application of the definition must lead ultimately to execution of $f(x)$, followed by execution of f upon the result, and so on, until f has been executed n times. Viewing the process of subtraction of 1 as atomic, along with whatever atomic processes are required in the definition of $f(x)$, we note that the sequence of completions of atomic tasks, if permitted, might allow the counting process to go far ahead of the steps that evaluate f. Thus we might get the task represented as $F(\underbrace{f \cdots f(x)}_{j\text{-times}}, n - j)$ without having evaluated f even once. While no logical error is thereby committed, the effect is rather useless and may fill up memory.

The executive routine is simply laying tracks ahead of the actual requirement. If we consider the counting operation as being composed of atomic tasks, however, the executive routine is achieving useful results.

Before commenting further on the point just raised, consider the possible alternative definition

$$F(x, n) = (n = 0 \rightarrow x, f(F(x, n - 1)))$$

Application of this equally valid definition would start laying down f's from back to front, while counting down from n; given a simple-minded executive routine, it would lay down all n of them before the first execution of f could take place. In this case, if n is very large, there might be inadequate storage to represent all n iterations, hence the task might fail to be executed. Before adopting a possible solution to the problem raised by the first definition, one must decide whether the solution should also cover the second. Ideally both definitions should lead to the same result, and indeed they would, given unlimited storage for use of the executive routine.

Some Observations

In the case of the first definition the difficulty may be overcome by protection against overrunning the allotted storage, in which case executions of f will always rescue the situation and permit the process to continue. In the case of both definitions the difficulty may be resolved by equipping the executive routine with its own counting process and with a compact representation for iterated processes corresponding to the familiar "do" statements. While it is reasonable to imagine the executive routine so endowed, this may not prevent the programmer from defining processes containing similar elements that need not be recognized as such by the executive routine. In this case, however, the problem is the same as that of representing, in finite space, a program which requires a larger space before any atomic task can be isolated. Universal solution of this problem would be miraculous.

We turn now to the matter of queuing disciplines, both with

267

respect to tasks assignable to appropriate processing units and with respect to unraveling of definitions by the executive routine. It would be reasonable to expect that a sensible executive routine, which operates rapidly compared with the execution of atomic tasks, would refrain from forming unnecessarily long queues for processing units. Given this property, the adoption of a "first-come, first-served" discipline for queues associated with like processing units would solve the particular difficulty raised by the first definition. The executive routine would assign atomic tasks belonging to the execution of f and continue unraveling task definitions only as long as processing units were available. The laying down of f's would proceed unnecessarily far only if the execution of f required different kinds of processing units from those required by the counting process, and then only if the counting process were rapid in comparison with the execution of f. A "first-come, first-served" discipline seems adequate because the major gain in efficiency very probably stems from the ability to determine dynamically the availability of processing units and the tasks assignable to available units. Intentional violations of this discipline may be used to provide interrupting facilities for the accommodation of "on-line" activities.

Other possible solutions to the difficulty may result from sequencing conventions adopted by the executive routine. Thus one might demand that task definitions be applied, whenever possible, by going inward with respect to parentheses. Such a rule leads to an attempt to evaluate all arguments of a task before expanding the task definition further. Returning to the discussion of Ackerman's function, just after the first application of A, we have the task $A(m - 1, U(m, n))$, with $m = 1, n = 1$. The above rule requires that $m - 1$ be executed, and then that $U(1, 1)$ be expanded as far as possible before $A(0, U(1, 1))$ is interpreted according to the definition of A. The sequence is $A(0, A(1, 0)), A(0, A(0, U(1, 0))), A(0, A(0, 1)), A(0, 2)$, and finally the result 3. The rule seems unnecessarily restrictive as a universal constraint. It corresponds, of course, to a weakened extension of the rule that atomic tasks shall not be assigned until all arguments are defined. Since many nonatomic tasks have the property that considerable work may be accomplished on them before all arguments are specified, this rule probably should be avoided.

An alternative convention may be made to depend on clues furnished by the programmer. We can view the assignment of a task to the executive routine as the beginning of a process in which the executive routine assigns derived subtasks to itself until atomic task assignments can be made. The process description then merely furnishes a list from which subtasks are assigned as they become appropriate. Assume that provision is made to mark particular subprocesses of a process so that the corresponding subtasks are automatically assigned to the executive routine at the same time the parent task is assigned. This would provide a partial control over the sequencing of the executive operations. In the case of the first definition of the iterative process, the subtask f could be so marked, as could specific subtasks of it. The effect would be to enforce early assignment of certain derived subtasks, thus imposing a preference pattern.

Other refinements of the executive procedure may be made to economize on storage requirements or to obtain improved efficiency in the absence of balanced over-all loads. As an example, it is not inconceivable that the executive routine might score assignments in terms of the unblocking they generate and choose first those assignments which enable the greatest number of derived assignments. Such a device is reminiscent of other scheduling problems, particularly the job shop problem. Indeed our problem is more than superficially related to other problems that require the description and scheduling of complex processes; we should expect the methods suggested here to have fairly general application.

Conclusions

In closing, it is appropriate to comment briefly on the probable methods of implementing a system of the type proposed and to point out some relationships between this approach and other recent developments. The presentation here has been informal; its formalization rests upon McCarthy's structure for representing functions of symbolic expressions as symbolic expressions. The fundamental operations defined by McCarthy are represented by corresponding operations of our executive routine. It is clear that an executive routine of the type suggested here will be primarily a list processor. Presumably arguments of processes and their outputs will be represented by symbols that are keys to lists and list structures; processes will be list structures and so will the derived dynamic task definitions. In view of the fact that list processing was devised to provide a powerful tool for symbol manipulation, it should not be surprising that it may provide the basis for implementing a system of the kind proposed.

There are, of course, some differences in points of view. Outright abandonment of sequence definition in program specification appears to be a radical proposal, in spite of my emphatic, continued advocacy. List processing, as programmed in existing systems, insists that sequences be nailed down. See, for example, Newell and Tonge[5] on IPL–V. In treating a problem closely related to ours, Evans, Perlis, and Van Zoeren[6] "thread" the computational sequence through their lists, because "tree" representations do not specify computation sequencing. Our position is that the "tree" representation ought to be substantially all that is required. Another departure is the separation between process lists and dynamically defined task lists. This eliminates the need for separate "push-down" lists and "depth counters"[7] to keep track of where the process is, since the assigned task list effectively acts, itself, as a set of push-down lists to keep track of progress and to update the various stages. "Two-way" links in the process and task lists will permit shuttling up and down in levels and will facilitate determination of when to release data lists. Admitting that somewhere, somehow, some process ultimately establishes sequences is far from admitting that programmers should define the sequences uniquely in advance.

In view of the relatively slow speed of present list-processing methods, the separation into two levels of program description may make the scheme practical. This follows since the processing time of atomic tasks may be reasonably large and the lists handled by the executive routine may be very short compared with complex programs written almost completely in list-processing language. It may be hoped that future hardware developments will facilitate list operations, at least on a scale adequate for operation of the executive routine.

Panel Discussion

HOPPER. When we discuss computer programs, we must realize that they exist at many levels. We must consider not the single instructions of the computer in isolation but how they come together to form a subroutine, how the subroutines come together to form a run, and how the runs come together to form a system. We must recognize that the system may not be operated entirely on the computer, but may include manual operations, punched-card operations, and reporting from various instruments. When we discuss the processes with which we must cope, we note that some processes are independent and can be accomplished at the same time, such as inventory and payroll, diagnostic testing and compiling, or data processing and card-to-tape conversion; some processes are partially dependent, such as payroll and labor distribution or project cost distribution; and some processes are completely dependent, such as sorting and matching, or the processes involved in defense against missiles. Projecting into the future, computing systems also fall into several classes. Some systems are *multiprogrammed,* with a single processor operating upon more than one program and doing its own scheduling; some systems are *multiprocess,* with several processing units sharing storage; and some systems are *multicomputer.*

I always think of the steps of getting a problem onto the computer as starting with a manager who needs intelligence. By intelligence I mean organized information. He goes to an analyst. If the manager is an engineer, he may go to a numerical analyst. If he is a businessman, he goes to a systems analyst. Even in the armed services there are analysts, although I think there they are called strategic planners. The manager says, "I need some information about such and such in order to make a decision. How do you get it for me?" There are two problems at this level. One is that the manager really does not know what he wants. The analyst must draw this out from the manager somehow and then determine how to obtain the necessary source information. The second problem is locating this source information and finding if it can be obtained and recorded. This reminds me of the Navy's attempt to learn why vacuum tubes were failing. The Navy attacked the problem by distributing some little cards to be filled out and returned every time a tube failed. Now the critical time for which this information is most important is during maneuvers, since this resembles wartime most closely. And of course this is the time when everybody marks that one cross which says "dropped it." Thus all tubes fail from being dropped during the critical period. Certainly better definitions and methods for obtaining source data are needed.

After the systems analyst has produced his flow chart, a programmer appears in the scheme of things to make the run charts and write the run specifications. His charts go to a coder who writes machine instructions, and these machine instructions go to the operator who runs the computer. Work in automatic coding has concentrated on getting rid of the coder. We have not yet tackled the job of automatic programming. When we do, we shall be tackling the job that Professor Brown has described. One step further is automatic system design, and this too may be attempted within the next ten years.

The question of parallelism carries certain other considerations with it. At present we write a program, and all too often we do not define the data upon which the program operates. In my mind the major difference between scientific problems and those of business data processing lies in the difference between the respective data. Mathematicians, engineers, statis-

272

ticians, and logicians operate on numerical or logical quantities. Data processing operates on information: anything from a bit to a name and address. The information may be in alphabetic, decimal, binary, or other form. The data description is essential to the program and cannot be omitted. We must include in any language with which we hope to describe complex data-processing situations the capability for describing data. We must also include a mechanism for determining the priorities to be applied to the data. These priorities are not fixed and are indicated in many cases by the data.

Thus we must have a language and a structure that will take care of the data descriptions and priorities, as well as the operations we wish to perform. If we think seriously about these problems, we find that we cannot work with procedures alone, since they are sequential. We need to define the problem instead of the procedures. The Language Structures Group of the CODASYL* Committee has been studying the structure of languages that can be used to describe data-processing problems. The Group started out by trying to design a language for stating procedures, but soon discovered that what was really required was a description of the data and a statement of the relationships between the data sets. The Group has since begun writing an algebra of processes, the background for a theory of data processing.

Clearly, we must break away from the sequential and not limit the computers. We must state definitions and provide for priorities and descriptions of data. We must state relationships, not procedures.

SAYRE. Rather than comment on Dr. Brown's paper, which treats a specific topic in considerable depth, I shall attempt to discuss programming as a whole, especially the forces that seem (to me at least) to be determining its development. During the earliest phase of the history of programming, applications were programmed for a particular machine starting from a very

* CODASYL is an acronym formed from the initial letters of the words that spell out the committee's objective: a common data systems language.

basic logical level, namely, that of the machine instruction. A wholly new program generally was written for each significantly different machine or application. Thus, human intelligence was expended lavishly in order to achieve near-optimal utilization of a given machine for a given application.

This state of affairs, besides being the natural way to begin, was also entirely appropriate so long as human intelligence was available for programming in adequate quantities and so long as machine capabilities were only barely sufficient for the desired applications. But a trend toward the exact opposite situation is now rapidly developing. It is becoming clear that the limiting factor in the growth of the use of machines is beginning to be mankind's ability to instruct machines in complex activities and not the machines' raw information-processing power. Programs are already being produced at the rate of some 300,000,000 words per year. By comparison, the material published for the people of the United States each year in book form is less than ten times that amount.

These circumstances naturally produce an intense pressure to economize on human intelligence in programming by developing machine intelligence as a substitute, so as to trade what is plentiful for what is scarce. In my opinion, the changing structure of computer programs can best be understood in terms of this force. In passing, we may note that similar pressures exist in many areas besides programming — these are what account for the acceptance of computing machines on such a large scale — and that developments there stimulate (and are stimulated by) developments in programming.

Some of the ways of saving programming effort require no comment. One way is simply to spend less effort in working toward optimal utilization of the hardware. This is a very noticeable feature of present-day practical programming. Another class of methods centers on better communication among programmers and the sharing of programs. And now a new and far-reaching method is at hand: It requires the computer manufacturers to make their machines more alike and not to change them, except of course for the purpose of making them faster and cheaper. This is not as easy as it sounds. Machines cannot be made faster and cheaper without introducing new hardware devices and organizations, and without producing different hardware configurations for different needs. More often than not these variations change the whole logic of the machine. Somehow this change in logic must be concealed.

Fortunately, a method for doing this has been found, and certainly its discovery and exploitation are the significant events of this stage in the history of programming. The method is to give to the machines themselves the ability to determine how their own hardware resources should be employed. Then the programmer can ignore this matter, and at the same time, machines which differ in their hardware can be made to look alike. This ability is carried in a large body of programming (automatic coding systems, automatic operating systems, and so forth), supplied by the computer manufacturer with the machine. Already this body of programming sometimes exceeds 100,000 words, particularly if it does a really good job of controlling the machine's hardware. From another point of view, it can be said that the manufacturer is beginning to supply a new kind of machine, composed partly of hardware and partly of *software* (the term that is beginning to be used for the body of programming which we are discussing). Such composite machines are rich enough in the control information they contain to resemble one another closely even though they consist of very different hardware arrangements and even though they cover a wide range of prices and performances. What we have here can be thought of as a clear instance of machine intelligence being substituted for human intelligence in one part of the programming problem.

Actually we software designers do not know at the present time how to cover up all aspects of hardware in this fashion. We can deal with the usual high-speed registers and storage of a machine, with the interrupt system, and with certain aspects of the assignment and overlay of input-output units. But we are still in the course of learning how to deal in a general fashion with auxiliary storage devices (such as tapes and discs) and with multiprocess machines. Dr. Brown's paper is an excellent example of the research that is needed. In the meantime, the composite machines that we know how to make do not yet reach the ideal of looking completely alike.

The development of the composite machine is bringing with it important changes in the computer industry. The user can switch comparatively freely from one composite machine to another, and he can easily get a fairly accurate comparison of their performances. Also, he can in concert with other users participate more effectively in setting specifications for composite machines than he could for purely hardware machines. The computer manufacturer is not at all sure that he likes these facts, but he is learning to live with them, and he knows that any trouble they bring him is more than offset by their stimulus to computing in general.

So much for the present and immediate future. What can we expect to happen next? I should like to approach this question by pointing out that the problem of economizing on the human intelligence which goes into programming is really one of programming the right things in the right order, of attempting at each stage to program what will most simplify what has yet to be done. (This is much like the principle that underlies the formation of any elegant formal theory; postulates and theorems are produced in such an order as to minimize the total argument necessary.) The matter we have just been discussing is a good example of this. Because hardware varies so widely and rapidly, it is desirable to neutralize the variation at a very basic logical level, so that all that lies above need not be constantly rewritten.

In my opinion, the next major phase in the development of programming will be the extension of this principle into the immense domain of applications programming, with the aim of neutralizing, as far as possible, the variations in applications. A continual attempt will be required to perceive and remove what is repeated in the body of applications programming and to reintroduce it into the structure at a lower level in more general form. To a slight degree we do this already: The mathematical subroutine is a good example. Moving downward in this way, we shall form successive levels of programming less and less specialized to individual applications, and more and more general in nature, gradually approaching the quality of basic statements of the laws and facts of our world. But this trend toward generality necessarily supposes the possession of more and more general techniques of reasoning. These techniques include the ability to deal with sentences in suitably rich languages (richer than computers can handle at present), the ability to devise classifications under which information may usefully be filed for later retrieval, and the ability to perform inference of various kinds.

To program these general techniques will require an edifice containing millions and eventually billions of words. The edifice will doubtless need continual improvement as well as occasional tearing down and rebuilding as our understanding of the principles that underlie its construction grows. But because it will be built on composite machines rather than on hardware, it ideally will be immune to changes in hardware. It will be the role of the software designer to keep it so. This edifice, and the intelligent machine activity that it permits, will naturally have costs and inefficiencies of utilization attached. An important aspect of the use of machines in the future, as now, will be to use only as much of what is available as is required by the application at hand. But the edifice will provide a high, broad, versatile foundation of abilities, and each new application will need to be built up only from that point. At present, each application must be built up from the bottom at an expenditure of human intelligence which we cannot afford.

To me programming is more than an important practical art. It is also a gigantic undertaking in the foundations of knowledge, and it is certain to add immensely to our understanding of what we know and how we know it.

BROWN. I should like to make a few closing remarks and perhaps take mild issue with one implication that has been made. I think the lack of predictability that Dr. Hopper mentioned and the difficulty of problem definition that both discussants stressed are adequate reasons for adopting the approach that I presented. I agree completely with the characterization of the problem as being one of dealing with diverse data descriptions. I think that is at the heart of the language problem.

I was interested and somewhat stunned to learn that there are 300,000,000 words of programming being written annually. I think the very existence of a programming bottleneck indicates that we had better not have programmers spending their time making decisions that do not matter for the logic. I should feel differently about it if I thought that all of the programmers' efforts which are supposedly expended on optimal machine performance really give optimal machine performance. Optimal machine performance in the small is very different from optimal machine performance over-all. I should agree that orientation toward machine utilization in the small is the improper place to put stress, but I should argue that in the large there is a great deal to gain. There are many places where we could gain factors of 2 or 3 more. I shall cite again a dissertation by Professor McKenney of the Harvard Business School.[3] This dissertation contains a simulation of an executive program of the type that I have discussed, and indicates that there really are factors of several lying around waiting to be picked up.

While I agree that the programming bottleneck is the thing that is really holding us back and that, in a sense, machines are cheap, they are not cheap for everybody. Every university machine that I have ever seen gets filled up right away. The things that are not getting done are suffering by virtue of the time we are using on the things that are getting done. Furthermore, I think factors of several are not to be sneezed at when major machine systems, in order to meet the requirements of university research, now begin to cost $10 million and more.

I should like to plead that efforts such as that of the CODASYL Committee indeed free themselves of dependence on statement sequence because I think that this is the easy part. I think that the difficult part is in the data description and specification relations. There is nothing to gain by retaining the dependence upon statement sequence which all of the language efforts still seem to have, at least in residual form. But there is a great deal to gain by deliberately abandoning sequential dependence. All I am saying is that a relationship should have the same implication, no matter where it sits in a list. Its implication should not be modified by what sits elsewhere on that list, provided the data descriptions are appropriate for the relationship as it sits.

My final observation is that the approach which I have described also happens to be applicable to the execution of the executive program itself. An analysis of examples has indicated that the executive program has the same kind of possibilities inherent in it that the standard programs have. This is an amusing thing to speculate about.

General Discussion

McKENNEY. I am curious if Dr. Sayre's preoccupation with software is not due in part to his fascination with manipulating machines and seeing how much more he can get out of them. It would seem preferable to study how to organize machines so that it would not be necessary to spend so much time worrying about how to manipulate them. There appears to me to be a tendency among machine manufacturers to see how much better machines can work, rather than how much better they can be organized.

SAYRE. Your statement is a little bit like saying that you are in favor of motherhood. Of course work on rationalizing the structure of machines is important. Nevertheless, I think that performance is the most desired and desirable of all the qualities that a machine can have. In software we have a technique for untying the hands of the hardware designer so that he can get performance without forcing a complicated machine upon the user. Let me give you an example. One way to make machines easy to use is to make all of their storage random access and of the same speed. But this kind of storage is expensive and impractical in comparison with other kinds of storage. The software that I have described can make a machine which is composed of heterogeneous storage look to the user as if it were homogeneous.

GRISOFF. I should like to ask Professor Brown two questions, if I may. First, don't you think that with just about all of today's methods of programming the programmer does not really have to make any extra effort in setting down the arbitrary ordering of his program steps? Yet wouldn't it require considerable additional effort to provide the information necessary to remove the nonessential ordering steps from the program? To my way of thinking this would require a very different way of programming from what we know or are even considering today. Second, you mentioned that it was not worth meshing two programs, or possibly more, without any prediction of their course on the machine. Don't you think in general that two or more programs running concurrently could make use of idle facilities on a queuing basis, with an almost certain saving in time? The worst you could possibly do would be the sum of the sequential running times; but the best you could do might be considerably better.

BROWN. If I may say so, I think that if I have not gotten my point across any better than this to the rest of the audience, I have more or less failed in my presentation. In answer to the first question, I believe that what the programmer does now *is* work, and I believe programmers make mistakes doing things that are of no consequence. I am not suggesting a different way of programming. I would not make programming harder; I would make it easier. It is true, however, that anybody who has learned to program a machine in some highly stylized manner will naturally fight anything that comes along and looks different.

In answer to the second question, queuing will provide tremendous efficiency with the parallel use and time sharing of units, but not for monolithic programs. Let me give you perhaps the classic example of this. The reason you cannot normally translate programs from one machine to another conveniently is the fact that even if you try to translate instruction by instruction you soon discover that there are instructions which the execution manufactures. You cannot translate in advance what you do not know in advance. This is the reason why most translation is done by simulators.

People fought such things as FORTRAN. They claimed that FORTRAN would never produce programs that had any kind of reasonable running time. The fact that FORTRAN compilation is now what takes all the time may only be a criticism of the professionals who wrote the compilers while seeking maximum machine utilization. FORTRAN programs after being compiled "run like the devil." They are faster than most programs that people write in an attempt to avoid using FORTRAN, and all our troubles are in the compilation written by those very professional programmers. If you stand and watch the FORTRAN system compiling (I am sorry to do this to IBM; I could do the same thing to Remington Rand), you see a roomful of equipment sitting idle while one lousy tape rewinds. We could do much better by letting the machines schedule themselves. I submit that we cannot do worse.

GARMAN. Dr. Brown, would you have these programs compiled and assembled every time they were rerun?

BROWN. No, that is not necessary at all. My executive program is an interpreter, operating at a sufficiently high level so that interpretation as a standard mode is fast and not wasteful. You know that if you tried to simulate one machine on another today — generally you simulate a slow machine on a fast machine — you are very lucky if the simulator runs as fast as the slow machine ran in the first place. This is because instruction-by-instruction interpretation is terribly slow. I am not suggesting that atomic processes be at the level of single machine instructions at all. But you do not have to get very far away from that before interpretation is a very efficient way to carry things out. What this means is that you are constantly in what is called a monitor state. This has tremendous advantages for program debugging, for understanding what is going on, and for keeping things rather close to the source language in which you kept track of your problem originally. So, no, I do not see this as a difficulty. I think we have an advantage here.

ABRAHAMS. I should like to bring up the current diversity of languages with which we are faced. It may be a symptom of a problem or it may be actually part of the problem itself. I noticed on the cover of a recent issue of the *Communications of the Association for Computing Machinery* a very nice drawing of a tower, representing the Tower of Babel. Each brick in the tower was a different programming language, and an amazing number of bricks were filled in. I wonder whether the ability to absorb programs written in currently available languages may be a very important feature of new programs, and new programming languages, especially considering the very large investment that we have in fixed programs and the difficulties in transferring them from one language to another and one machine to another.

BROWN. The only thing I shall say is that if we do not do something soon about accepting a reasonably standard image of what gross logic in computers looks like, then this problem will just get worse and worse. We already have seen situations where manufacturers are unable to free themselves of a program structure because of their great investment in programming, and the longer this goes on, the bigger the investment gets. Even if our programs did not have complete translatability at the lowest levels, even if only the major structure had this translatable property, then at least we would only have to worry about the atomic processes and relating them. So we should have that much improvement. As to the further step of ultimate universality of language, I am not an expert on this, but it is perfectly clear that the great impediments to standardization are the externals: the differences in tape structures, printer structures, and even cards. Dr. Hopper probably can say ever so much more than I on this subject.

HOPPER. The sooner we stop describing data on cards or data on tape, and just describe data, the better. Unfortunately we have programmers who like to make data designs, even though it is clear that the computer is more capable of creating good data designs than are programmers. The computer does not mind in the least breaking up a man's name and address to use as stuffing around quantities, a very convenient device which makes for efficient programs. A programmer would not do this because then he could not "look through" the tape and read off the names and addresses.

We should not only take away the programmer's freedom to allocate storage and time, we should also take away his freedom to arrange characters on cards and tapes. The programmer exists in a world of human prejudice. When he looks through a file, he thinks that he must look alphabetically by name and address. It disturbs him greatly to have a name scattered over eight or nine or ten words in various positions. But the fact that he can never read a tape does not seem to upset him. Programmers are a very curious group. They arose very quickly, became a profession very rapidly, and were all too soon infected with a certain amount of resistance to change. The very programmers whom I have heard almost castigate a customer because he would not change his system of doing business are the same people who at times walk into my office and say, "But we have always done it this way." It is for this reason that I now have a counterclockwise clock hanging in my office.

McCARTHY.   I should like to make two comments. The first one concerns the use of devices for eliminating unnecessary specification of sequence in programming. Professor Brown hit the nail on the head there. I devised conditional expressions precisely for this purpose. My motivation was not so much to achieve scheduling efficiency, but was simply that in a mathematical sense it seemed inappropriate to specify more than was necessary. Unfortunately, even with such devices there is still a great deal of unnecessary specification of sequence. For example, commutative operations such as addition and multiplication allow us freedom to choose the order in which the operations are performed. But it is quite difficult to leave this up to the compiler. The freedom can be pushed only so far, and eliminating all unnecessary specification of sequence turns out to be impossible.

My second comment is an expression of accord with the remarks made about the importance of data description. The main gap one finds in examining this Tower of Babel is the relatively few control structures in all these languages. I agree with Professor Brown that a universal control structure is possible, but because no ways of describing new data structures exist as yet (except in rather primitive form in some of the business data-processing languages), the main distinction between the various programming languages is still in the data structures that they allow. Now it seems to me that the tools for describing data structures have been with us all the time. They are the mathematical operations of Cartesian product of sets and union of sets, which are really fairly simple mathematically. It seems to me that with the aid of these tools a universal means of describing data could be created, and we could clear up this jungle of programming languages.

BROWN. I certainly agree that you cannot carry sequence freeness all the way down. This is another reason for organizing programs on two levels. Atomic processes may or may not have some sequence freedoms of their own, but it is the control language which definitely should be free of sequence specification; and it can be.

With respect to the data descriptions, none of the so-called universal languages around has taken the step of adopting a control language like the one I described. I think this is a sad mistake. Indeed this is not the hard part of the problem, and yet it is the part that has been ducked. I see no reason why the macrolevel should have a control language that suffers from the defects of the microlevel. This is the situation today.

HOPPER. I should like to add one thing to that, however. I think it is awfully nice that mathematicians, logicians, engineers, and statisticians have exact languages in which they converse with each other. But one of the difficulties with programmers is that the symbolisms that they have invented leave management and systems analysts ignorant of what is going on.

When it recently became possible to use the English language to write programs, an Air Force colonel was heard to say, "Now we can take back command of the Air Force from those damned programmers."

There is a very great danger here. I think we mathematicians have to use and construct exact languages. However, I must meet a data-processing world that has not been trained in Boolean algebra. If I said to a certain salesman, "But the first thing I have to do is evaluate this truth function," he would probably say, "Well, I sold the darn thing, didn't I?" We must not lose sight of the users, and we must not forget that a part of the reason for these languages has been to re-establish communication between managers, programmers, computers, and all of the surrounding people who until now have been cut off from the mathematicians.

BROWN. I have no objection whatsoever to your writing, "If so and so, then so and so, otherwise, so and so," in the data description. I find this perfectly acceptable and it meets my requirements.

HUGHES. I want to comment on the reference to the English language. My programmers are using an English language compiler to write their programs, but looking over their work I still don't know what they are doing. Because English is cumbersome and highly redundant, they end up with a set of abbreviations which I cannot understand. I have all the disadvantages of the English language (namely, I have to write out long sentences to express short ideas), and I also have the problems of computers. That is, the slightest variation from the prescribed English language form causes the computer indigestion. The redundancy does me no good and actually does me great harm. I think we have to find a language acceptable to the people analyzing business processes which can be translated by the computer into a language that management can understand.

HOPPER. I have to answer that because we ran into it too, particularly the tendency of programmers to abbreviate, misspell, and forget periods at the ends of sentences. The first thing we did was to invent a young lady called a "pseudocoder" and put her in charge of all abbreviations. No one was allowed to use an abbreviation unless it was registered with her. The second thing we did (having discovered that programmers could not write in English after we carefully had made programs so that they could write in English) was to isolate the programmers and have them write English language flow charts and nothing beyond. Then the pseudocoders typed English sentences from the flow charts, always using the same abbreviations in the same program, always putting periods on the ends of sentences, and always putting in all the redundancies necessary to make sense. They know that they are the ones who are really programming the computer.

BRUNOW. Must not the speed, the storage capacity, and the input-output capabilities of the computer undergo a sharp upward change before we can achieve the desirable powers of software spoken of tonight?

SAYRE. In this business of software we are dealing with the fundamental economic question of the relative cost of human intelligence versus machine intelligence. You cannot go very far toward machine intelligence until you have lowered its relative cost below that of human intelligence. At the present time, machine intelligence is still very costly and can be efficiently and economically employed only in the most favorable circumstances. In answer to your question, yes, we have to bring the cost of machine intelligence down. On the other hand, I think it is evident that it is going to come down. I think we shall have a hard time developing methods for realizing machine intelligence as fast as its decreasing cost will warrant.

HOPPER. Up until a year ago software was unrecognized, applications were unrecognized, and programmers were pretty well unrecognized by engineers. When we programmers objected to something, it usually led to our stalking out of the room saying, "O.K., build it anyway you like and we'll program around it." Only within the last few years have programming, software, and applications been given equal status with engineering. I think there is more to come. I think we have only started on this path.

MORSE. George [Brown], do you have any final words?

BROWN. Only the reminiscence that physical scientists once upon a time used to accuse social scientists of the error of thinking that they understood something once they had given it a name. I hope we do not think, because people now have the word "software," that we fully understand the problems and that they are solved. They are not.

REFERENCES

1. Nekora, M. R., "Comment on a Paper on Parallel Processing," *Communications of the Assoc. for Computing Machinery*, Vol. 4, 60 (Feb., 1961).

2. Ryle, B. L., "Multiple Programming Data Processing," *Communications of the Assoc. for Computing Machinery*, Vol. 4, 99–101 (Feb., 1961).

3. McKenney, J. L., *Simultaneous Multi-Programming of Electronic Computers*, Research Report No. 69, Management Sciences Research Project, U.C.L.A., Los Angeles, Calif. (Feb., 1961).

4. McCarthy, J., "Recursive Functions of Symbolic Expressions and Their Computation by Machine, Part I," *Communications of the Assoc. for Computing Machinery*, Vol. 3, 184–195 (Apr., 1960).

5. Newell, A., and Tonge, F. M., "An Introduction to Information Processing Language V," *Communications of the Assoc. for Computing Machinery*, Vol. 3, 205–211 (Apr., 1960).

6. Evans, A., Jr., Perlis, A. J., and Van Zoeren, H., "The Use of Threaded Lists in Constructing a Combined ALGOL and Machine-Like Assembly Processor," *Communications of the Assoc. for Computing Machinery*, Vol. 4, 36–41 (Jan., 1961).

7. Irons, E. T., and Feurzeig, W., "Comments on the Implementation of Recursive Procedures and Blocks in ALGOL 60," *Communications of the Assoc. for Computing Machinery*, 65–69 (Jan., 1961).

8

What
Computers
Should
Be Doing

8

What Computers Should Be Doing

Speaker	JOHN R. PIERCE Executive Director of Research Communications Principles Division Bell Telephone Laboratories, Inc.
Discussants	CLAUDE E. SHANNON Donner Professor of Science Massachusetts Institute of Technology WALTER A. ROSENBLITH Professor of Communications Biophysics Massachusetts Institute of Technology
Moderator	VANNEVAR BUSH Honorary Chairman of the Corporation Massachusetts Institute of Technology

PIERCE.   When I was asked to deliver a lecture in this series, no one expected me to talk about computers. I am not an expert in the field, and I certainly could not hope to present the sort of inside story of computer design, programming, and simulation that the other lecturers have provided.

My lack of familiarity with the details of computers is not going to deter me, however, for I have numerous examples to encourage me. A number of years ago a publisher who knew a great deal less than I do suggested that I write a book about the cybernetic revolution and about machines that outthink man. He outlined, almost chapter by chapter, the fantasy for which I was to supply words and circumstantial detail. When I ventured to say that I did not believe that all of those things were true, the publisher misunderstood me completely and said, "You don't have to be for it, you can be against it."

Since that day various people have written the book the publisher was seeking, and I have gone on to encounter computers at shorter range. A couple of years ago I suddenly found the Bell Laboratories' mathematical research department, together with its IBM 704 computer, in my department. The 704 has now been somewhat painfully exchanged for a 7090. I have observed programmers struggling with problems that came to them from AT&T and Western Electric as well as with research problems, including theorem proving. Somewhat earlier, I had watched acoustic and visual researchers in my department use the computer to simulate the performance of electrical circuits and devices, and to process, analyze, and recognize acoustic and visual data. More recently, as head of the library committee, I have watched librarians' efforts to grapple with the problems of information retrieval.

It has occurred to me that this casual association with computers and my speculations concerning their use may have involved a number of matters important to management and the computer of the future. If I do not understand the computer in fine detail, neither will many of the managers who will make use of the computers of tomorrow. For that matter, I am neither a physiologist nor a card-carrying psychologist. I have more ignorance than knowledge about the functioning of the human beings with whom I associate every day, but somehow I manage to get along with them, by and large.

Managers will have to get along with computers and programmers on these same terms. But, just as some sense of the abilities and fallibilities of human beings is necessary if one is to work with them, so some knowledge of the abilities and fallibilities of computers and programs is necessary if one is to get along with computers. It is obvious that one should not treat men like machines, and I hope that it is equally obvious that one should not treat machines like men.

I think that the first thing one needs concerning computers is some sense of their powers and limitations. The research of today is embodied in the operations of tomorrow, or at least, the successful research of today is. It seems to me that a good way to discuss management and the computer of the future is to discuss research and the computer of today, and I propose to review a few triumphs and flubs of today's computer research.

Mechanical Translation versus Satellite Tracking

I was talking to an Air Force officer recently about the translation of Russian into English. I said that it seemed urgent to teach more people Russian. He said that this takes too long and the Air Force cannot wait. Instead, a large number of projects on machine translation are being supported. With the aid of an excellent book from the National Science Foundation on current Research and Development in Scientific Documentation, I counted up twenty projects on mechanical translation, of which six are supported by the Air Force, four by the National Science Foundation, two by the Army, and one by the Navy.

Machine translation has already taught us a great deal. It has taught us how little we actually know about the mechanics of language and translation and how hard the problem is. It has taught us the fallibility of a few appealing ideas. The study of language and translation with the aid of computers promises to be an active, worthwhile, and fruitful field of research for many years.

Where do we stand as far as actual translation goes? Word-for-word translations, or a little better, have been produced at a number of places. A Special Investigating Committee of the U.S. House of Representatives Committee on Science and Astronautics had an eminent chemist evaluate a translation of a paper in the field of chemistry. The chemist reported that he found the translation intelligible, but that he spent about four times as long in reading it as he would have in reading a version translated into English by an expert human being.

Machine translations are not easily read. Unexpected machine behavior sometimes creates confusing artifacts. It is clear that if *much* Russian is to be read, the reader will save time in the long run by learning Russian. But, if the problem is not that of translating and reading much Russian, why the mass-production implication of the machine? I am afraid that gambling on machine translation rather than teaching Russian can only have the effect of hindering access to Russian sources for an *indefinite*, unforeseeable period. This does not mean that work on machine translation should not be carried out, but such work should not be counted on as providing a solution for a real and pressing problem.

Let us consider another matter. I have been interested in satellite communication for a number of years. I used to hear assertions that the only practical satellites are those that revolve 22,300 miles high above the equator and hang stationary in the sky. The problem of tracking lower-orbiting satellites that rise and set was proposed as very difficult and expensive if not insuperable. I knew that quite large steerable antennas could be purchased for much less than the cost of launching a satellite, and there are lots of fine computers at large, so I was skeptical of this. During the Echo experiment data from the Minitrack network were sent to the Goddard Space Flight Center. There the orbit was computed, and pointing data were computed for the JPL Goldstone antennas and the BTL Holmdel antennas for every 4 seconds of each pass of the satellite. These data were received at Goldstone and Holmdel on teletypewriter tape. A digital-analog converter read the taped data at appropriate times and controlled the servos steering the antennas.

While the system suffered from some errors in data transmission, and occasionally from stale orbital data, its operation left no doubt that satellites can be tracked successfully in this manner. The computations involved in the satellite tracking can be specified explicitly. The auxiliary equipment that is needed can be built using known digital arts.

Without the use of a computer, satellite tracking of the sort I have described would be impossible. Translation is not difficult for a skilled linguist, yet translation of an adequate quality is at present impossible for a computer, and we have no reason to believe that human translation will be substantially replaced by machine translation in the near future.

It is perhaps instructive to compare the problems of satellite tracking and translation a little further. In satellite tracking, the speed of the computer is absolutely essential. Without this speed the refinement of orbital data and the conversion of co-ordinates could not be completed in time. Suppose, however, that a machine translated a large bulk of Russian text instantaneously. Human beings would still have to pore over the translated text in order to make use of it. A reduction of time of translation to zero might not appreciably reduce the time of utilization.

Some may object that the machine itself could carry out certain operations, such as searching for key words or combinations of key words, or indexing, or even abstracting. This is certainly true. The machine can, however, carry out such operations in a foreign language as well as in English. They are essentially information-retrieval, not translation, functions.

Theorem Proving, Game Playing, and Pattern Recognition

We see that computers are not inherently good or bad; they are good for some problems and bad for others. One can go further, and say that whether computers are good or bad, that is, successful or unsuccessful, depends on whether they are used well or poorly.

One of the show problems for electronic computers is the proving of theorems. Several people have made computers prove theorems. Gelernter at IBM has made a computer prove elementary theorems in Euclidean plane geometry. Newell, Shaw, and Simon have made a computer prove simple theorems in mathematical logic. So has Wang. As far as *results* go, Wang's program has clearly done best. It has, in fact, enabled the IBM 704 computer to prove all the (approximately 350) theorems in the first thirteen chapters of *Principia Mathematica*, by Russell and Whitehead, in 8.4 minutes.

Now the method of proof used by Wang differs markedly from those of the others. Wang takes great care to frame his problems in a language suitable for machine use, and he provides a foolproof, mechanical method of finding a proof. Newell, Shaw, and Simon, and Gelernter, on the other hand, try to ape human behavior. Particularly, Newell has observed how mathematically unsophisticated subjects go about proving theorems, and has tried to make the computer do likewise. "Heuristic" devices are sought, which will lead the computer to promising but not infallible courses of action. So far, such heuristic devices have not been shown to be very helpful.

Suppose that you are interested in human behavior and in laying a groundwork for machine behavior that is in some way analogous to human behavior. You will find the work of Gelernter and of Newell, Shaw, and Simon fascinating, while that of Wang may seem simple, elegant, mathematically ingenious, but cold and unappealing. The simulation of human behavior would call for a procedure very different from Wang's. Perhaps, as Minsky suggests, a program to solve real mathematical problems will have to combine with the mathematical sophistication of Wang the heuristic sophistication of Newell, Shaw, and Simon.

But suppose one's objectives are different. Suppose one wants to use computers to do something they can do very much better than human beings can. Wang has shown that computers can outdo human beings at one rather complicated task. Newell, Shaw, and Simon have shown that computers can imitate human behavior imperfectly and with only moderate effectiveness at an equivalent task.

Here we see quite clearly a divergence of views about computers which permeates much work, thought, and writing. The playing of games by machine is a prime example. Computers play ticktacktoe and nim as well as these games can be played, and unerringly. It would be simple to invent games at which a computer would quickly and unerringly beat any human being. One would merely have to make success dependent on complicated calculations, infallible memory, the simultaneous application of many invariable criteria.

Checkers and chess are different. These games were devised with human beings, not computers, in mind. It is a tribute to programming skill that computers have played chess poorly and checkers well, though not as well as a very good checker player.

Samuel's checker-playing program even includes learning by experience. Right now, however, it would be cheaper to hire a checker player or a chess player than to seek equivalent performance from a computer. To make a computer excel a chess champion is a noble intellectual challenge, but it is not a paying proposition. Further, it is not clear that such game playing is the road to progress in the improvement of computers and programs, though of course it may be.

Next to game playing, a favorite pastime of computer experts is character recognition and the recognition of spoken words. No one can argue that computers cannot read words; they read words off punched cards, perforated tape, and magnetic tape every millisecond (or less). Selfridge has even made a computer read hand-sent Morse Code. This is no small feat, for in hand-sent Morse some dots are longer than some dashes.

What computers do not do very well, despite the efforts of Selfridge and others, is to read varieties of type faces in various orientations, or to read handwritten script, or to recognize many words when spoken in a variety of voices. Several reasons for this fallibility are clear. In the case of speech, for instance, computers can find only slowly and fallibly features that are clearly present to the eye in a speech spectrogram. It is difficult to make computers recognize classes of features that the eye or ear picks out unerringly. Beyond this, we obviously make use of context in puzzling out the meaning of script, and our ignorance of the nature of language makes it hard for us to tell a computer how to do this. Let it be said, in addition to this, that there is no guarantee that any amount of research will give us satisfactory recognition equipment in any specified time. Recognition, like translation, is a fruitful field for research rather than a resource to be counted on.

In contrast, my bank's accounting machinery has no trouble with the numbers printed in magnetic ink on my checks, though to me they are strange and obscure. Further, we should contemplate the fact that the overwhelming bulk of the world's records are as yet unrecorded, that most of the world's books are as yet unwritten. I am sure that beyond some point in the

297

future, material to be processed by machine will be set down in machine-readable language, and that this will include almost everything that is set down. Someday, the majority of all recorded material *will* be in machine-readable form. Unhappily, today money will not buy a device for producing a machine-readable record that compares in convenience and speed with a good typewriter. I wish that some of the ingenuity that is spent on recognition would go into producing such a machine, and a cheap one as well.

If a machine is to be forced to read records, and at a rapid rate, the task should be made easy for the machine. The characters should be unambiguous, and the machine should be allowed to run through tape or sort through cards; it should not have to thumb through dog-eared pages. On the other hand, the user is entitled to some consideration. He should find it simple to give orders to a machine, and he should receive information from the machine in an easily intelligible form. Special-purpose computers have been designed with this in mind. The telephone dial does not tax the user's ingenuity severely, and yet it controls what is certainly the most complicated (though not the most versatile) computer system in the world. The reservation machines in airline offices are admirably easy to use.

General-Purpose Computers, Special-Purpose Computers, and Compilers

When we think of computers, however, we usually think of huge general-purpose computers. These are given their orders in a language composed of hundreds of different instructions by a special caste called programmers. Very astute programmers construct special, sophisticated languages to help in programming computers to undertake recondite tasks such as chess playing and theorem proving. Clever programmers have also constructed extremely simple languages by means of which people who know nothing about computers or about programming in general can cause computers to solve certain limited classes of problems. The "program" that the user writes can be as simple as a line-per-block listing of the blocks, parameters, and interconnections of the block diagram of a circuit whose performance is to be simulated.

By means of a compiler, the computer itself translates unambiguous instructions in such a simplified user language into a long, detailed program in its own language. Successful compilers have been made for a large variety of special purposes, ranging from exploratory research to the carrying out of mundane chores such as minimizing the length of connecting wires by locating subassemblies most advantageously on a chassis.

Part of the gain achieved through a compiler is in providing a language that accords with ingrained habits of human thought and speech, including mathematical habits. An essential part of the gain achieved through the use of a compiler is that of using the computer itself to take the step between the setting of a specified task and the writing of a long list of instructions for the carrying out of the necessary steps in the required calculation. In order to gain any advantage, however, it is necessary that the compiler be in some sense specialized. A compiler allows us to reduce the burden of programming a class of problems more restricted than everything, senseless and sensible, that the computer could be made to do. Indeed, compilers most reduce the programming burden when they are designed for a very restricted range of problems; when, in effect, they enable us to use a large general-purpose computer as if it were a highly specialized computer.

Why not use a highly specialized computer instead? A general-purpose computer cannot be as efficient as a special-purpose machine. If many machines are required to do highly similar work continuously in many places for many years, it will probably be advantageous to design a special-purpose computer for the function. Indeed, as the computer art matures, a large variety of computers of various sizes and capabilities have come on the market, and these are certainly not interchangeable. Too, it has sometimes proved extremely time consuming and costly to program general-purpose computers to carry out special functions. The SAGE system provides a notable example of this. The mere fact that a general-purpose computer *can* do anything is no universal advantage.

However, many specialized jobs can best be explored (tried out first) on a general-purpose computer. Many jobs take so little computer time that they do not justify designing a special-purpose computer. Many are not done in enough different places, or over a long enough period. Further, the design and production of a new computer and the distribution and servicing of the new machine are not to be undertaken lightly. New machines have a sad history of fallibility, even those produced by competent manufacturers. The building of special digital equipment of any great complexity is something that appeals to novices but sends shivers down the spines of those who have experienced its tribulations. Debugging a new program is sometimes difficult, but debugging a new machine is far, far worse. A new computer design is justified only if widespread usage and very substantial gains are assured.

Some Assertions

Let me sum up my background summary with a few assertions.

The fact that a general-purpose computer can do almost anything does not mean that computers do all things equally well. Some things they do much better than human beings; some things they do worse. Machines are not people. While it is highly desirable to strengthen their weakness, the greatest immediate gains, and some long-range ones as well, will come from exploiting their strengths.

Partly, the strengths of computers are associated with certain types of problems, problems necessarily involving a great deal of straightforward computing on a great deal of input data, as opposed to game-playing or recognition problems. Partly, however, the strengths may be associated with ingenious preparation of the problem, ingenious methods of solution, and ingenious programming, as in Wang's theorem proving.

This emphasizes the obvious fact that while machines are not men, they are useless without the aid of skilled programmers.

300

A skilled and ingenious programmer can do quickly, accurately, and with a minimum of running time a job that would be done slowly and with much computation, or perhaps not at all, by a less skilled man. Further, a skilled programmer can turn a general-purpose machine into a variety of special-purpose machines for the use of less skilled programmers, or even for the use of men with no programming skill at all. Thus, he can circumvent the the novice's love for special machines.

The Future

With these observations as background, let us ask what sort of things computers are likely to do for management in the future, and how can management go about reaping any benefits there are to be gained.

I think that one thing should not be overlooked. Next to having a good idea oneself, the best thing to do is to copy someone else's new idea — providing that it is a good one. Here we should of course take into account a common sort of guile. The King and the Duke in Huckleberry Finn persuaded the audiences of the Royal Nonesuch to bamboozle their friends into being swindled. Companies afflicted with architectural monstrosities recommend the architect to their rivals, and I suppose that this attitude might extend to the victims of computers as well. Nonetheless, we should try to learn all we can from the *successful* experience of others. It really is the cheapest way.

The use of computers is advancing so rapidly, however, that a certain amount of novelty (yes, let us admit it) of research is a necessary adjunct even to routine operation. Anyone who wants to use computers effectively will have to be willing to try things that are at least a little different from what has been done before. What sort of things, and what sort of new things, should management turn to the computer for? One obvious area is that of information handling, analysis, and retrieval.

In the simplest case, if information of any sort, whether it be accounting data or the answers to questionnaires, is in machine-readable form, it can in principle be rapidly presented in any form, averaged, correlated, or abstracted for a variety of purposes. The manager can in principle have up-to-the-minute data to base his decisions on. Or, if he does not like the presentation of data, he can have it reworked in another format or summarized in a different way painlessly by the computer.

We must always remember, of course, that the results will be no better than the data. Further, suppose one were inclined to act more promptly on fresh data than on stale data. If the fresh data were in any way misleading, or if the consequences of action were not fully understood, such action could conceivably have violent and useless effects on the operation of an otherwise stable business.

Questionnaires are even more suspect than data. It is much easier to accumulate the answers to questions than it is to interpret the meaning of the answers. To cite an extremely simple instance, a more-contented-than-average attitude toward the management of a particular office may reflect the fact that the office is in a small community rather than any aspect or attitude of management. After drastic simplification of data by a computer, such a fact may become completely hidden.

This all makes it clear that, while computers can be put to good use in information processing, it is easy to put them to bad use. The computer will not assure that its summaries of operating data are trustworthy and useful. Some very smart person must take responsibility for this. Surveys must be devised by competent social scientists and the results combed over by competent statisticians if any useful data are to be extracted from them by means of a computer. A computer cannot turn bad data into good data.

Beyond the processing of information, information retrieval is often proposed as a computer function. The first problem one encounters is that information cannot be handled by a computer unless it is in machine-readable form. If there were any convenient way of putting information into machine-readable form, it might not be too early to start putting reports and even correspondence into such a form on a routine basis. However, we do not have such means. Even when we do have such means, many seemingly niggling little problems of transliteration of foreign letters and mathematical and chemical formulas will have to be worked out.

In the immediate past, information-retrieval systems have foundered because of the cost of putting past records into machine-readable form. This indicates that we should think first of processing moderate amounts of information, and work toward more grandiose plans as we find ways of obtaining more machine-readable material.

Indexing may seem a trivial start, but need not be so. Titles are brief, and it takes no skill to identify them. An up-to-date permutation index can call to one's attention many or most reports or papers bearing on a matter of particular current interest. Beyond the step of indexing, there are many more elaborate proposals for information retrieval. These can be evaluated only through experiments which will determine their usefulness and systems-engineering studies which can estimate their cost.

It is not only through gathering, digesting, and locating information that computers will serve management. One important general area is that of exploring the consequences of proposed actions. In engineering research, simulation is an example of this. The computer can be used to simulate the operation of a new device, perhaps a device to transmit speech with reduced bandwidth, or a device to recognize or to generate speech. Or a computer can simulate the operation of a control system or a switching system. Such research simulation does not solve the problem of building a new device. It answers the question, what sort of results would we obtain if we did build a successful model of the device?

In production, linear programming can go beyond the determination of operating costs for a given distribution of work; it can find, under certain assumptions, an optimum distribution of work. Linear programming can be used as a routine operating tool. As a more strictly management device, however, it can be used to evaluate past assignment procedures.

In the telephone industry, and in some others as well, a change in classes of service and rate structures may open up new business opportunities, but it will certainly cause some present customers to fill present needs under different classes of service at new rates. Even if we assume the simplest sort of fully informed, economically motivated behavior, the consequent changes in service pattern and revenue can be worked out only with the aid of the largest existing computers and the most advanced programming techniques.

Simulation, linear programming, studies of the consequences of changes in rates and classes of services are in principle simple examples of instances in which the computers can help men to explore the consequences of decisions, or even to arrive at better decisions. It is easy to propose to go further than this, and people will no doubt try to. It has been proposed to simulate on computers the behavior of chemical plants that involve chemical processes. If we really understood how a business functioned, we presumably could simulate the business on a computer, or at least one aspect of the business. This indeed is in the spirit of what the military does in its endless war gaming.

Such elaborate simulations must depend on the availability of valid, useful information and on an understanding of business operation which I doubt that we have. Such over-all simulation must evolve gradually through the ideas and experiments of highly competent people who are interested in the operation and problems of businesses.

The Management of Machines

Of course, none of this can be done without machines, and the acquisition and management of machines pose serious problems in themselves. In acquiring and processing data, how much should be done at remote points and how much by a central computer? How is electrical communication to be provided? What will the reliability and cost of various equipment be?

Most industries have business computing machinery for payroll and other accounting purposes. Some data-processing and other studies can be done by this equipment, but some work calls for a large scientific computer. Can time be rented on an outside machine? Especially if outside programming is involved, is this consistent with company privacy? Perhaps the research department has a large computer. If so, can this be used without disrupting research work?

Finally, when a large computer is available, should different locations have their separate computers, or should one central computer serve several locations? Can a remote computer be operated from a distance as flexibly and readily as if it were on the premises? How can one get data for a host of small problems into and out of a fast computer and still carry out large-scale jobs efficiently?

Summing Up

I have said a variety of things about computers and their use which I hope will be rather disturbing to managers. Among them are the following:

In applying computers to management problems, new ground must be broken. This can be done effectively only by very competent men.

Machines are not men. Just because a computer *can* do something a man might do does not mean that it should. Amid a hullabaloo of enthusiastic aspirations and sales talk, management must find out what sorts of things computers *should* do for it.

What computers should do depends not only on the computer and the problem but on the ingenuity of the programmer.

Ingenious programming can make computers useful for *special* purposes to persons with no programming background.

While machines can process data, the results are no better than the data, and information may be lost in the processing.

While machines can process the results of surveys, it takes a good social scientist to plan a survey, and a good statistician to evaluate the results.

An information-retrieval system can succeed only if it is operable and economical. It takes a great deal of expert knowledge to work out and to evaluate even the machine side of such a system.

Further, all sorts of systems considerations arise in connection with any large-scale use of computers, considerations having to do with dispersal as opposed to centralization, with electrical communication, and with enabling the over-all computer installation to cope efficiently with a variety of large and small problems.

Management is management, but machines are not men. Somehow management must learn the management of computers. This may not be easy, especially in large organizations.

Wise use of, and wise decisions about, computers are not to be mastered quickly or easily. They call for brains of the highest order. They call for close and protracted application. There is real doubt whether they can be made by a man harassed with the routine of a large, multilevel organization. They certainly cannot be made by even a bright specialist in management unless that specialist is willing to devote years of hard effort to learning things quite outside of his specialty, things that have to do with machines and systems of machines, with data and information, rather than with organizations of people and with human idiosyncrasies.

How can a man capable of dealing effectively with machines and machine problems be given his proper reward, status, and responsibility in management? How can he and the expert programmers who work for him be kept from fleeing to the large material rewards and the great freedom and personal responsibility of research? How can management find a way to reward success in such a job other than by transferring the man into one of a large number of specialized and more-or-less interchangeable management jobs? How can management resist the temptation to give such a job to a man because he has been highly successful in a number of management jobs which shared a specialized content quite different from that called for in managing machines?

The problems raised are a little like those of properly relating lawyers and doctors to management, but it would be wrong to think that they are identical. And, unless management finds a way to acquire, use, and keep the services of first-rate people who are capable of managing machines, it will not exploit the full potentialities of the computers of the future.

Panel Discussion

BUSH. Dr. Pierce has told us about a race of machines and a race of men. Both races appear to be prospering and proliferating. The only difficulty seems to be that the rapport between them is not all that might be desired. Norbert Wiener mentioned to me the other day that he is now ready to build a machine that would duplicate itself. What Wiener means by duplication and construction and what I mean may be very different things. But it is possible to visualize a machine in the desert, surrounded by its numerous progeny, busily computing all sorts of things to which no one is paying any attention whatever. I think that Dr. Pierce has placed before us a number of interesting problems on this matter of the interconnection between the human mind and the machine. I am going to ask Dr. Shannon to open the discussion. Dr. Shannon is the father of the modern theory of communication, insofar as it has a father. I need take no more of your time introducing a man whose work is known to all of you.

SHANNON. A mathematician friend of mine, Ed Moore, who enjoys classifying people as well as mathematical concepts, once showed me a chart on which he had placed many of the scientists working with computers. The chart formed a kind of spectrum, ordered according to how much one believed computing machines were like the human brain or could be said to perform intelligent thought. On the far right were those who view computers as merely glorified slide rules useful only in carrying out computation, while at the far left were scientists who feel computers are already doing something pretty close to thinking. Moore had placed me, to use a phrase of Roosevelt, "a little left of center." I think Dr. Pierce has taken a very sound position quite close to dead center. Many of the differences between people along this spectrum relate, I think, to a lack of careful distinction between computers as we now have them for working tools, computers as we are experimenting on them with learning and artificial-intelligence programs, and computers as we visualize them in the next or later generations.

One of Dr. Pierce's main points, with which I completely agree, is that there are some jobs for which computers are better and others for which men are better. One should not send a machine to do a man's job, and vice versa. I should like to explore a bit further the differences between computers as we have them today and the human brain. On the one hand, we have the fact that is often pointed out that computing machines can do anything which can be described in detail with a finite set of instructions. A computer is a universal machine in the sense of Turing: It can imitate any other machine. If the human brain is a machine, a computer with access to sufficient memory can, in principle, exactly imitate the human brain. There are, however, two strings on this result. One is that no mention is made of time relations, and, in general, one machine imitating another is greatly slowed up by the mechanics of describing one machine in terms of the second. The second proviso is even more important. One machine can imitate another or carry out a computing operation only if one can describe exactly, and in all detail, the first machine or the desired computing operation. Of course, this we cannot do for the human brain. We do not know the circuitry in detail or even the operation of the individual components.

As a result of these and other considerations, our attempts to simulate thought processes in computers have so far met with but qualified success. As Dr. Pierce has pointed out, there are some things which are easy for computers to do, operations involving long sequential numerical calculations, and others which are unusually difficult and cumbersome. These latter include, in particular, such areas as pattern recognition, judgment, insight, and the like.

As viewed from the outside, as a behaviorist psychologist might, there are other important differences between computers and brains. Machines are "taught" how to do something by giving them complete and detailed instructions with regard to their action in each specific situation. People, on the other hand, are taught most often by example. One gives a child a few examples of an action, and the child automatically generalizes to cover a wide variety of similar situations. Until it is possible to set up our computers so that this form of instruction can be easily done, artificial intelligence will be limited by programming ingenuity. I might mention, however, that various programs have been set up which do, in fact, learn limited types of response by generalization of special cases.

If there are these important differences at the psychological level between computers as we have them today and brains, one may raise the question as to whether this is a reflection of a different internal organization, and if so, what are the chief differences? I believe that, in fact, there is very little similarity between the methods of operation of the computers and the brain. Some of the apparent differences are the following. In the first place, the wiring and circuitry of the computers are extremely precise and methodical. A single incorrect connection will generally cause errors and malfunctioning. The connections in the brain appear, at least locally, to be rather random, and even large numbers of malfunctioning parts do not cause complete breakdown of the system. In the second place, computers work on a generally serial basis, doing one small operation at a time. The nervous system, on the other hand, appears to be more of a parallel-type computer with a large fraction of the neurons active at any given time. In the third place, it may be pointed out that most computers are either digital or analog. The nervous system seems to have a complex mixture of both representations of data.

These and other arguments suggest that efficient machines for such problems as pattern recognition, language translation, and so on, may require a different type of computer than any we have today. It is my feeling that this computer will be so organized that single components do not carry out simple, easily described functions. One cannot say that this transistor is used for this purpose, but rather that this group of components together performs such and such a function. If this is true, the design of such a computer may lead us into something very difficult for humans to invent and something that requires very penetrating insights. Most machines are invented by breaking the over-all problem down into a series of simple and perhaps previously solved problems and combining these to effect the final design. In such designs, particular components have simple functions — a carburetor mixes gasoline and air, a spark plug ignites the mixture. In a machine of the type I am suggesting, it would be impractical to describe the purpose or action of any single component. I know of very few devices in existence which exhibit this property of diffusion of function over many components. One example is certain types of relay switching circuits arrived at by mathematical design procedures in which the mathematical techniques keep our design procedure in order in spite of human limitations.

If this sort of theoretical problem could be solved within the next few years, it appears likely that we shall have the hardware to implement it. There is a great deal of laboratory work in progress in the field of microminiaturization, the use of thin-film memories and the like. We are almost certain to have components within a decade which reduce current transistor circuits in size much as the transistor and ferrite cores reduced the early vacuum-tube computers. Can we design with these a computer whose natural operation is in terms of patterns, concepts, and vague similarities rather than sequential operations on ten-digit numbers? Can our next generation of computer experts give us a real mutation for the next generation of computers?

BUSH. Dr. Shannon has told us a number of things, among them that we are making our machines too obedient, that they follow our instructions too literally, and that perhaps they learn from their experience too little. Of course, the human race itself has gotten into trouble a number of times by being too obedient and too regimented. It also can get into trouble by not

combine the assets which a long evolution has be-
pon man with those which man's inventiveness has
and will bestow upon the computers of tomorrow. I
efore less tempted to stress what computers can do
an men than to envisage the benefits that we might
om an intelligent division of labor between man and
r. Such arrangements are very likely to enhance hu-
acities in just those areas that are crucial to the func-
f a world whose technology is rapidly evolving.

he industrial revolution, which bore the imprint of the
ngine, and the cybernetic revolution of automation,
symbolized by the computer, have given rise to diffi-
These difficulties affect the coupling of man to his
is well as relations between men. Both revolutions have
tically altered man's image of himself.

romise of the cybernetic era resides in the fact that the
hnology may prove capable of providing more than
bstrata for a rational flow of communication and con-
ssages; it is likely that it will furnish some of the needed
r the development of the sciences of man. We may
tain the instrumentalities for the successful manage-
f human wants and institutions, and perhaps even for
management of human behavior.

he now be more specific and turn to some explicit tech-
bints. The first deals with the role that computers play
recognition of patterns. Dr. Pierce has, in my opinion,
lued this role by selecting as his principal examples the
and written word, which demand indeed a great deal of
g of the relevant features of certain patterns by human
Transplant a man into a foreign language environment,
will be quite poor at discriminating and especially at re-
ng linguistic events that are child's play to the natives.
arch in fields of science which lack adequate physical
s or mathematical foundations is often characterized by
perimenter's inability to control his many interacting
es. In such situations, computers, especially when they
used "on-line," often enable the experimenter to detect

being disciplined or regimente
expect carries over to our par
on the problem of the relation
know them and the human b
have two types of machines,
that the brain is probably neitl
teresting machines built by ma
I think that this field is some
lies much of the promise for th
been too closely associated witl
out looking at the intermediate

With respect to the relation:
the functioning of the brain, w
qualified to speak on that subje
known to all of you as one of
biophysics of sensory communio
as deeply as any man living in
cinating problem of the similari
brain and the computer operate
may mislead us, but at the sam
which to start. I take great plea:
fessor Rosenblith.

ROSENBLITH. The following
"discussant," if we accept the ro
who tries to tear the speaker asu
him or not. Instead I shall atte
own limited experience with co
different emphasis, Dr. Pierce's a

The topic for this evening rem
sion that an acquaintance of mir
he designates certain questions
all they ask is, "Who is ahead?"
has reformulated the topic as the
My inclination is to substitute co
competition. The real challenge
novel, more powerful, self-modifi

that wi
stowed
bestowe
am the
better t
derive f
comput
man ca
tioning

Both
steam
which
culties.
devices
also dra

The
new te
mere s
trol me
tools f
thus o
ment
the sel

Let
nical p
in the
underv
spoken
learnin
brains
and he
produ

Res
theori
the e:
variab
can b

312

distinctive features in the patterns of behavior whose significance he is trying to assess. He may often be able to do more: By including himself, his experimental subject, and the computer in a closed loop, he may be able to formulate and discard his hypotheses quickly enough so they can be tested in a multivariate configuration that has remained sensibly the same. Whether one wants to call this pattern recognition is a matter of definition and perhaps even taste, but it is a fact that the combination of man *and* computer is capable of accomplishing things that neither of them can do alone.

Such uses of computers have started to affect profoundly research in certain areas of the life and behavioral sciences. Tomorrow our practices in medicine, human genetics, and education will find themselves modified in turn. The nation's health record system will affect management practices in hospitals, in industrial medicine, in the Veterans Administration, in social service organizations: The effect may perhaps not be as dramatic as Dr. Kemeny's vision of the library system of the year 2000, but something of this kind is likely to occur.

These changes will, of course, not occur overnight or automatically. In many fields in which there is a temptation to apply computers, the established professions are hardly prepared to take advantage of the opportunities. It is just not enough to transfer existing unsatisfactory and outdated practices onto punched cards and trust that programmers will do the rest. A new generation of professionally trained scientists or practitioners presumably will grow up and will know enough about computers to deal with the basic problems of programming, of peripheral equipment, and so forth. They will then be able to judge which aspects of their data are computer-compatible or worth "hardening," to use the phrase in vogue; indeed, they should then be able to decide whether the time-honored questions and practices of their profession are still valid in the context of the new technology.

Whenever computers are under scrutiny, it seems obligatory to compare their performance with that of *the* brain. Most often *the* brain turns out to be the human brain, and at that not just any human brain but one that can prove theorems, do problems in mathematical logic, and preferably play chess. On the other hand, casual observation reveals that evolution has produced an incredible variety of brains: Some are genetically quite rigidly precoded and capable of only a very restricted repertory of behaviors, while others are capable of many learnings, including the manipulation of abstract symbols. We do not know of a universal IQ test that would permit us to rank order the brains of all species along a single continuum. A *fortiori* we cannot expect to make valid over-all comparisons between the two parallel races, one of which is just barely emerging from the ylem or ur-state. Instead we must at present be satisfied with comparing specific performances of a given computer and a given brain, and with increasing our understanding by simulating the performance of the latter with the aid of the former.

We are hopeful that we shall gain added insight into both brains and computers by analyzing their structural principles in relation to their programmability. Some of Claude Shannon's remarks on serial versus parallel operation, on diffused-function operation which hark back to a theme of von Neumann's, make this hope more explicit. Present-day neuroanatomy and neurophysiology do not furnish us with recipes of what mix of hierarchical organization, specificity, randomness, and redundancy will yield a particular performance in the sensory domain, for instance. These sciences are likewise incapable of telling us today how evolution came to make such extended use of analog-to-digital (and vice versa) recoding and interaction schemes. Perhaps those who preside over the evolution of computers will contribute to the study of brain function by developing a series of *calculi of relations* that will in some sense transcend the digital versus analog dichotomy.

From all we know, it seems reasonable to assume that in universities, colleges, and eventually even in high schools the young will learn how to talk and listen to computers, and how to use them in their thinking and planning. Few aspects of life will be able to resist such a massive reconsideration. Computers are likely to affect their environment the way cars did, provided the rapport between human beings and computers will become sufficiently widespread and intimate. Cars have given us a mobility that far exceeds what evolution has provided us with; computers may constitute a comparable evolutionary step with respect to man's intellect.

No technology comes with a built-in guarantee against misuse. Thus life with computers may be better or just different. Norbert Wiener in his book, *The Human Use of Human Beings*, has alerted us to the problem: For what human and humane purposes will we use computers tomorrow?

General Discussion

BUSH. The meeting is now open for general discussion. It is perfectly legal and ethical to ask a question of anyone on this panel as long as you do not ask it of the presiding officer. I was qualified to engage in this type of discussion twenty or thirty years ago.

MCCARTHY. I should like to "discuss" the paper in the etymological sense. I think what Dr. Pierce said concerning present computer applications is true, but I think his general picture of things is almost completely false. His picture is static. It is based on computers as they are today and on practices already obsolete in some cases. I think that the picture of programmers as a highly trained group is misleading. None of us has received any particular training; we simply have had a little practice. I think that the picture of programming languages as designed to make the machine easier for the duffer is out of date. The new programming languages are not particularly easier to learn than machine code. Their purpose is to be more powerful, to permit an idea that can be expressed verbally in five minutes to be programmed in two weeks instead of six months, as is now required using straightforward machine languages.

On the question of information retrieval one would ask, "Why is this difficult?" Dr. Pierce's answer is that it takes time;

it is too expensive to put the data into machine-readable form. The problem unfortunately is not as simple as this. If it costs $200 to type a book onto IBM cards, then for $1,000,000 you can type 5000 books. The trouble is that you will not know what to do with the 5000 books once you have them on IBM cards, because no present computer has the memory capacity to handle such a quantity of data properly.

The distinction that Dr. Pierce made between what is suitable for computers and what is not suitable for computers seems to reduce to, what is simple has already been programmed and what is complicated is taking longer. The reason for my annoyance is a belief that unfamiliarity at the practical level is more of a handicap in the computer field than it is in most others. In most other fields it is possible to take a general view. But since computation is the subject of what intellectual processes are like in detail, it is a subject for which there is almost no theory worthy of the name. Practical experience is really all that we have, and even this is extremely tenuous.

PIERCE. I am not at all converted by what Dr. McCarthy has said. In the first place, as I stated at the outset, I addressed myself primarily to the problems of management. As I mentioned, what management will be doing with the computer tomorrow is what some people in research and development laboratories are doing with the computer today. In the second place, don't let anyone fool you. Although Dr. McCarthy may pick up programming without quite knowing he is doing it, when you bring a person with a Master's degree and lesser talents into the job of writing programs, it is only after some years that he gets really good at it, and the supposition is that he has been learning something during this period. Now, about the programmers as intermediaries; this is indeed bad in the routine use of computers, but the way it is overcome is not by learning programming without trying, nor is it by writing more powerful languages that will enable one to assail problems that no one has approached yet. It is by writing very simple languages which enable the engineer to use the computer to simulate electrical equipment, which enable the equipment builder to determine where the modules should go in the assemblies in order to minimize the length of wire required, and which enable the designer to design logical circuitry without the customary mental pain.

With respect to information retrieval, I did not mean to imply that reducing data to machine-readable form was the only problem. I shall say this, however. If data were reduced to machine-readable form, some very simple things could be done by devices that are not as complicated as full-scale computers; for example, sorting through correspondence for the mention of a particular name. I shall say also that information-retrieval schemes of a very simple-minded sort (one was tried at the patent office) have foundered on this very point of reducing information to machine-readable form.

Concerning the future of computers: The airplane is a very wonderful device even though it does not resemble the pigeon, and the automobile is a very wonderful device despite the fact that it will not clamber around mountains as goats can. In a similar way, the computer is a very wonderful device even though it only does some things that Dr. McCarthy regards as "old hat." I think that there are many possible advances in computers which will come from looking for problems, sometimes very unexpected problems, which are easily accessible to computers and which computers will do very well. One of these advances occurred in engineering research when computers were employed to simulate the operation of circuits. Other examples are the preparation of drawings by computers, the checking of logical design by computers, and the determination of optimum assembly layouts by computers. It seems to me that human beings are very fallible. They do not foresee the future very well. They find the future by doing things. If they do simple things first, they may get to the future faster than if they set themselves very remote goals and then get discouraged.

One of the things that has bothered me is people setting themselves rather artificial goals, such as language translation, which is very remote in a practical sense, or such as a baseball information program, which is just an illustration and not very useful. It seems to me that the sort of goal which will lead to an advance in computer applications is the goal which is accessible in the not too distant future and which will be highly useful once you attain it. I should contrast algebraic manipulation with theorem proving as an illustration. I think that computers within the next few years may very well perform many of the chores of algebraic manipulation which occur in orbital calculations, quantum-mechanical calculations, and electron-beam problems. For instance, in fitting boundary conditions you run headlong into lengthy manipulations that, by hand, you get wrong the first five times. Computers some day may do these manipulations very nicely. They may be doing them right now at M.I.T., but I do not believe that this has reached a stage at which it is highly useful to mathematicians.

I have one last point, and it concerns something which Walter Rosenblith mentioned. What is a pattern? There are many patterns that human beings find easy to recognize, and they are very important to us: the spoken word, the written word, and so forth. But these are hard for computers. On the other hand, we all know that the world is full of patterns that human beings find difficult to recognize. Chemical tests and urinalyses are simple examples. An electrical filter will filter a sine wave out of a lot of noise, while the filter in our ear is broad-band and cannot do this. Recently at the Bell Laboratories, Bela Julesz has been inserting patterns of various sorts into a configuration of random dots. Some patterns are recognizable by eye immediately and some are not, but one is just as easy as another for a computer. Thus, many simple-minded recognition tasks, which are not as complex as recognizing script or speech, but nevertheless which require a property that the human eye does not have, will undoubtedly be done in a very practical way by computers. Indeed, Walter Rosenblith has been doing just this type of thing.

LICKLIDER. As McCarthy implied, computers give us for the first time the tools with which to come to grips in a serious way with intellectual processes. We have never had them before, and we have made more progress since getting them than in decades past, despite the flowering of mathematics in the early part of the century. I should like to reinforce what Rosenblith said about developing a real feeling of rapport with the computing machine. He suggested the analogy of the car and implied, I think, that anybody who does not feel the extension of the human body into a machine does not really have a basis for feeling what the intellectual extension might be. Some people who have spent hours at tennis can hardly believe that the racket is not alive. People who have spent hours with computers have comparable difficulty.

BUSH. When you speak of rapport between men and machines and illustrate it by the automobile, I wonder how often you drive home in commuter traffic.

ANONYMOUS. I wonder if Professor Shannon would comment further on one of his earlier remarks. If I understood him correctly, he considered the fact that the brain is not hooked up at all the way a computer is as a roadblock in the way of simulating brains or brain-like machines on computers. Why is this an obstacle? As Dr. Pierce has said, airplanes are nothing whatever like pigeons, yet in some ways they fly much better. Is it not possible that a highly parallel machine has significant disadvantages which we do not happen to know about at the moment?

SHANNON. I did not say that parallel machines would be better, but only that they would be different and might lead to the possibility of doing more easily some of the things which seem difficult in serial machines: the things which are easy comparatively speaking for brains to do. I agree that the automobile is fine as an automobile, and I agree that the serial machine is fine for the kinds of things for which it is designed, for example, numerical calculations of great depth and number. So there is no argument there. But computing machines as we have them today, the analog and the digital, are only two of a vast population which we have not yet explored. What I am saying in my challenge is that we should look to other possible machines in the same general area of information processing. Just because we have bicycles, we should not stop looking for automobiles and airplanes. Carrying the point a bit further, there are two courses open at our present state of technology. We can attempt to refine and improve what we have as much as possible — in the case of computers we can try to develop our programming skill to the utmost — or we can take a completely different tack and say, "Are there other types of computing machines that will do certain things better than the types we now have?" I am suggesting that there well may be such machines.

BUSH. Have you any comments at this point, Professor Rosenblith?

ROSENBLITH. When we talk about The Brain, we are certainly overgeneralizing almost as much as when we talk about The Machine. Brains come in all sizes. As Adrian has remarked, unless they are about as large as an apple, we do not expect much evidence of our kind of reasoning and generalization. Those who work today in the field of artificial intelligence deal often with types of problems that cannot yet be studied in any meaningful way by analyzing the electrical activity of the brain. But brains are multipurpose devices, and the intellectual aspects of their activity are not the whole story by any means. Brains are programmed partly by hereditary factors and partly by learning; they are reprogrammed, almost minute by minute, as they are stimulated by the environment. If one records, for instance, by means of a microelectrode from a cell in so-called association cortex, one may find that the cell seems interested in auditory stimuli to begin with; it then shifts its interest to visual events, then to what happens on the skin, and so forth. This kind of flexible arrangement may be the chief characteristic of a large tribe of brain cells. Obviously, not all parts of the brain are as flexibly connected as this, but it would seem that the brain disposes of a certain reserve of uncommitted neurons that can be applied wherever and whenever there is a need for information processing. This unusual and only partially understood combination is far from being readily duplicable by our current machines. In order to understand this type of behavior, we need to know not only the neuroanatomical circuitry and the neuroelectric events, but we also need to know a great deal more neurochemistry, and to get a grasp of how the varieties of memory are coded. In the meanwhile, we should emphasize in computer simulation studies the range and combinations of performances that living brains are capable of. Thus, we may develop a catalogue of programmable machines exhibiting a whole gamut of behavior repertories. The brain systems of tomorrow are then likely to combine and match the capabilities of logical machines with the flexibility and sloppiness of biological ones.

DREYFUS.* After hearing Dr. Pierce's remarks attacked by the computing fraternity's vociferous far left, we feel that a few comments are in order. We undertake this defense primarily to show that M.I.T. has not yet been taken over entirely by machines. We use machines to characterize the relentless prophets of the omniscient computer, since it appears, in this matter at least, that they lack the fundamental attribute of the human brain mentioned by Dr. Rosenblith — a few uncommitted neurons.

Specifically, we should like to address ourselves to the frequent and rather immodest claim of manyfold progress in artificial intelligence. How much progress has been made toward the world champion chess machine (so confidently predicted) when, in the past few years, the rules of chess and a few simpleminded heuristics of its play have been committed to the punched card? How much progress did the cave man make toward space flight when he climbed his first mountain? Something fundamental to significant progress is lacking in both cases — the conceptual, or technical, or technological breakthrough. Work in the fields of language translation, game playing, and pattern recognition has contributed nothing to the understanding of the nature of intelligence or insight. This suggests that the solution of profound problems touching upon

* These remarks by H. L. and S. E. Dreyfus were not made at the Pierce session itself, but were submitted in writing a short time thereafter.

the nature of thought may not be the sum of many minute steps.

If programmers set themselves glamorous tasks as difficult to execute as they are appealing to the press (which includes some so-called technical journals), let them report progress when the necessary breakthrough occurs, and not until then. Such researchers should run the same risks as the alchemist trying to synthesize gold from base materials: obscurity until success. Artificial intelligence seems to be operating instead on the principle of fame until failure. In contrast to Dr. Pierce's sober remarks, the claims of the far left read like fiction, and bad fiction at that, since the ending is always "deus ex machina."

MINSKY. The present-day stored-program serial computer is presumably in a very early phase, and I have a strong objection to "computer" being used to point to the IBM 704 or any other particular representative, although perhaps this is necessary in order to avoid using a long string of qualifiers. Every designer of programming languages nowadays is thinking about more complex associative memories for serial computers. Parallelism is in the air. The next generation of machines, or the one after the next generation, will certainly have large parallel aspects. But looking at a conventional computer of the caliber of the IBM 7090, despite the comments from the platform, we are not sure that it cannot solve many of the difficult intellectual problems that face us. The brain has had a billion years to make good use of its neurons, and the programmers have not. In the last two years we find the IBM 704 solving problems of an order of magnitude more difficult than it did in 1958 or 1959. Although I doubt it, it still remains possible to me that the IBM 704 with its crude serial mode of operation could be as intelligent as man in fairly broad areas, just provided it had a larger memory.

This is not a closed issue. We are nowhere near the limits of good heuristic programming which, to parallel what Dr. Rosenblith said, have partly hierarchical and partly disorderly arrangements. And the situation is improving fairly rapidly. Still, the parallel computer shows great promise.

Concerning pattern recognition, just as a specific matter, I should bet that the serial IBM 704, if properly programmed, could read printed letters faster than a human, even though present programs do not. I should bet that eventually the 704 even could read script faster than a human.

PIERCE. These are nice bets, but how long do we have to wait? Will I live so long? I do not doubt that it will read script faster, if you do not care how well it reads it. There is a wonderful tendency to talk about things that lie in the future and that you cannot prove will not happen. This is good clean fun because it is the only way we have of giving variety to the future. When the future comes there is going to be just one future, but here in anticipation we can enjoy a lot of different futures, and I am pleased to see that everyone is enjoying himself. As for me, I do not know what is going to happen, and I find the future more difficult to talk about. There is a certain dullness in talking about things that are either in our grasp or are just coming into our grasp, but I think that it is legitimate to talk about these things, even though they are less glamorous, because they are the things that seem to be neglected.

ABRAHAMS. I should maintain, Dr. Pierce, that in a sense you are placing your bet on the wrong horse. You recommended that effort should be shifted from machine translation to human translation, but I think there are fairly broad classes of problems which are in a sense simply beyond human capabilities, problems characterized by the fact that we do not know algorithms for solving them or they do not appear to be within human capabilities. One example is the problem of information retrieval where the amount of information that a human being needs to digest is just too much for him. Another example is the problem of translating from an unknown language. We do not know algorithms for solving such problems, yet computers might be able to solve them by generating programs, perhaps by heuristic methods that we cannot understand. In other words, programs may grow essentially by accretion. The programs which you have restricted yourself to are those which the programmer can understand. I feel that this is a very strong restriction. Learning programs may open up a new avenue of approach, and this has already been explored to some extent by Newell and Simon; but there remains a great deal to be done.

PIERCE. There sure does. I want to say something about the problem of information retrieval and the flow of information. In my view, the greatest step that could be made in this direction is fewer journals and more stringent editorial policies for journals now being published.

BAR-HILLEL. I first of all want to agree with Dr. Pierce that we have very little prospect of knowing what is going to happen in the future, even in the near future. In spite of this uncertainty, we must make up our minds as to which types of future we should like to encourage, and we must recognize that certain types are unachievable. One such decision soon must be made by computer people. Do we want computers that will compete with human beings and achieve intelligent behavior autonomously, or do we want what has been called man-machine symbiosis? I admit that these two aims do not definitely exclude each other, but there has been an enormous waste during the last few years in trying to achieve what I regard as the wrong aim at this stage, namely, computers that will autonomously work as well as the human brain with its billion years of evolution. Of course, it may turn out that ten or fifteen years from now certain unforeseen developments will enable computers to perform much more marvelously than seems possible today. But I think computer people have the obligation to decide now which of the two aims they are going to adopt.

PIERCE. In the matter of making a decision now on the basis of an unknown future, I am reminded of a remark inadvertently made by Mr. Webb, Administrator of the National Aeuronautics and Space Administration. (I am sure this remark does not really describe the operation of the agency.) Mr. Webb stated on television that "We have a step-by-step program in which each step is based on the next."

References

Bar-Hillel, Y., "The Present Status of Automatic Translation of Languages," in *Advances in Computers*, Vol. 1, Alt, F. L., Ed., Academic Press, Inc., New York, 1960, pp. 91–163.

Carr, J. W., III, "Programming and Coding," Chap. 2 of *Handbook of Automation, Computation and Control*, Vol. 2, Grabbe, E. M., Ramo, S., and Wooldridge, D. E., Eds., John Wiley & Sons, Inc., New York, 1959.

Gotlieb, C. C., and Hume, J. N. P., *High-Speed Data Processing*, McGraw-Hill Book Co., New York, 1958.

Kelly, J. L., Jr., Lochbaum, C., Vyssotsky, V. A., and others, "A Block Diagram Compiler," *The Bell System Technical Journal*, Vol. 40, 669–676 (May, 1961).

Leagus, D. C., Lee, C. Y., and Mealy, G. H., "Verification of the Logic Structure of an Experimental Switching System on a Digital Computer," *The Bell System Technical Journal*, Vol. 38, 467–476 (Mar., 1959).

Ledley, R. S., *Digital Computer and Control Engineering*, McGraw-Hill Book Co., New York, 1960.

Lyapunov, A. A., Goodman, R., and Booth, A. D., Eds., *Problems of Cybernetics*, Vol. 1, Pergamon Press, Inc., 1960 (translated from the Russian).

Mathews, M. V., "An Acoustic Compiler for Music and Psychological Stimuli," *The Bell System Technical Journal*, Vol. 40, 677–694 (May, 1961).

Minsky, M., "Steps Toward Artificial Intelligence," *Proceedings of the IRE*, Vol. 49, 8–30 (Jan., 1961).

Oettinger, A. G., *Automatic Language Translation*, Harvard University Press, Cambridge, 1960.

Proceedings of the International Conference on Scientific Information, Washington, D. C., 1958, Vols. 1 and 2, National Academy of Sciences and National Research Council, Washington, D. C., 1959.

Samuel, A. L., "Programming Computers to Play Games," in *Advances in Computers*, Alt, F. L., Ed., Vol. 1, Academic Press, Inc., New York, 1960, pp. 165–192.

Wang, H., "Toward Mechanical Mathematics," *IBM Journal of Research and Development*, Vol. 4, 2–22 (Jan., 1960).

Wang, H., "Proving Theorems by Pattern Recognition — II," *The Bell System Technical Journal*, Vol. 40, 1–41 (Jan., 1961).

Selected Bibliography

Social Issues and Management Implications

Shultz, G. P., and Whisler, T. L., Eds., *Management Organization and the Computer*, The Free Press of Glencoe, Illinois, 1960.

Simon, H. A., "The Corporation: Will it be Managed by Machines?," *Management and Corporations, 1985*, McGraw-Hill Book Co., New York, 1960.

Simon, H. A., *The New Science of Management Decision*, Harper & Brothers, New York, 1960.

Wiener, N., *The Human Use of Human Beings*, Houghton Mifflin Company, Boston, 1950.

Wiener, N., "Some Moral and Technical Consequences of Automation," *Science*, Vol. 131, 1355–1358 (May 6, 1960).

Simulation of Large Systems

Cohen, K. J., and Cyert, R. M., "Computer Models in Dynamic Economics," *The Quarterly Journal of Economics*, Vol. 75, 112–127 (Feb., 1961).

Conway, R. W., Johnson, B. M., and Maxwell, W. L., "Some Problems of Digital Systems Simulation," *Management Science*, Vol. 6, 92–110 (Oct., 1959).

Forrester, J. W., *Industrial Dynamics*, The M.I.T. Press and John Wiley & Sons, Inc., New York, 1961.

Geisler, M. A., "The Simulation of a Large-Scale Military Activity," *Management Science*, Vol. 5, 359–368 (July, 1959).

Orcutt, G. H., Greenberger, M., Korbel, J., and Rivlin, A. M., *Microanalysis of Socioeconomic Systems*, Harper & Brothers, New York, 1961.

Orcutt, G. H., Shubik, M., Simon, H. A., and Clarkson, G. P. E., "Simulation: A Symposium," three articles in *American Economic Review*, Vol. 50, 894–932 (Dec., 1960).

Pool, I. de S., and Abelson, R., "The Simulmatics Project," *Public Opinion Quarterly*, Vol. 25, 167–183 (Summer, 1961).

327

Selected Bibliography

ARTIFICIAL INTELLIGENCE

Gelernter, H. L., Hansen, J. R., and Loveland, D. W., "Empirical Explorations of the Geometry Theorem Machine," *Proceedings of the Western Joint Computer Conference*, San Francisco, Calif., May, 1960, The Institute of Radio Engineers, New York, 1960, pp. 143–149.

Minsky, M., "Steps Toward Artificial Intelligence," *Proceedings of the IRE*, Vol. 49, 8–30 (Jan., 1961).

Newell, A., Shaw, J. C., and Simon, H. A., "Chess Playing Programs and the Problem of Complexity," *IBM Journal of Research and Development*, Vol. 2, 330–335 (Oct., 1958).

Samuel, A. L., "Some Studies in Machine Learning, Using the Game of Checkers," *IBM Journal of Research and Development*, Vol. 3, 210–229 (July, 1959).

Selfridge, O. G., and Neisser, U., "Pattern Recognition by Machine," *Scientific American*, Vol. 203, 60–68 (Aug., 1960).

Shannon, C. E., "Programming a Digital Computer for Playing Chess," *Philosophical Magazine*, Vol. 41, 256–275 (Mar., 1950).

Wang, H., "Toward Mechanical Mathematics," *IBM Journal of Research and Development*, Vol. 4, 2–22 (Jan., 1960).

COMPARISON WITH LIVING ORGANISMS

Ashby, W. R., *Design for a Brain*, 2nd ed., John Wiley & Sons, Inc., New York, 1960.

McCulloch, W. S., and Pitts, W., "A Logical Calculus of the Ideas Immanent in Nervous Activity," *Bulletin of Mathematical Biophysics*, Vol. 5, 115–137 (1943). Articles also in *ibid.*, Vol. 7, 89–93 (1945), and Vol. 9, 127–147 (1947).

Rosenblith, W. A., "The Quantification of the Electrical Activity of the Nervous System," in *Quantity and Quality*, Lerner, D., Ed., The Free Press of Glencoe, Inc. (Crowell-Collier Publishing, Co.), New York, 1961, pp. 87–102.

Turing, A. M., "Can a Machine Think?," in *The World of Mathematics*, Vol. 4, Newman, J. R., Ed., Simon and Schuster, Inc., New York, 1956, pp. 2099–2123.

von Neumann, J., *The Computer and the Brain*, Yale University Press, New Haven, Conn., 1958.

Walter, W. G., *The Living Brain*, W. W. Norton & Company, Inc., New York, 1953.

Wiener, N., *Cybernetics*, 2nd ed., The M.I.T. Press and John Wiley & Sons, Inc., New York, 1961.

THEORY OF COMPUTATION

Davis, M., *Computability & Unsolvability*, McGraw-Hill Book Co., New York, 1958.

McCarthy, J., "A Basis for a Mathematical Theory of Computation, Preliminary Report," *Western Joint Computer Conference*, Los Angeles, Calif., May 9–11, 1961, The Institute of Radio Engineers, New York, 1961, pp. 225–238.

Turing, A. M., "On Computable Numbers, with an Application to the Entscheidungsproblem," *Proceedings of the London Mathematical Society*, Ser. 2, Vol. 42, 230–265 (1937).

von Neumann, J., "The General and Logical Theory of Automata," in *The World of Mathematics*, Vol. 4, Newman, J. R., Ed., Simon and Schuster, Inc., New York, 1956, pp. 2070–2098.

MECHANICAL TRANSLATION

Delavenay, E., *An Introduction to Machine Translation*, Frederick A. Praeger, Inc., New York, 1960.

Edmundson, H. P., Ed., *Proceedings of the National Symposium on Machine Translation*, Prentice-Hall, Inc., Englewood Cliffs, N.J., 1961.

Locke, W. N., and Booth, A. D., Eds., *Machine Translation of Languages*, The Technology Press of M.I.T. and John Wiley & Sons, Inc., New York, 1955.

Mechanical Translation (MT), journal published irregularly at M.I.T. (Room 20D–102), Cambridge, Mass.

Oettinger, A. G., *Automatic Language Translation*, Harvard University Press, Cambridge, 1960.

Research on Mechanical Translation, Hearings Before the Special Investigating Subcommittee of the Committee on Science and Astronautics, U.S. House of Representatives Report 2021, 86th Congress, 2nd Session, U.S. Government Printing Office, Washington, D. C., May, 1960.

INFORMATION STORAGE AND RETRIEVAL

Brownson, H. L., "Research in Handling Scientific Information," *Science*, Vol. 132, 1922–1931 (Dec. 30, 1960).

Bush, Vannevar, "As We May Think," *Atlantic Monthly*, Vol. 176, 101–108 (July, 1945).

Current Research and Development in Scientific Documentation,

329

National Science Foundation, U.S. Government Printing Office, Washington, D. C. (published twice yearly).

Documentation, Indexing, and Retrieval of Scientific Information, Staff of U.S. Senate Committee on Government Operations, Senate Doc. 113, 86th Congress, 2nd Session, U.S. Government Printing Office, Washington, D. C., 1960.

Mooers, C. N., "The Next Twenty Years in Information Retrieval: Some Goals and Predictions," *Proceedings of the Western Joint Computer Conference,* San Francisco, 1959, The Institute of Radio Engineers, New York, 1959, pp. 81–86.

Nonconventional Technical Information Systems in Current Use, National Science Foundation, U.S. Government Printing Office, Washington, D. C., No. 1, 1958, No. 2, 1959, and Supplement, 1960.

Proceedings of the International Conference on Scientific Information, 2 vols., National Academy of Sciences and National Research Council, Washington, D. C., 1959.

Swanson, D. R., "Searching Natural Language Text by Computer," *Science,* Vol. 132, 1099–1104 (Oct. 21, 1960).

Taube, M., and Wooster, H., Eds., *Information Storage and Retrieval,* Columbia University Press, New York, 1958.

TIME SHARING AND MAN-MACHINE INTERACTION

Cohen, K. J., and Rhenman, E., "The Role of Management Games in Education and Research," *Management Science,* Vol. 7, 131–166 (Jan., 1961).

Licklider, J. C. R., "Man-Computer Symbiosis," *IRE Transactions on Human Factors in Electronics,* Vol. HFE-1, 4–11 (Mar., 1960).

Strachey, C., "Time Sharing in Large, Fast Computers," in *Information Processing,* Proceedings of the International Conference on Information Processing, UNESCO, Paris 15–20 June 1959, UNESCO, Paris, 1960, pp. 336–341.

Teager, H. M., "Systems Considerations in Real-Time Computer Usage," *Proceedings of Conference on Application of Digital Computers to Automatic Instruction,* John Wiley & Sons, Inc., New York, forthcoming 1962.

PROGRAMMING LANGUAGES

Bemer, R. W., "Survey of Modern Programming Techniques," *Computer Bulletin* (British), Vol. 4, 127–135 (Mar., 1961).

COBOL — 1961, U.S. Government Printing Office, Washington, D. C., June 13, 1961.

Gill, S., "Current Theory and Practice of Automatic Programming," *Computer Journal* (British), Vol. 2, 110–114 (Oct., 1959).

McCarthy, J., "Recursive Functions of Symbolic Expressions and Their Computation by Machine, Part I," *Communications of the Assoc. for Computing Machinery,* Vol. 3, 184–195 (Apr., 1960).

McCracken, D., *A Guide to FORTRAN Programming,* John Wiley & Sons, Inc., New York, 1961.

Naur, P., Ed., Backus, J. W., and others, "Report on the Algorithmic Language Algol 60," *Communications of the Assoc. for Computing Machinery,* Vol. 3, 299–314 (May, 1960).

Orchard-Hays, W., "The Evolution of Programming Systems," *Proceedings of the IRE,* Vol. 49, 283–295 (Jan., 1961).

Ross, D. T., "The Design and Use of the APT Language for Automatic Programming of Numerically Controlled Machine Tools," *Proceedings of the 1959 Computer Applications Symposium,* Armour Research Foundation of Illinois Institute of Technology, Chicago, Ill., 1960, pp. 80–99.

Yngve, V. H., "COMIT as an IR Language," *Communications of the Assoc. for Computing Machinery,* Vol. 5 (Jan., 1962).

PROCESSING AND CONTROL

Gotlieb, C. C., and Hume, J. N. P., *High-Speed Data Processing,* McGraw-Hill Book Co., New York, 1958.

Grabbe, E. M., Ramo, S., and Wooldridge, D. E., Eds., *Handbook of Automation, Computation and Control,* John Wiley & Sons, Inc., New York, Vol. 1, 1958, Vol. 2, 1959, Vol. 3, in press.

Gregory, R. H., and Van Horn, R. L., *Automatic Data-Processing Systems,* Wadsworth Publishing Company, Inc., San Francisco, 1960.

Kozmetzky, G., and Kircher, P., *Electronic Computers and Management Control,* McGraw-Hill Book Co., New York, 1956.

Ledley, R. S., *Digital Computer and Control Engineering,* McGraw-Hill Book Co., New York, 1960.

Malcolm, D. G., and Rowe, A. J., Eds., *Management Control Systems,* John Wiley & Sons, Inc., New York, 1960.

Truxal, J. G., "Computers in Automatic Control Systems," *Proceedings of the IRE,* Vol. 49, 305–312 (Jan., 1961).

CONFERENCE PROCEEDINGS AND SPECIAL COLLECTIONS

Alt, F. L., Ed., *Advances in Computers,* Vol. 1, Academic Press, Inc., New York, 1960.

Editors of Scientific American, *Automatic Control*, Simon and Schuster, Inc., New York, 1955.

Information Processing, Proceedings of the International Conference on Information Processing, UNESCO, Paris 15–20 June 1959, UNESCO, Paris, 1960.

Lyapunov, A. A., Goodman, R., and Booth, A. D., *Problems of Cybernetics*, Vol. 1, Pergamon Press, Inc., 1960 (translated from the Russian).

Mechanisation of Thought Processes, 2 vols., Her Majesty's Stationery Office, London, 1959.

Proceedings of the Computer Applications Symposium, Armour Research Foundation of Illinois Institute of Technology, Chicago, 1959, 1960.

Proceedings of the Eastern and Western Joint Computer Conferences, The Institute of Radio Engineers, New York, 1955 and later years.

Shannon, C. E., and McCarthy, J., Eds., Princeton, N.J., *Automata Studies*, Princeton University Press, 1956.

Yovits, M. T., and Cameron, S., Eds., *Self-Organizing Systems*, Pergamon Press, Inc., New York, 1960.

BIBLIOGRAPHIES

Malcolm, D. G., "Bibliography on the Use of Simulation in Management Analysis," *Operations Research*, Vol. 8, 169–177 (Mar.–Apr., 1960).

Minsky, M., "A Selected, Descriptor-Indexed Bibliography to the Literature on Artificial Intelligence," *IRE Transactions on Human Factors in Electronics*, Vol. HFE-2, 39–55 (Mar., 1961).

Shubik, M., "Bibliography on Simulation, Gaming, Artificial Intelligence and Allied Topics," *Journal of the American Statistical Association*, Vol. 55, 736–751 (Dec., 1960).

Index

Abrahams, P. W., 176, 282, 323
Abstracts, 153–159, 161, 167–169, 172, 173, 175, 178, 295
Access time, 167, 214, 215
Ackerman's function, 265, 268
Air battle and defense, 52–54
Alexander, S. S., 94, 123, 129
Algebraic equations, numeric evaluation of, 240
Algol language, 187, 210, 228, 259, 261, 287
Algorithms, 184, 185, 189, 195, 196, 215, 216, 261, 323
Alt, F. L., 131
Amdahl, G. M., 220, 238, 247
American Chemical Society, 175
Analog computer, 246
    combined with digital computer, 247
    vs. digital computer, 309, 311, 314, 319
Apprehensions caused by computer, 6, 15, 26
    avoidance of responsibility, 25, 26
    closed decisions, 10, 14
    gadgetry, 12, 15, 25, 26, 28
    lack of control, 23, 24, 32, 34
    society bypassed, 12, 13
    tendency to oversimplify, 17, 18
    wrong or foolish questions, 15–17, 21
Apt language, 228
Arden, D. N., 86
Armed Services Technical Information Agency (ASTIA), 174, 175

Artificial intelligence, 68, 114–116, 121, 130, 207, 217, 227, 251, 308, 309, 320–322
Ashby, W. R., 95
Atomic processes and tasks, 258–271, 281, 282, 284
Automation in libraries, 139

Bar-Hillel, Y., 324, 325
Baumann, D. M. B., 175
Beach, P. E., Jr., 128
Beecher, N., 30
Bell Telephone Laboratories, 238, 292, 318
Berkeley, E. C., 124
Berry, M. M., 178
Books, miniaturized, 139, 145
    sentiment about, 141, 177
Booth, A. D., 325
Boring, E. G., 130
Bottleneck, library, 149, 174
    programming, 274, 278
Brain, 314, 320, 321
    relation to computer, 307–309, 311, 313, 319, 324
Brown, G. W., 250, 251, 277, 280–282, 284, 285, 287
Brunow, G. P., 286
Buckland, L. F., 172
Burroughs B–5000 computer, 241
Bush, V., 222, 248, 290, 307, 310, 315, 319, 320
Bush differential analyzer, 182, 246
Business games, 23, 185, 186, 208, 217

Calculus, 119, 120, 190, 195, 196, 200, 201, 209, 215
Cameron, S., 131
Capital Airlines, 245
Carnegie Institute of Technology, 184, 188
  computer, 199, 214
  course in computers, 189
  management game, 185, 186, 208
  programming systems, 189
Carr, J. W., III, 325
Cathode-ray-tube console, 231
Checkers and chess machines, 22, 23, 25, 30–34, 63, 96, 97, 114, 296–298, 314, 321, 325
Chomsky, N., 120
Clapp, L. C., 32
Clark, W. A., 95, 96, 205
COBOL language, 228
Cocke, J., 239, 242
CODASYL committee, 273, 278
Coding, automatic, 272
Cohen, K. J., 217
Communication between computers, 238, 254
Communications of the Association for Computing Machinery, 282
Companies, stability of, 83
  successful vs. unsuccessful, 82
Compilers, 254, 298, 299, 325
Complex processes and structures, 251, 255, 257, 269
Cooke, G., 157
Corbató, F. J., 222
Course in computers, first, 188–190, 202, 203
  grading by computer, 183, 189, 193, 194
  problems for, 191, 195, 196, 217
  role of processes, 184, 189–191, 196, 209, 210, 215
Creativity, 129–131, 205, 206
Cybernetics, 12, 95, 291, 312, 325
Cyert, R. M., 70, 217

Dartmouth College, 238
Dartmouth College library, 135–137

Data, 302
  problem of describing, 272, 273, 278, 279, 282–284
Data processing, 251, 272, 273, 287, 304, 325
Debugging, of machines, 300
  of programs, 223, 281, 300
Decision making, 6, 33, 34, 304
  as Brownian movement, 6–9, 33
  education example, 7, 8
  health service example, 7
  legalistic diagrams, 6
  levels of abstraction, 49, 64, 65, 67, 68
  policy, 46–51, 55, 56, 68, 69
  radar example, 9
  scientists in, 10, 11, 29, 30, 34
  in secret by the few, 8–10, 30, 34
  strategic bombing example, 9, 11, 18
Design, automatic system, 272
Dewey Decimal System, 142, 167
Diffuse-operation computer, 310, 311, 314, 320
Dill, W. R., 217
Dinneen, G. P., 96
Dreyfus, H. L., 321
Dreyfus, S. E., 321

Economics, use of computer in, 185
Education, 7, 8
  computer in, 216, 217
  sensitivity, rationality, and table look-up, 188, 204
  to use computer, 186, 187
Efficiency of memory referencing, 242, 243
Einstein, A., 81, 129
Electronic computer, early, 237, 252, 253
Elements of programming, 191–193
  attention to all eventualities, 192
  definitions, 192
  iteration, 191
  mechanical syntax, 192, 193
  parameters, 191, 196, 213
  proof construction, 190, 193
  recursion, 191, 260, 265–269, 287

Elements of programming, representation, 192
simulation, 193
Elias, P., 180, 199, 212, 215
Emery, J. C., 127
Employment, fluctuations of, 57, 58, 61, 84
English language programs, 285, 286
ENIAC computer, 237
Equilibrium, and stability, 29
static vs. dynamic, 29
Evans, A., Jr., 270, 287
Executive program, 258, 259, 261–271, 279, 281, 284
Experimentation, on models, 68, 69
using history, 11, 19–21, 27

Factorization, 106–109, 113, 119, 130
Fano, R. M., 134, 162, 174, 177
Farley, B. G., 95, 96
Fatehchand, R., 131
Federal Reserve Board, 48
Feedback, 17, 34
ataxia vs. paralysis, 34
vs. feed forward, 71
information, 39–42, 70, 71
Feurzeig, W., 287
Flow chart, 189, 190, 264, 265, 272, 286
Ford Foundation, 187
Ford Motor Company, Aeronutronic Division, 240
Forecasting, 51, 71, 185
Forgie, J. W., and C. D., 131
Forrester, J. W., 36, 37, 80–91, 214
FORTRAN language, 182, 228, 259, 281
Fredkin, E., 177, 205, 235
Futrelle, R. P., 126

Game, management, 23, 185, 186, 208, 217
war, 23, 304
Game playing, 295–298, 300, 321, 325
GAMMA 60 computer, 247

Garman, C. G., 281
Gelernter, H., 295, 296
General Problem Solver (GPS), 97–104, 108–110, 115–117, 122–125
goals, 100, 101
individual differences, 128, 129
means-end analysis, 101, 102, 110
objects, differences, and operators, 99, 100, 108–110, 131
planning and abstracting, 102, 130
self-improvement, 117, 122, 123, 127
side conditions, 124, 125
state-process dichotomy, 110–113
General-purpose computer, 298–301
Godkin lectures, 8, 34
Goodman, R., 325
Gotlieb, C. C., 325
Government, science and, 34
Grisoff, S. F., 32, 280
Growth of computers, 254
Gyftopoulos, E. P., 33, 172

Hardy, G. H., 4, 5
Harvard University library, 135, 136
Herzog, S., 29
Heuristic programming, 115, 322
Heuristic technique, 70, 113, 116, 122, 184, 296, 321, 323
Heuristic value of computers, 216, 217
Hierarchy of final causes, 96, 114, 124
History, disasters in, 28
discontinuity in, 26, 27, 166
examples from, 16
experimentation, 11, 19–21, 27
Hnilicka, M. P., 29
Holt, C. C., 36, 68, 81, 82, 86–88, 90
Hopper, G. M., 250, 271, 282, 284–286
Howard, R. A., 36, 74, 84, 85, 88–90
Hughes, J. H., 285
Hull, C., 120
Hume, J. N. P., 325

335

IBM (International Business Machines Corporation), 181, 182, 228, 281, 295
IBM 704 computer, 171, 212, 292, 295, 322, 323
IBM 709 computer, 224, 225, 228, 242
IBM 7090 computer, 222, 229, 292, 322
IBM STRETCH computer, 234, 243
Image, man's and machine's own, 19, 31, 312
Imitation and theory, 114, 126, 127
Indexes, 167, 168, 295, 303
Industrial dynamics, 74–80, 84, 88, 90, 91
  evaluation of, 77–80
  example, 56–62
  future of, 80
  levels and flow rates, 42–45
  methodology of, 76
  noise and nonlinearity, 45, 56, 85, 89, 90
  phenomena of study, 75, 76
  research philosophy, 76, 77
  stability, structure, delay and amplification, 40, 41
  state of the art, 77
  viewing distance, 45, 62, 63, 71
Information, digestion of, 176
Information-feedback system, 39–42, 70, 71
Information processing, 207, 301, 302
Information search and retrieval, 137, 144, 148–160, 163–166, 177, 178, 292, 295, 301–303, 305, 316, 317, 323–325
Insight, 87, 127, 182
Intelligence, artificial, 68, 114–116, 121, 130, 207, 217, 227, 251, 308, 309, 320–322
  machine vs. human, 32, 33, 118, 274–277, 286
Interpreter, 256, 281
Invention, 48, 49, 72, 80
Inventory, fluctuations of, 57, 58, 61

Inventory problem, 18
Irons, E. T., 287

Jacobs, W. W., 23, 34
Job shop problem, 252, 269
Johnson, H. W., 2
Journals, reorganization of, 144, 161, 324
Judgment, art and, 86, 87
  human, 11–13
Juhasz, S., 177
Julesz, B., 318

Kailath, T., 216
Kelly, J. L., Jr., 325
Kemeny, J. G., 134, 135, 168, 172, 176, 222, 226, 313
Kent, A., 178
Kessler, M. M., 164, 169
King, G. W., 134, 166, 173, 176
Kirsch, R. A., 178
Kuhns, J. L. 178

Lanczos, C., 184, 217
Language, and communication, 130, 131
  computer, 184, 187, 202, 203, 227, 228, 238–240, 254
  for data processing, 273
  machine-readable, 298, 302, 303, 316, 317
  for psychological theories, 119–121
  speech and, 130
  for stating procedures, 200, 211, 228, 240, 242, 273
  upper- and lower-level, 258–260
Laws of nature, 83
Leagus, D. C., 325
Learning machine, 20, 22–25, 27, 30–32, 130, 156, 237, 238, 297, 308, 309, 324
Ledley, R. S., 325
Lee, C. Y., 325
Liberman, A. M., 131
Library, centralized vs. decentralized, 140, 152, 160, 174, 175
  classification into subject, branch, and item, 141–151, 163, 167, 169

Library, code for, 144, 148, 149
  costs of, 139, 140, 147, 167, 170, 171, 173, 175
  National Research, 140–152, 158–162, 172, 174
  personal, 150, 151, 169
  projected growth of, 135, 136, 138, 143
  reading unit for, 148–150
  for 2000 A.D., 134–178, 226, 313
Library of Congress, 166, 171, 175, 176
Licklider, J. C. R., 180, 203, 204, 213, 216, 222, 247, 318
Linear programming, 303, 304
LISP language, 228, 242, 243
List processor, 243, 262, 270, 271
Literature explosion, 135, 162, 166, 168, 172, 324
Lochbaum, C., 325
Locke, W. N., 134, 177
Logic, symbolic, 120, 314, 325
  two levels of programming, 258, 271, 284
Logic-processing computer, 240
Lowen, J., 33
Lucas, E. F., 81
Luddites, 5, 6, 14, 19
Luhn, H. P., 175, 177, 178
Lyapunov, A. A., 325

McCarthy, J., 31, 170, 205, 211, 220, 221, 242, 244–247, 260, 261, 263, 270, 283, 287, 315
McCulloch, W. S., 120
Machine, adaptation to new, 13, 14, 28
  built by humans, 125
  communicating with, 203, 212
  composite, 275–277
  language of, 277
  vs. man, 139, 291, 292, 305, 306, 308, 324
  management of, 304, 306, 307
  self-reproducing, 31, 307
Machine habit, 28

Machine-readable form, 298, 302, 303, 316, 317
Machine translation, 25, 30, 31, 161, 293–295, 309, 317, 321, 323, 325
McKenney, J. L., 259, 278, 279, 287
McLanahan, J. C., 81
Magic, Monkey's Paw, 23, 24, 31, 34
Magnetic discs, 167, 194, 198
Magnetic tapes, 145–148, 167, 255, 281
Man, as calculator, 51, 52, 69
  in computer loop, 197, 313
  vs. machine, 139, 291, 292, 305, 306, 308, 324
Man-machine interaction, 25, 154, 155, 158, 163, 172, 176, 199–202, 206–208, 212–214, 222–227, 247, 312, 313, 315, 319, 324
Management, automatic, 66
  and information, 37–39
  of machines, 304, 306, 307
  middle, 66, 67
Management laboratory, 54
Management science, 62, 70, 87, 90
Manager and computer analyst, 272
Maron, M. E., 178
Marquis, D. G., 180, 212
Massachusetts Institute of Technology (M.I.T.), 3, 80, 182, 187, 203, 209, 222–224, 228, 233, 246, 318, 321
Mathematical Reviews, 143, 144, 153–155, 169, 171
Mathematics library, 142, 146, 148–150
Mathews, M. V., 325
Mauchly, J. W., 220, 236, 246
Mealy, G. H., 325
Michigan, University of, 187
Military command systems, 53, 54, 251
Miller, G. A., 94, 95, 104, 115, 118, 130, 131
Miniaturization, of books, 139, 145
  of computer components, 310

Minsky, M. L., 27, 94, 95, 114, 120, 124, 126, 130, 205, 207, 212, 222, 296, 322, 325
Model, experiments on, 68, 69
vs. reality, 83
simulation, 58, 68, 69, 73
standard criteria for, 81
validation of, 68, 69, 73, 78
Modigliani, F., 89
Mooers, C. N., 174, 178
Moore, E. F., 307
Morison, E. E., 2, 3, 13, 26, 28, 30, 31, 34
Morse, P. M., 250, 287
Multicomputer systems, 271
Multiprocessing, 234, 235, 239, 241, 243, 244, 256, 271, 276
Multiprogramming, 256, 271, 287

National Research Library, 140–152, 158–162, 172, 174
National Science Foundation, 181, 182, 293
Naval Ordnance Test Station, 171
Nekora, M. R., 256, 287
Newell, A., 94, 96, 130, 131, 270, 287, 295, 296, 324
Newman, S. M., 178
Numerical analysis, 183, 187, 201
course in, 183, 187

Oettinger, A. G., 215, 325
Operation of computer, 223–225
with interlock, 233
with interruption, 232, 233
nonstop, 232
with program relocation, 233, 241, 243
Operations research, 74–80, 88, 90
evaluation of, 77–80
future of, 80
methodology of, 76
phenomena of study, 75, 76
research philosophy, 76, 77
state of the art, 77
Operator systems, automatic, 254
Optimization, problems of, 74
self-, 117

Orcutt, G. H., 70
Organizing machines, 279
Oscillations and fluctuations, 57, 58, 61, 78, 84
Osgood, C. E., 130

Parallel operation, 237
Parallel-type computer, 309, 319
Parallelism, 251–255, 272, 287, 322
Parameters, binding, 191
Pattern recognition, 96, 114, 292, 295, 297, 300, 309, 312, 313, 318, 321, 323, 325
Perlis, A. J., 180, 181, 204, 209, 214, 217, 222, 270, 287
Perry, J. W., 175, 178
Photographic reduction, 166, 172
Physical Review, 164, 169, 170
Piaget, J., 120
Pierce, J. R., 290, 291, 316, 323, 324
Piore, E. R., 220, 246, 247
Pitts, W., 96, 114, 120, 124
Polya, G., 115, 122
Prediction, 84, 85, 89
Priorities, 273
first-come, first-served, 268
round-robin, 230, 235
Private computer, 222–225, 229
Probability theory, 120, 121, 153, 157
Program debugging, 223, 281, 300
Programmer, 256, 257, 272, 278, 280, 283–286, 298, 301, 305, 315
Programming, as art of stating procedures, 211
automatic, 272
computer, 184, 325
continuously, 183
discipline of, 216
elements of, 191–193
history and development of, 273–277
knowledge required for, 245
levels of, 258, 271, 277
teaching of, 195, 201–203, 211, 215

Programming language, 184, 187, 189, 197, 201, 282, 284, 285, 315
Programming services, 236
Psychology, 126, 127
  language for, 119–121
Public utility, computing as, 236

Questionnaires and interviews, 72, 272, 302
Queuing in programs, 267, 268, 280

Ramo-Wooldridge polymorphic computer, 245
Rath, G. J., 126
Ray, L. C., 178
Reaction time, human, 213–215, 230
Recursive functions, 191, 260, 265–269, 287
Referencing, and bibliographies, 161, 163, 168, 170
  cross, 165, 167, 174
  forward, 164, 170, 174
Remington Rand, 281
  real-time computer, 245
Research and development, 40
Reservation machine, 298
Revolution, 8, 312
Reynolds, J. C., 245
Rome Air Development Center, 240
Rosenblith, W. A., 290, 311, 320
Rowe, A. J., 70
Russell's theory of types, 33
Russian translation, 293–295
Ryle, B. L., 256, 287

Sage system, 299
Samuel, A. L., 23, 34, 297, 325
Satellite tracking, 293–295
Sayre, D., 250, 273, 279, 286
Science and government, 34
Scientists as in-group, 29, 30
Search, example of, 136
  experiments in, 153, 154, 157, 169
  machine, 153–156, 159, 164, 175, 176

Search, problem of, 137, 152–159, 163, 167, 168, 172, 175
  service for, 160
  statistical, 175
  trial-and-error, 105, 107, 109, 113
  work in progress, 171, 174
Self-optimizing mechanisms, 117
Self-organizing systems, 95, 114, 116, 123, 131
  postponement in, 117
Self-reproducing machine, 31, 307
Selfridge, O. G., 96, 297
Sequence constraints, 253, 254, 257, 260, 264, 270, 278–280, 283, 284
Serial computer, 319, 322
Serial processor, 235, 236
Shannon, C. E., 164, 290, 307, 319
Shaw, J. C., 130, 131, 295, 296
Shedd, E. F., 82
Shubik, M., 70
Simon, H. A., 94, 95, 121, 124–131, 295, 296, 324
Simulation, 68, 69, 193, 208, 251, 303, 304, 321
  of electrical equipment, 292, 299, 303, 325
  of human thinking, 19, 21, 94–131, 296, 308, 314
  of one computer on another, 255, 256, 281, 308
  of organizations, 185
  ultimate test of, 123, 128
Skinner, B. F., 216
Slagle, J. R., 215, 228, 248
Snow, C. P., 2, 3, 26, 27, 29, 32–34
Software, 275–277, 279, 286, 287
Sony Company, 175
Specialization of processing units, 252, 256
Special-purpose computers, 240, 247, 298–301
Spectrum of views on computer, 307, 308
Speech, acquisition of, 104–108
  computer work on, 131

Speech, factorization of, 106–109, 113, 119, 130
  and language, 130
  perceptual and motor symbols, 105, 111, 126, 131
  trial-and-error search, 105, 107, 109, 113
Sprague, R. C., 36, 56
Sprague Electric Company, 56
  model, 81, 82
Square root, example, 261, 262
Stability, of companies, 83
  in feedback systems, 40, 41, 55
  and world change, 8, 20, 26, 27, 29
Standardization, 275, 282
Statistical methods, 72, 73, 80, 81
Stevens, H. H., Jr., 245
Stibitz, G., 238
Storage, computer, 227, 280
  primary, 231, 232, 246
  secondary, 233, 246
Strachey, C., 222, 247
Symbol manipulation, 97, 225, 228, 229, 246–248, 270, 318

Taube, M., 178
Teaching machine, 194, 195, 208, 216, 226, 246
  learning, 237, 238
Teager, H. M., 222
Technician, computer as, 196, 227
Tetley, W. H., 53
Texts on computer, 198, 199
Theorem-proving machines, 97, 114, 173, 292, 295, 298, 300, 314, 318, 325
Thinking, creative, 129–131, 205, 206
Time sharing, 159, 172, 247, 252, 256, 257, 280
  computer requirements for, 231–233, 241, 245
  computer system for, 171, 197, 203, 205–209, 212–214, 220–248
  console for, 229, 231
  memories for, 244
Tizard-Lindemann story, 8

Tonge, F. M., 270, 287
Transfer function, 46
Translating machine, 25, 30, **31**, 161, 293–295, 309, 317, 321, 323, 325
Translating programs, 255, 256, 281, 282
Trends in computer design, 221, 237
Turing machine, 308
TX-0 computer, 224, 225
Typewriter console, 229–231, 238, 242

Undecidability theorem, 131
University, computer requirements of, 197–199
  computer's first role in, 195, 205
  computer's ultimate role in, 196–199, 203, 205
  cost of computer in, 198, 199
  role of, 209

Validation, 72, 84
  of models, 68, 69, 73, 78
  tests of, 89
Values, transfer of human, 22, 24, 25, 30, 31
Van Zoeren, H., 270, 287
Voice input to computers, 245
von Neumann, J., 314
Vyssotsky, V. A., 325

Walter, G., 95
Wang, H., 295, 296, 300, 325
War, thermonuclear, 23, 27, 31
War games, 23, 304
Weather prediction, 223, 236
Wegner, P., 176
Whirlwind computer, 182
Wiener, N., 2–6, 21, 27–34, 95, 307, 315
Wolf, T., 103
Wooster, H., 178
World Wars, 8, 9

Yovits, M. C., 131